Table of Co

Month 1..3

- matching objects that are the same
- identifying objects that are different
- pairs of objects
- parts and wholes
- classifying and grouping objects
- objects that belong and do not belong
- matching objects that go together
- cut-out matching cards: objects

Month 2..35

- identifying colors (red, yellow, blue, green, orange, purple, brown, black)
- completing a color pattern
- identifying shapes (circle, square, triangle, rectangle)
- matching shapes
- finding shapes in a picture

Month 3..65

- matching sets of objects
- counting and showing 1-5 objects
- recognizing numerals 1-5
- matching numerals to sets
- matching sets with the same amount
- more and less
- comparing sizes
- sizes (big/little, biggest/littlest, long/short, longest/shortest)
- cut-out matching cards: sets

Month 4..97

- rhymes and word families
- opposites (long/short, hot/cold, push/pull, old/new, clean/dirty, day/night)
- cut-out opposite cards
- names for people
- names for animals
- pull-out storybook: rhyming riddles

Month 5..129

- identifying same beginning sounds
- identifying beginning letters and sounds: consonants
- identifying beginning letters and sounds: vowels
- reviewing beginning sounds

Month 6..161

- tracing lines from left to right
- tracing lines from top to bottom
- tracing slanted and curved lines
- tracing paths
- tracing lines to make pictures
- drawing shapes (circles, squares, rectangles, triangles)
- more fine motor skills practice (dot-to-dots, mazes, drawing pictures)
- pull-out drawing book

Month 7..193

- matching objects that are the same
- recognizing items that are different
- matching objects to shapes
- recognizing items that face a different direction on a page (directionality)
- finding objects in a picture (visual discrimination)
- drawing missing parts (visual discrimination)
- identifying what's wrong with a picture (visual discrimination)
- drawing conclusions
- predicting what comes next
- story sequence (first, next, last)
- cut-out sequence cards

Month 8..225

- matching sets of objects
- reviewing 1-5
- counting and showing 1-10 objects
- recognizing numerals 1-10
- matching numerals to sets
- number order: dot-to-dots
- writing numerals 1-10
- writing numbers in sequence

Month 9..257

- recognizing uppercase letters A-Z
- recognizing lowercase letters a-z
- reviewing letter recognition

Month 10..291

- rhyming words and word families
- names for places
- names for things
- names for actions
- cut-out word cards
- position words (top/bottom, in/out, on/off, left/right, next to/between)
- following directions

Month 11..321

- tracing and writing uppercase letters A-Z
- tracing and writing lowercase letters a-z
- cut-out alphabet cards

Month 12..353

- matching words that are the same
- making words by filling in beginning letters
- matching pictures and words
- reading words with common phonograms
- reading common sight words
- reading simple sentences
- cut-out word cards
- pull-out storybook

Index..383

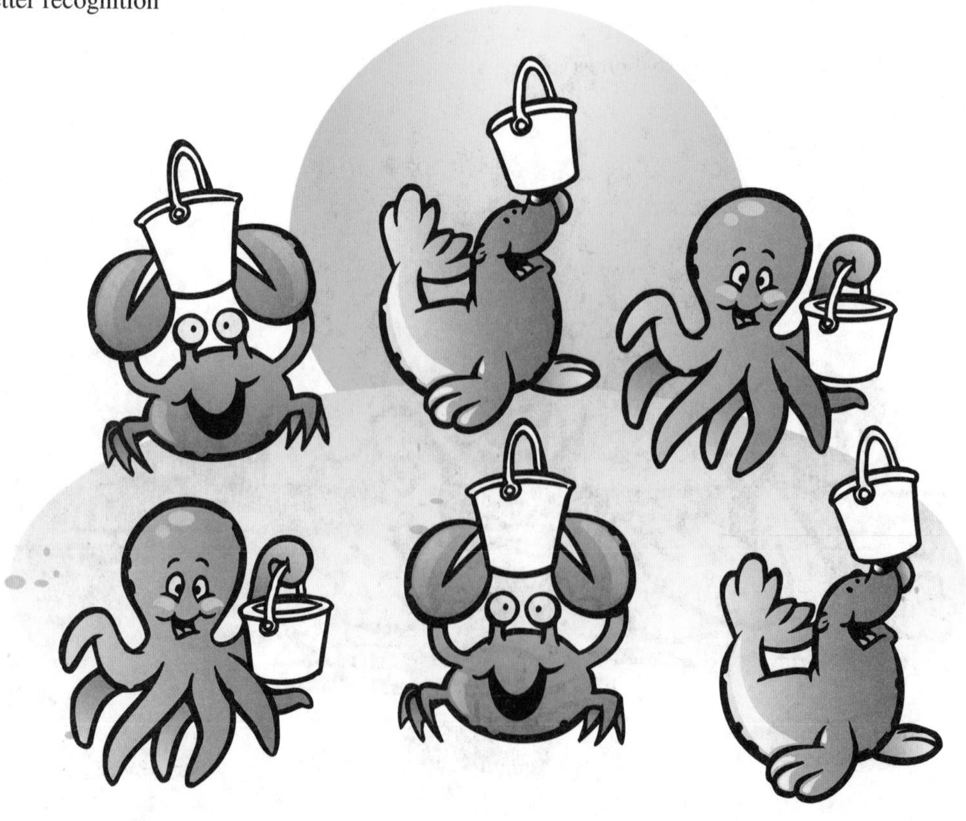

Month 1 Checklist

Hands-on activities to help prepare your child for school!

PREREADING

Same and Different: pages 5–14
Matching Pairs: pages 15–16, 33–34

As your child begins to identify objects, he or she is developing the ability to focus on details and recognize similarities and differences. This will later play a role in distinguishing between letters and words when learning to read. Help your child build this skill through the following activities:

- ❑ Complete the worksheets.
- ❑ Have your child look through a bowl of dry alphabet cereal or uncooked alphabet macaroni and find the letters that are alike.
- ❑ Place three coins that are alike on a table and one that is different. Have your child find the one that is different.
- ❑ Look through the newspaper or magazines with your child and cut out pictures of automobiles. Have your child explain how they are alike and how they are different.
- ❑ Make a pile of shoes belonging to family members. Have your child find the matching pairs.

Part and Whole: pages 17–18

Identifying parts of a whole requires not only the skill of visual discrimination, but also the ability to make associations and think about "the bigger picture." The following activities will give your child opportunities to practice this skill:

- ❑ Complete the worksheets.
- ❑ Play a game in which you remove a piece from different fruits and have your child match the parts to the wholes. For example, cut a slice from an apple, remove the stem of a strawberry, separate a grape from the bunch, and take the peel off an orange or banana.
- ❑ Have your child look at articles of clothing and name the parts, such as buttons, pockets, zippers, and shoelaces.

PREREADING

Classification: pages 19–28
Go-Togethers: pages 29–32

The skill of sorting involves identifying the different features of items, and then separating those items into categories, or classifying them. Identifying items that belong in a group further advances the skill of classification. Grouping items offers an opportunity to associate ideas. These skills can be practiced at home using the following activities:

- ❑ Complete the worksheets.
- ❑ Have your child help you sort tableware into sets of forks, spoons, and knives. Be sure that an adult handles the knives!
- ❑ Ask your child to sort toys into like groups—e.g., balls, stuffed animals, board games, and toys with wheels.
- ❑ Have your child draw or name three things that he or she would need to bring to the beach or a birthday party.
- ❑ Place objects that go together on a table and have your child pair them—e.g., cup and saucer, hammer and nail, pencil and paper, sock and shoe, and toothbrush and toothpaste.

Hats Off!

Match the ones that are the same.

PREREADING

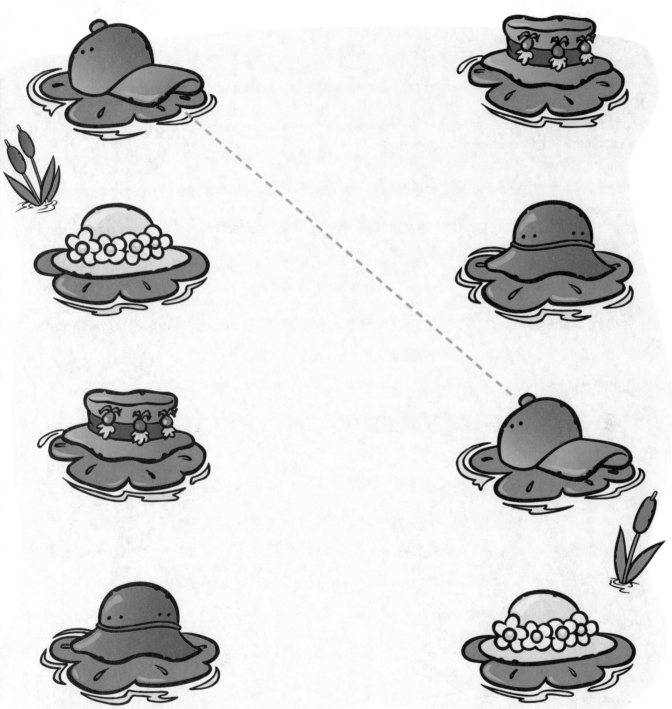

Parents: Help your child identify each hat and then ask him or her to draw a line to connect the hats that are the same.

Animal Crackers

Match the ones that are the same.

Parents: Have your child name each animal in the left-hand column and then ask him or her to draw a line to connect each of those animals with the matching one on the right.

Look in the Forest

Color the two that are the same in each row.

Parents: **Ask your child to find the matching animals in each row and color them.**

At the Toy Store

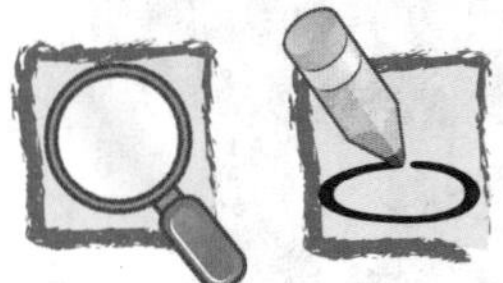

Circle the ones that are the same in each group.

Parents: Have your child point to and circle the toy cars that are the same. Ask, "How are all three cars the same? How is the uncircled car different?" Then have your child circle the tops and balls that are the same.

Look in the Garden

Circle the ones that are the same in each group.

Parents: **Have your child point to and circle the butterflies that are the same. Ask, "How are all three butterflies the same? How is the uncircled butterfly different?" Then have your child circle the flowers and snails that are the same.**

Rolling Along

Circle the one that's the same as the first one in each row.

Parents: Have your child look closely at the first object in each row. Ask him or her to find and circle the object that is the same in that row.

Come to the Circus

Color the one that's different in each group.

Parents: Have your child identify the animals in each group. Ask him or her to find and color the one that is different. Talk about what makes the animal different.

PREREADING

Fun at the Beach

Color the one that's different in each group.

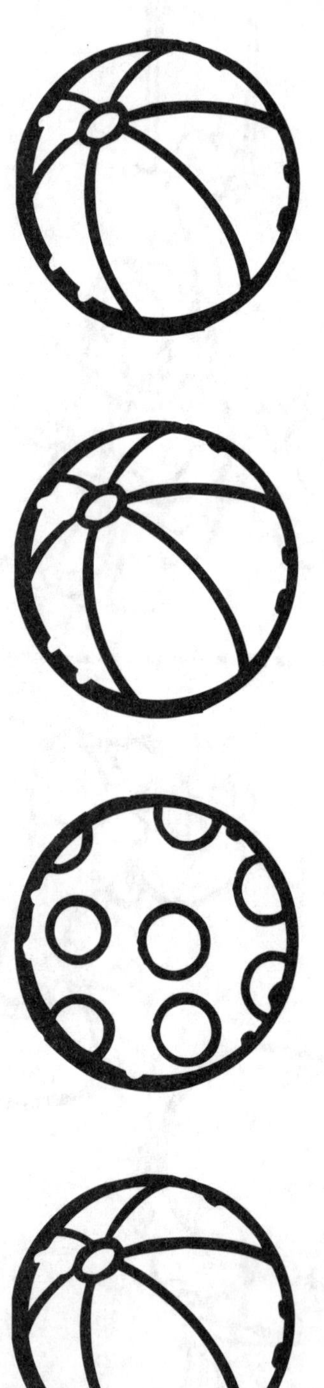

Parents: Have your child identify the objects in each column. Ask him or her to find and color the one that is different. Talk about what makes the object different.

Time to Plant

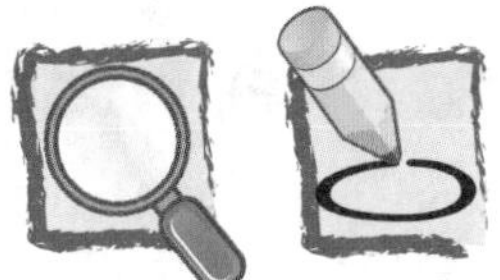

Circle the one that's different in each group.

Parents: Have your child identify the objects. Ask him or her to find and circle the one that is different in each row. Talk about what makes it different.

Identifying objects that are different

More Circus Fun

Circle the one that's different from the first one in each row.

Parents: **Have your child look closely at the first picture in each row. Ask him or her to find and circle the picture that is different in that row.**

Winter Fun

Match the ones that go together.

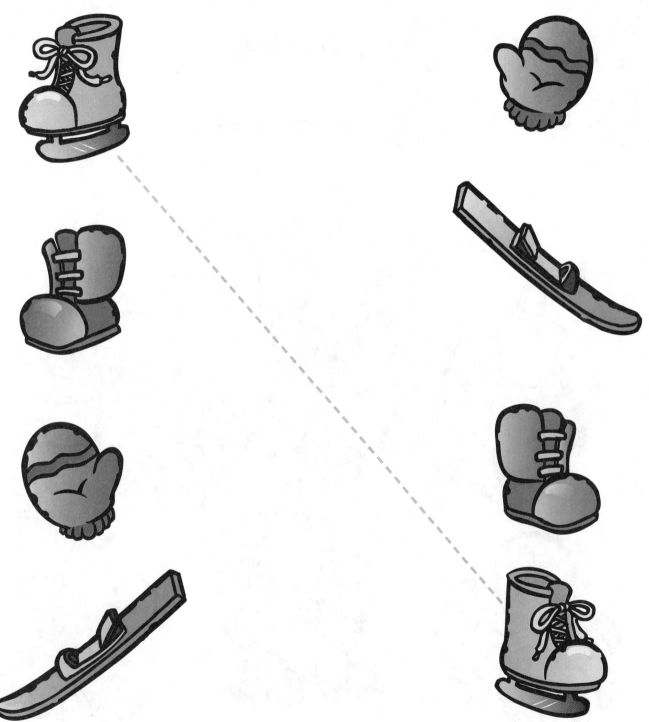

Parents: Ask your child to draw a line from each object on the left to the matching one on the right.

PREREADING

Summer Fun

 **Color the**  **s' pails red.**

 **Color the**  **s' pails blue.**

 **Color the**  **s' pails purple.**

Parents: Have your child find each pair of animals that are the same and color their pails to match.

What's Missing?

Match the part to its whole.

Parents: Say, "Look at the flower petal. Draw a line to what it goes with." Then have your child continue with the other objects. Talk about where each missing part fits on the whole.

Animal Parts

Match the whole to its part.

Parents: Say, "Look at the bird. What's missing? Draw a line to its missing part." Then have your child continue with the other animals. Talk about where each missing part fits on the whole.

Which Group?

Match the ones that go together.

Parents: Help your child name the objects in each group on the right and talk about how they are alike. Then have your child identify each object on the left and draw a line to the group where it belongs.

What Belongs?

Look closely. Color the things that belong in the picture.

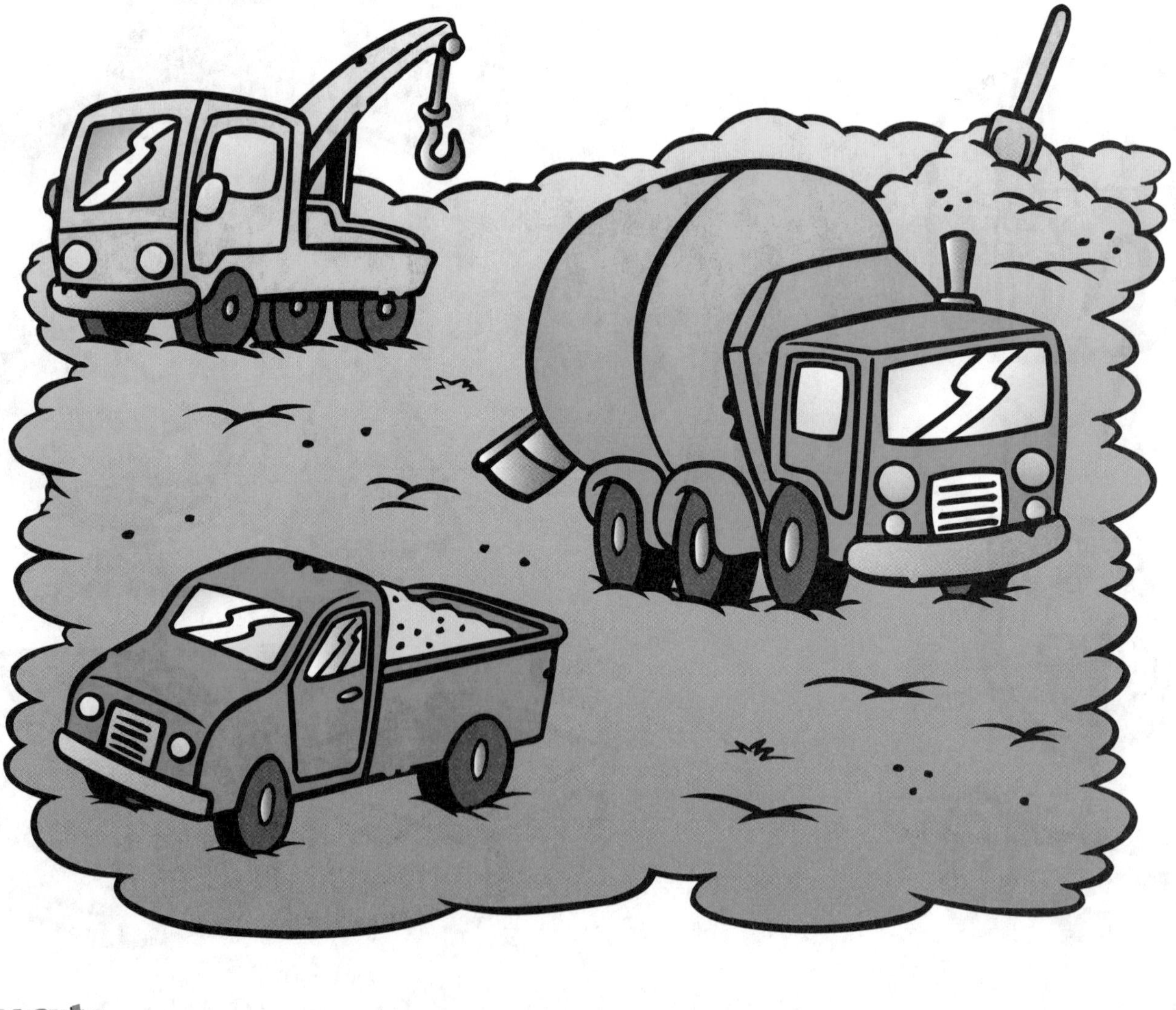

Parents: Have your child name the vehicles in the scene and talk about how they are alike. Then have him or her identify the vehicles above and color the ones that belong in the scene.

Get Ready for School

Circle what belongs in the  **.**

Parents: **Ask your child to name all the objects on the page. Then say, "Circle all the things that belong in the backpack."**

What Goes Where?

Cut out and paste the pictures.

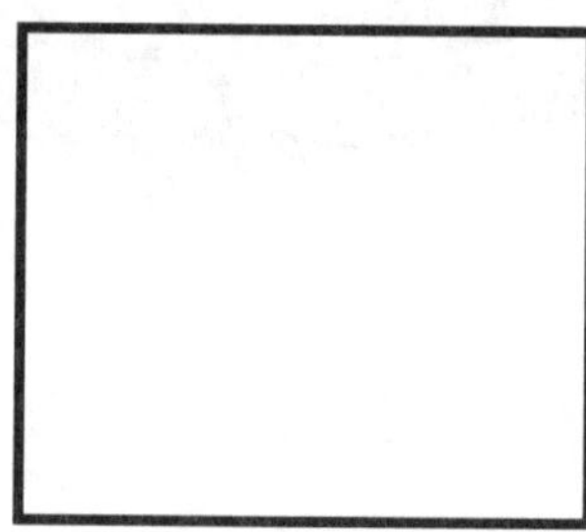

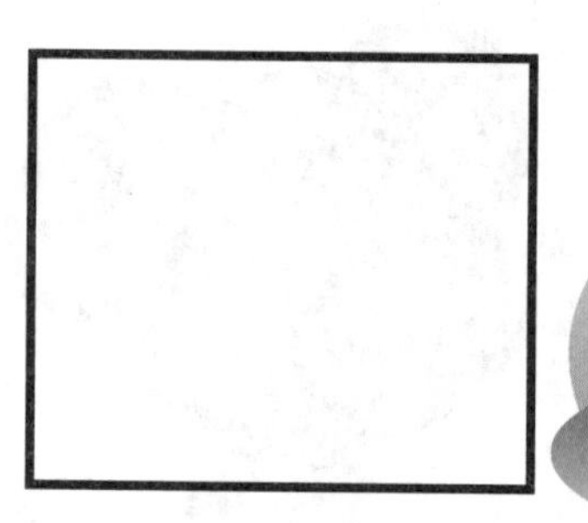

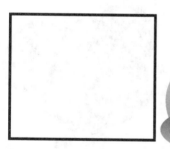

Parents: Have your child identify the animals that move in the air, on the land, and in the water. Then help him or her cut out the animal pictures above and paste them where they belong.

Get Ready for the Beach

Circle each thing  will need.

Parents: Have your child make a path to the beach by circling the things the hippo will need.

At the Playground

Circle what belongs at the playground.

Parents: Ask your child to name the objects on the page. Then say, "Circle all the things that belong at the playground."

The Grocery Store

Look closely at the grocery store.

Circle the things that do not belong.

Parents: (Top) Ask your child to tell you about the grocery store. (Bottom) Then point to the items below the picture and say, "Circle the things that are not in the grocery store."

What Doesn't Belong?

Color what doesn't belong.

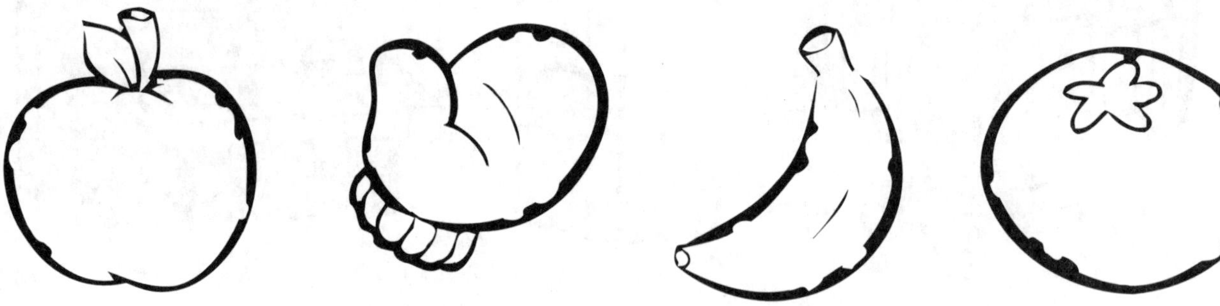

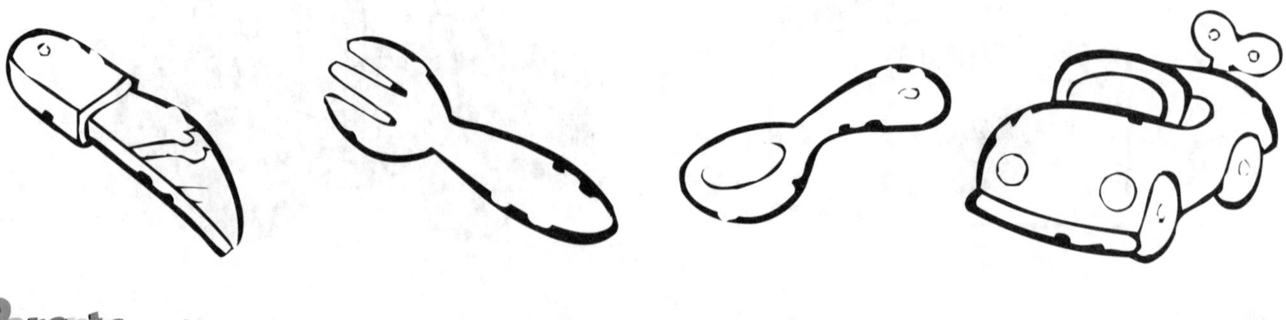

Parents: **Ask your child to name the objects in each row and color the one that does not belong. Encourage him or her to say why it doesn't belong.**

At the Library

Circle what doesn't belong.

Parents: Have your child find two things that do not belong in a library and draw a circle around each one.

PREREADING

Does It Belong?

Circle what doesn't belong.

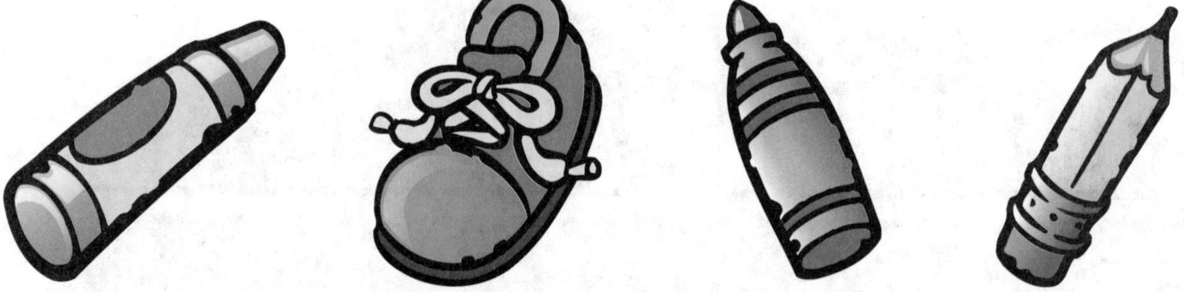

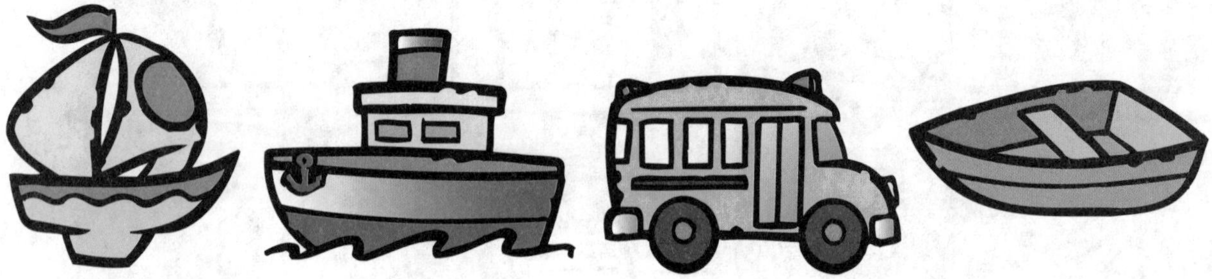

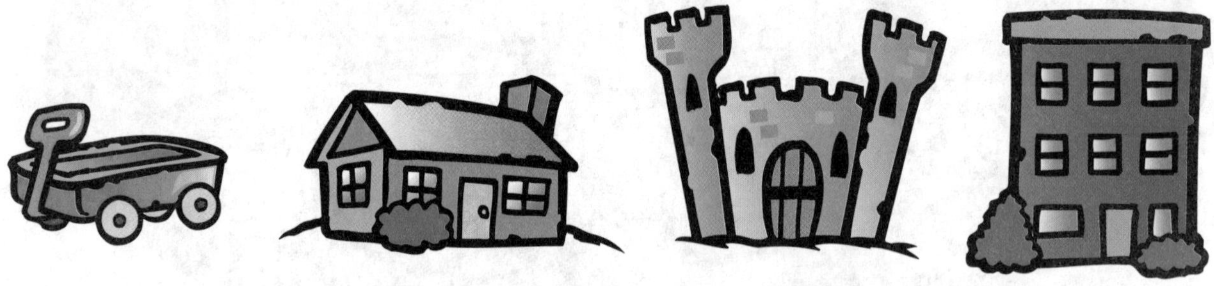

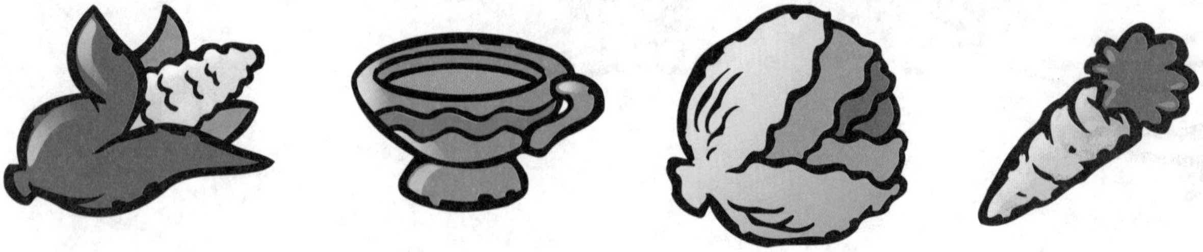

Parents: Ask your child to name the objects in each row and circle the one that does not belong. Encourage him or her to say why it doesn't belong.

Go-Togethers

Match the ones that go together.

Parents: Ask your child to name each item in the left-hand column. Then have him or her draw a line from each of those items to the one it goes with on the right. Talk about how the objects go together.

We Go Together

Circle what belongs.

Parents: Have your child name the first object in each row. Ask him or her to circle the object in that row that goes with it. Encourage your child to say how the objects go together.

More Go-Togethers

Color two things that go together.

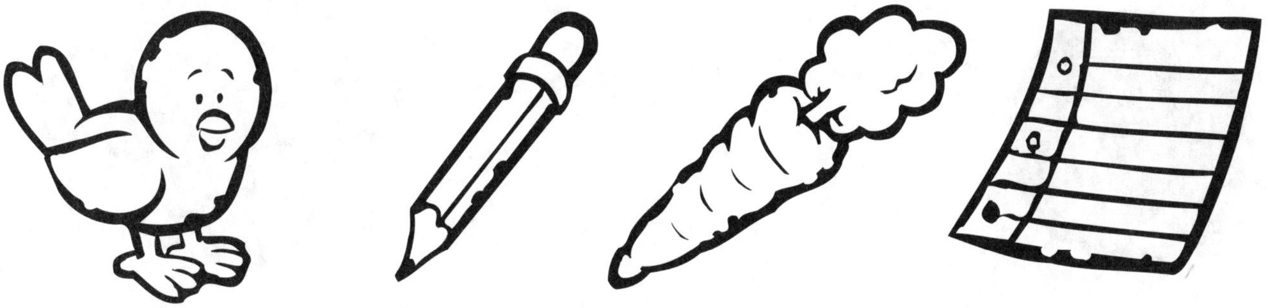

Parents: Ask your child to name the objects in each row and color the two that go together. Encourage your child to say how the objects go together.

Weather Go-Togethers

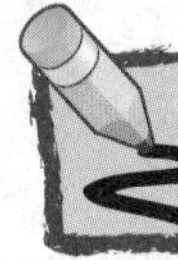

Match the ones that go together.

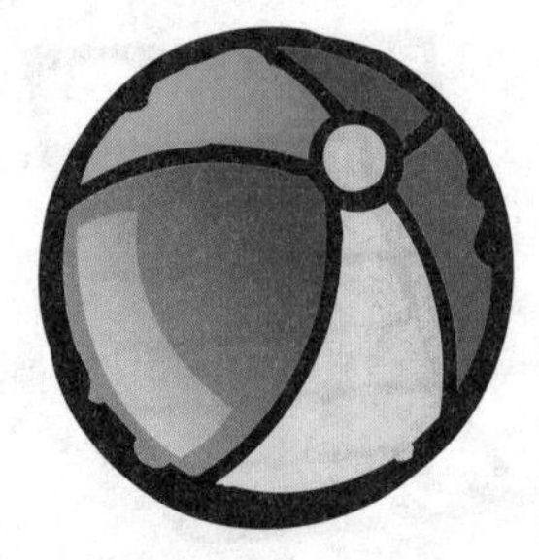

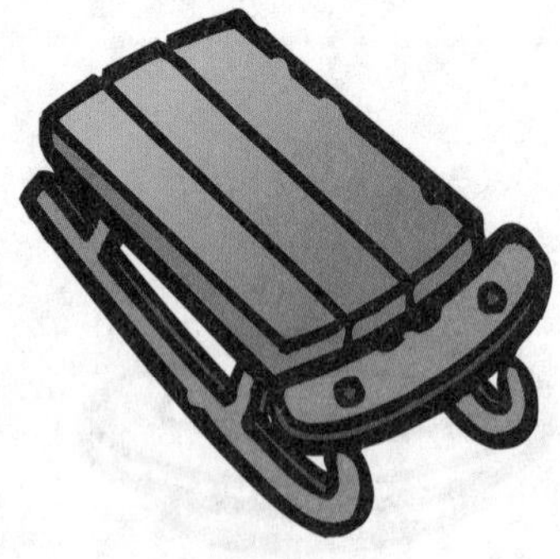

Parents: Ask your child to draw a line from the kite to the windy picture on the right. Ask, "In what kind of weather can you fly a kite?" Then have him or her draw a line from the other objects to the type of weather they go with.

Matching Mittens

Cut out the cards.

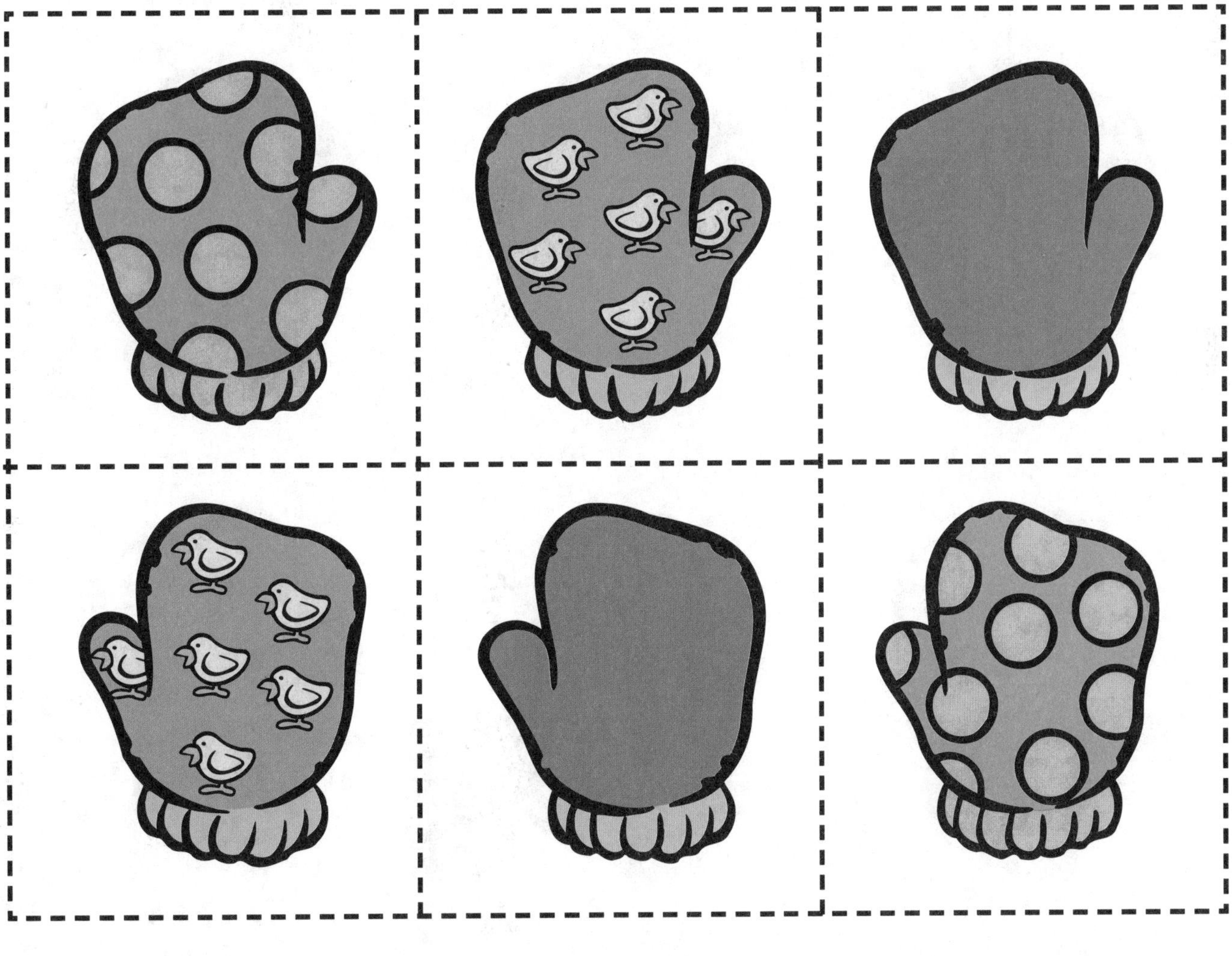

Parents: Cut out the mitten cards and place them on a table in random order. (Work with three matching pairs.) Say, "Help the three little kittens find their mittens." Have your child match the three pairs. Repeat for the mittens on the backs of the cards.

More Matching Mittens

Cut out the cards.

Month 2 Checklist

Hands-on activities to help prepare your child for school!

COLORS AND SHAPES

Colors: pages 37-48
Sorting and classifying are important beginning math skills. Children can develop these skills by learning to recognize and differentiate attributes such as color. Use the following activities to help your child build these skills.

- ❑ Complete the worksheets.
- ❑ Have a "Color Day" after completing a worksheet for a specific color. For example, complete the activities on page 38 then have a "Red Day." Help your child select red clothing to wear that day. If possible, try to serve some red foods, such as apples, strawberries, and pizza.
- ❑ Put together a collection of small objects that are different colors. You might gather colored blocks, beads, paper clips, buttons, crayons, or paper scraps. Put the items into a paper bag. Ask your child to reach into the bag and select two items. Have your child tell if the items are the same color or a different color. Then have your child name the color(s).
- ❑ Using the same collection of objects, ask your child to sort the objects into piles or containers so that all the objects are separated by color.
- ❑ Provide your child with red, blue, and yellow food coloring or paint. Ask him or her to name each color. Then let your child try mixing the colors to create new colors—e.g., red and yellow make orange, red and blue make purple, and yellow and blue make green.
- ❑ Help your child look for colors outside. Play a game where you pick a color, such as green, and you and your child see how many things you can find that are that color.
- ❑ Make a "Color Book." You may choose to do this activity over several days. Give your child a piece of paper and a crayon and ask him or her to draw something at the top of the page to create a color "title" for the page. Together, look through magazines for pictures of things that are that color. Help your child cut and paste the pictures onto the page. Repeat for other colors. After your child has created pages for several colors, put the pages together and add a cover to create a book.
- ❑ Use colored objects such as blocks to create a simple pattern—e.g., yellow, blue, yellow, blue, yellow, blue. Say the colors as you place them on a table to create the pattern. Then ask your child, "What color comes next?" Encourage him or her to continue the pattern.

COLORS AND SHAPES

Shapes: pages 49-64

Recognizing shapes is important for learning how to sort and classify. Also, learning the names of basic shapes helps children develop vocabulary based on geometry. Foster these skills with the following activities:

- ❑ Complete the worksheets.
- ❑ Ask your child to go on a shape hunt. Pick a shape, such as a circle, and a room in your house. Ask your child to point to things in that room that have a circle shape. Choose a different shape and start again. You might also extend the hunt to look for shapes in the neighborhood when you go outdoors.
- ❑ Cut sandwiches into different shapes—squares, rectangles, triangles, and circles. Talk about the name of each shape and its characteristics. For example, a triangle has three sides. A rectangle has four sides—two long and two short.
- ❑ Cut out paper squares, rectangles, circles, and triangles of different sizes. Have your child arrange the shapes on paper to make a picture of a person, vehicle, or design. Help your child paste the shapes onto the page. Talk about what shapes he or she used.
- ❑ Look through magazines for pictures of circle-shaped objects. Help your child cut them out and paste them on a circle-shaped piece of paper. Repeat for squares, rectangles, and triangles.
- ❑ Provide crackers in as many of these shapes as possible: square, rectangle, triangle, and circle. Set out a plate for each shape. Help your child sort the crackers by shape, placing all the round crackers on one plate, all the square crackers on another plate, and so on.
- ❑ Use index cards to create and play a matching game. Make two cards for each shape: circle, square, rectangle, and triangle. Mix the cards and place them face down on a table. Take turns turning over two cards at a time. If the shapes match, the player keeps the cards. If they don't match, the player turns them face down again and it's the next player's turn. Play until all the cards are matched.
- ❑ Play "Name that Shape." Draw a circle, square, rectangle, and triangle on a piece of paper. Tell your child you are thinking of one of these shapes. Have your child guess the shape by listening to clues you give to describe it. For example, say, "I'm thinking of a shape that has four sides. All the sides are the same size." (square)
- ❑ Make shape prints. Cut sponges into circles, triangles, squares, and rectangles. Show your child how to dip a sponge shape into paint and then press it onto a piece of paper to make a print.

Party Colors

Circle the ones that are the same color.

Parents: Ask your child to circle the items in each row that are the same color. Then help him or her name the colors.

Red

Look closely.
Circle the one that is  **.**

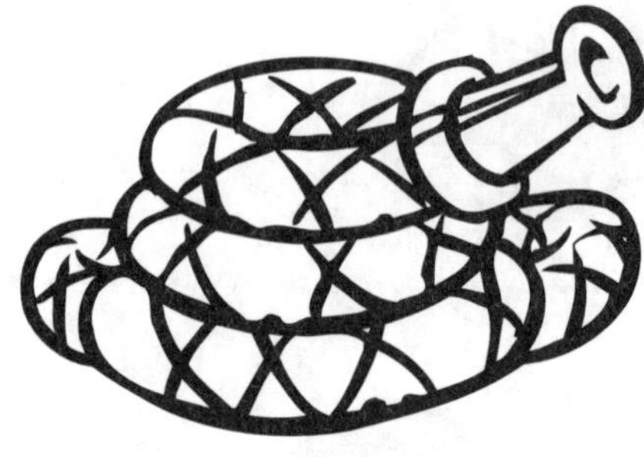

Parents: Have your child point to the fire hat and say what color it is. Ask him or her to point to the boots that are the same color and circle them. Then ask your child to identify each of the pictures at the bottom of the page and color them red.

Yellow

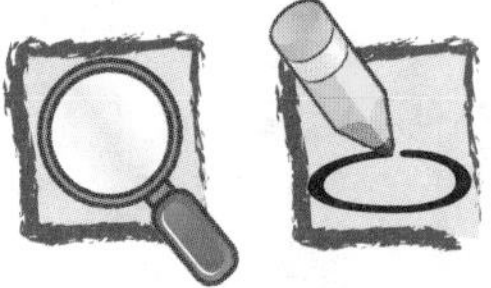

Look closely.
Circle the one that is  **.**

Parents: Have your child point to the bananas and say what color they are. Ask him or her to point to the other fruit that is the same color and circle it. Then ask your child to identify each of the pictures at the bottom of the page and color them yellow.

Blue

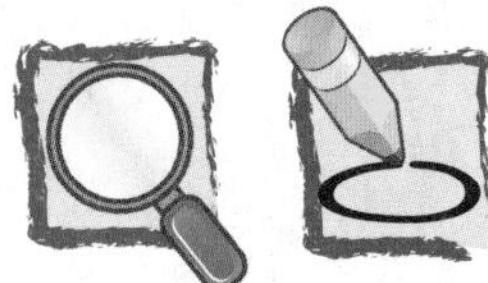

Look closely.
Circle the one that is  **.**

Parents: **Have your child point to the pants and say what color they are. Ask him or her to point to the sneakers that are the same color and circle them. Then ask your child to identify each of the pictures at the bottom of the page and color them blue.**

Understanding colors; recognizing color names

Green

Look closely.
Circle the one that is  **.**

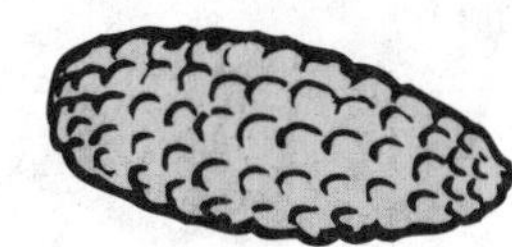

Parents: Have your child point to the peas and say what color they are. Ask him or her to point to the other vegetable that is the same color and circle it. Then ask your child to identify each of the pictures at the bottom of the page and color them green.

Understanding colors; recognizing color names

COLORS AND SHAPES

Orange

  **Look closely.**
Circle the one that is  **.**

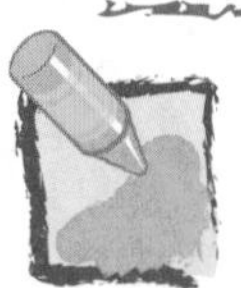

Parents: Have your child point to the pumpkin and say what color it is. Ask him or her to point to the other fruit that is the same color and circle it. Then ask your child to identify each of the pictures at the bottom of the page and color them orange.

Purple

Look closely.
Circle the one that is  **.**

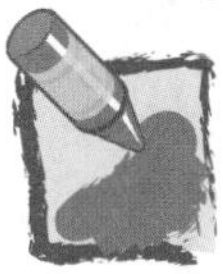

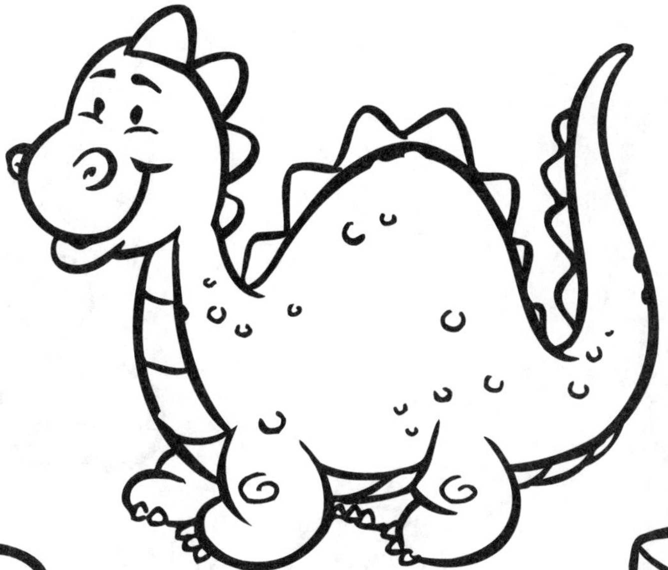

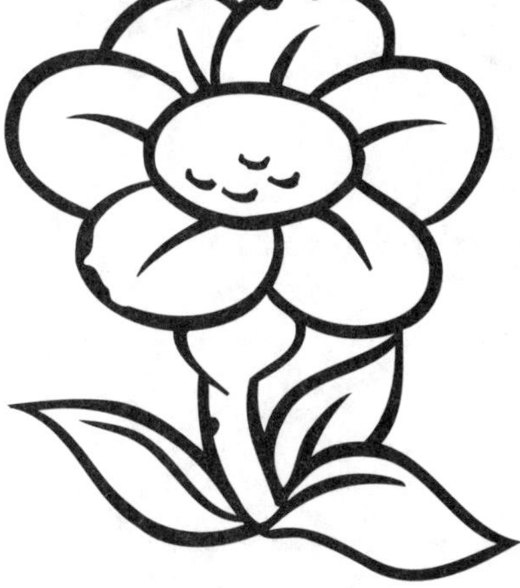

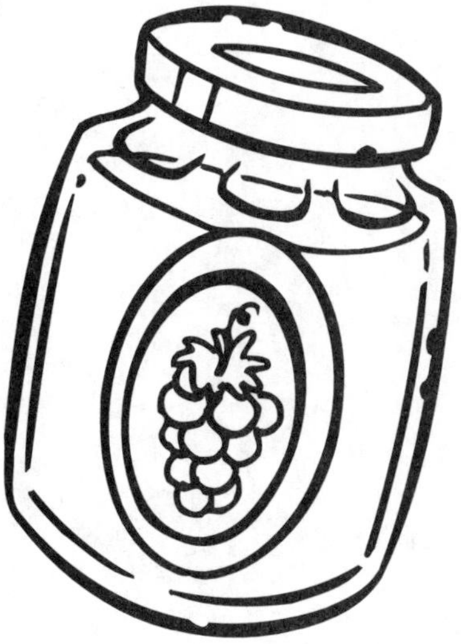

Parents: **Have your child point to the grapes and say what color they are. Ask him or her to point to the other fruit that is the same color and circle it. Then ask your child to identify each of the pictures at the bottom of the page and color them purple.**

Brown

Look closely.
Circle the one that is  **.**

Parents: Have your child point to the mitt and say what color it is. Ask him or her to point to the ball that is the same color and circle it. Then ask your child to identify each of the pictures at the bottom of the page and color them brown.

Understanding colors; recognizing color names

Black

Look closely.
Circle the one that is  **.**

Parents: Have your child point to the tire and say what color it is. Ask him or her to point to the car that is the same color and circle it. Then ask your child to identify each of the pictures at the bottom of the page and color them black.

Understanding colors; recognizing color names

On the Move

Match the ones that are the same color.

Parents: Ask your child to point to and name the color of each item. Then ask him or her to draw a line to connect the items that are the same color.

Colorful World

Color the [sun] [crayon]. Color the [butterfly] [crayon].

Color the [flower] [crayon]. Color the [bird] [crayon].

Parents: Help your child read each direction line and identify the color of each crayon. Then ask him or her to color the items in the picture using the crayon code.

Hats Off!

Color the hat to continue the pattern.

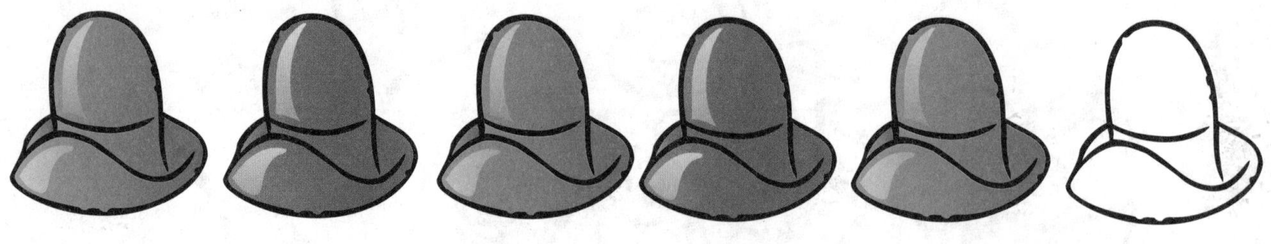

Parents: Have your child point to each hat in the first row and say what color it is. Repeat the color names after your child, emphasizing the pattern. Then ask, "Which color comes next?" Have your child color the last hat yellow to continue the pattern. Repeat for each row.

Shapes in a Row

Circle the ones that are the same shape.

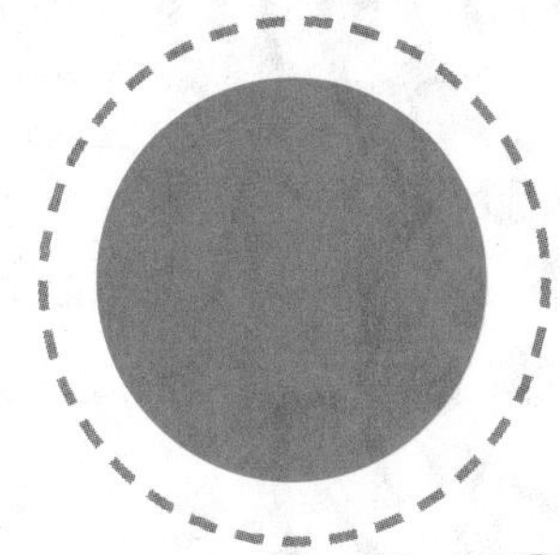

Parents: Ask your child to circle the shapes in each row that are the same. Then help him or her name the shapes.

Circle

Look closely.

Color the ◯s.

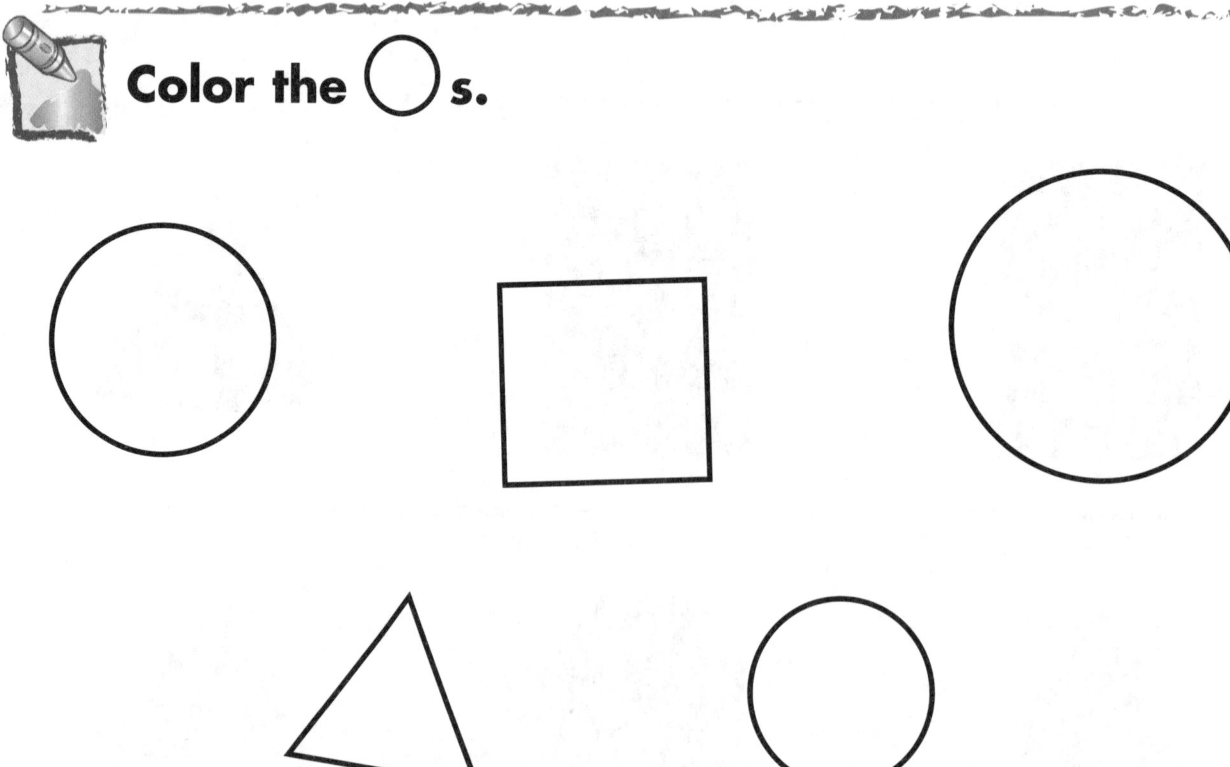

Parents: Point to the circle at the top of the page. Trace the shape with your finger as you say, "This is a circle. The line is curved." Ask your child to color all the circles on the page.

Understanding shapes; recognizing shape names

Circle Search

Look closely. Color the ◯s.

Parents: Ask your child to point to all the circles in the scene and color them.

Square

Look closely.

Color the □ s.

Parents: Point to the square at the top of the page. Trace the shape with your finger as you say, "This is a square. It has four sides that are the same size." Ask your child to color all the squares on the page.

Square Search

Look closely. Color the □s.

Parents: Ask your child to point to all the squares in the scene and color them.

Triangle

Look closely.

Color the △s.

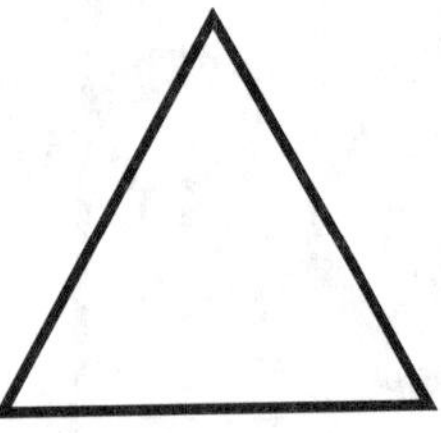

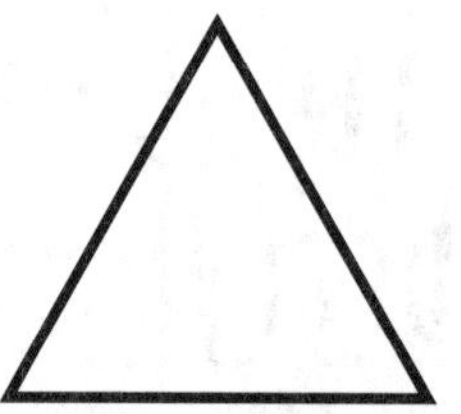

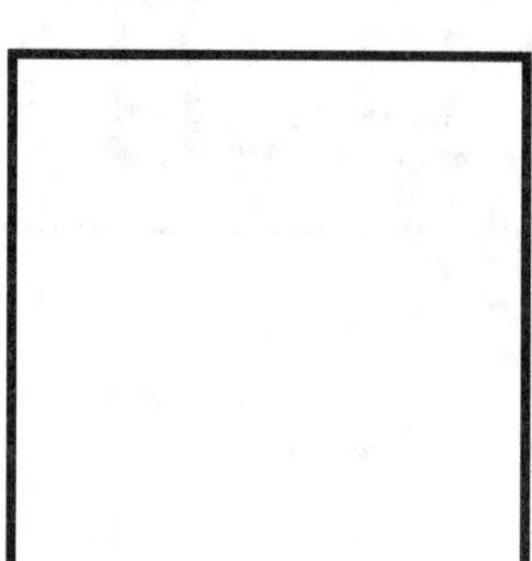

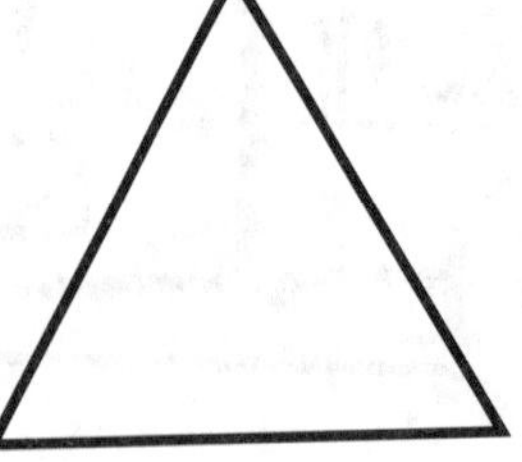

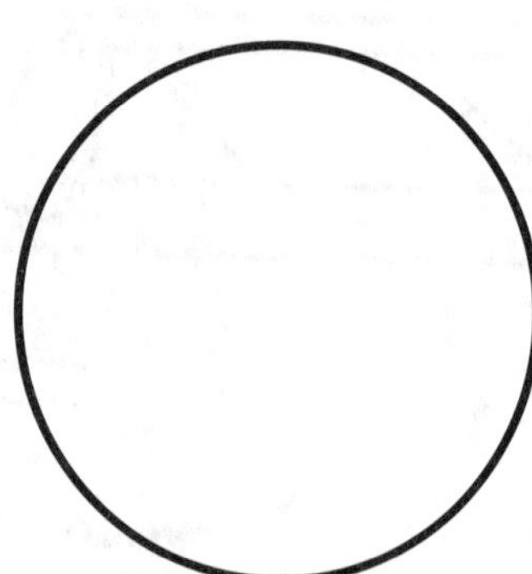

Parents: Point to the triangle at the top of the page. Trace the shape with your finger as you say, "This is a triangle. It has three sides." Ask your child to color all the triangles on the page.

Triangle Search

Look closely. Color the △s.

Parents: **Ask your child to point to all the triangles in the scene and color them.**

Rectangle

Look closely.

Color the ☐ s.

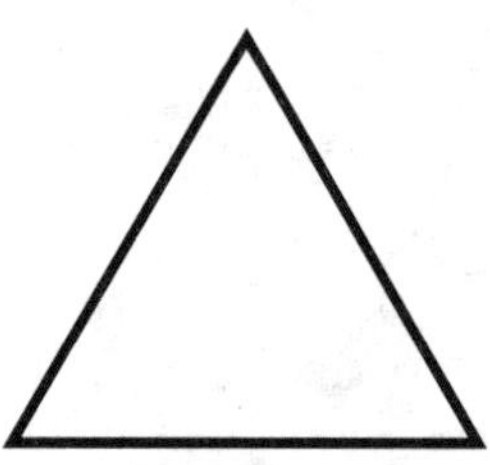

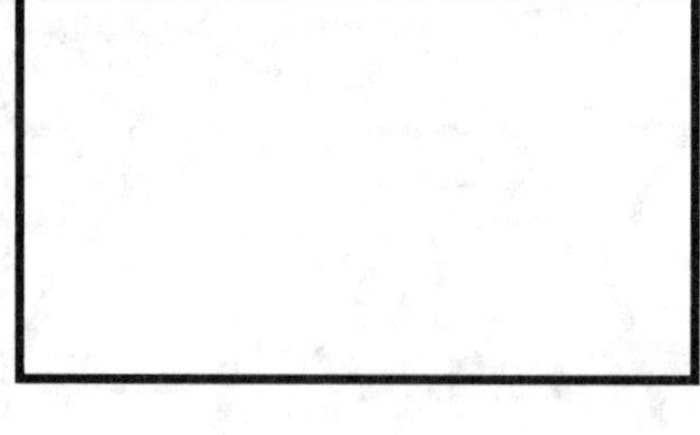

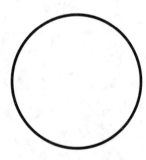

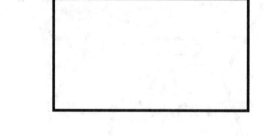

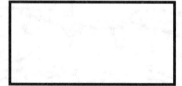

Parents: **Point to the rectangle at the top of the page. Trace the shape with your finger as you say, "This is a rectangle. It has two long sides that are the same and two short sides that are the same." Ask your child to color all the rectangles on the page.**

Rectangle Search

Look closely. Color the ▭s.

Parents: Ask your child to point to all the rectangles in the scene and color them.

Shape Match

Match the shapes that are the same.

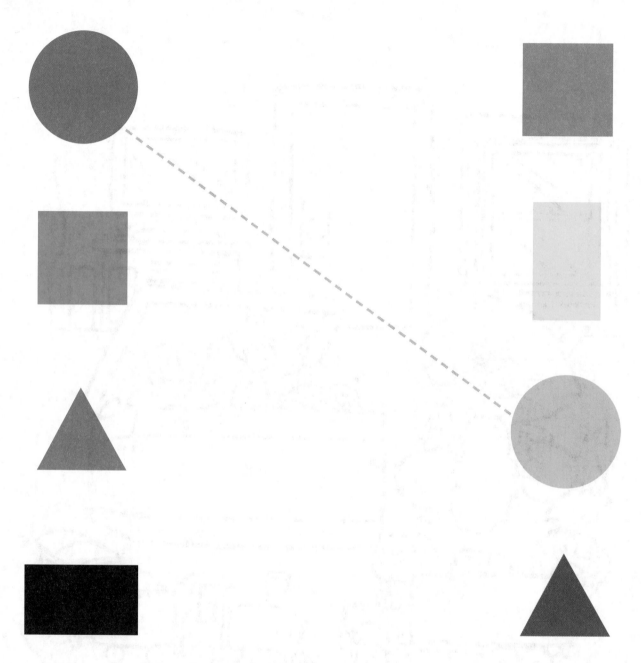

Parents: Ask your child to point to and name each shape. Then ask him or her to draw a line to connect the shapes that are the same.

Snack Time

Match the shapes that are the same.

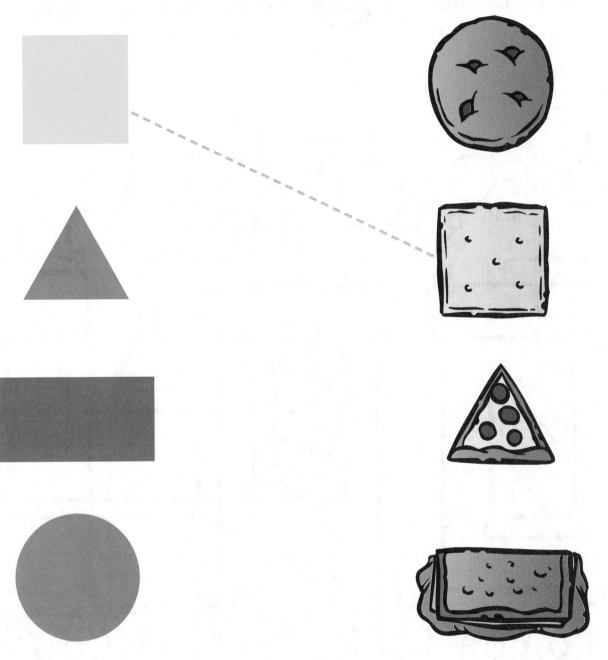

Parents: **Ask your child to point to and name each shape in the left-hand column and the shape of the snacks in the right-hand column. Then ask him or her to draw a line to connect the shapes that are the same.**

All Aboard!

Color the □s . Color the ○s .

Color the △s. Color the ▭s.

Parents: Help your child read each direction, making sure he or she identifies the colors and shapes correctly. Then ask your child to color the shapes in the picture using the color code. Have your child color the shapes on the next page using the same code.

TICKETS

In the Kitchen

Look closely. Color the shapes.

Parents: **Help your child find and color the circles, squares, triangles, and rectangles.**

A-Maze-ing

Color the □s.

Parents: **Ask your child to identify the different shapes on the page. Then have him or her color all the squares to make a path from the dog to the doghouse.**

Home Sweet Home

Color the △s.

Parents: **Ask your child to identify the different shapes on the page. Then have him or her color all the triangles to make a path from the bird to the nest.**

Month 3 Checklist

Hands-on activities to help prepare your child for school!

MATH

Counting from 1 to 5: pages 67-89, 95-96

This month introduces number concepts. Children learn to identify sets of one to five objects and recognize the numerals that represent each set. You can help your child with these skills through the following activities:

- ❑ Complete the worksheets.
- ❑ Provide assorted sets of small objects such as beans, buttons, pasta, or cereal pieces for your child to count. Display a group of objects and ask your child to count and tell how many there are. Also, display two groups of items with different amounts—e.g., two pieces of cereal and five pieces of cereal. Ask your child to tell you which group has *more*. Continue with other examples for the concepts *fewer* and *same*.
- ❑ Write the numerals 1 to 5 on separate index cards or paper slips. Set the number cards on a table. Give your child objects to count. Ask him or her to read each number and then place that many objects next to the number.
- ❑ Visit the library with your child and borrow a variety of counting books. Explore them together.
- ❑ Play "Simon Says." Be sure to use directions that involve numbers 1 through 5. For example, say, "Simon says, clap your hands three times."
- ❑ If you are setting the table for five or fewer people, invite your child to help. He or she can count out the appropriate number of napkins, forks, spoons, plates, and so on.
- ❑ When you and your child are out in your neighborhood, point out groups of one to five. For example, say, "I see one stop sign at the corner, and I see three children playing on the swings."
- ❑ Ask your child to draw pictures that show 1, 2, 3, 4, and 5.

Comparing Sizes: pages 90-94

Children develop spatial awareness as they compare the size and length of different objects. The following activities will help your child build his or her vocabulary and develop skills relating to measurement:

- ❑ Complete the worksheets.
- ❑ Give your child practice comparing sizes in everyday situations. For example, you might call attention to two different-sized boxes of cereal or cans of food and ask your child to tell you which is big and which is little. Similarly, you can point out three different-sized items and ask, "Which one is the biggest? Which is the littlest?"
- ❑ Cut a straw or string into two pieces. Ask your child which piece is long and which is short. Or, have your child compare three pieces and tell you which one is the longest and which is the shortest.
- ❑ Have your child compare the length of his or her shoe with yours.
- ❑ Point to two items in your home and encourage your child to compare their sizes.
- ❑ Compare the sizes and lengths of different fruits and vegetables.
- ❑ Invite your child to create balls out of clay and compare their sizes. Then have him or her roll the balls into snakes and compare their lengths.

Treat Time

Match each animal to a treat.

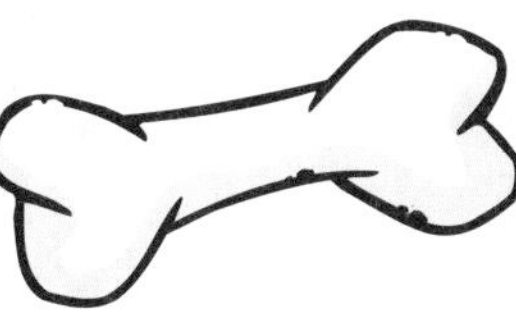

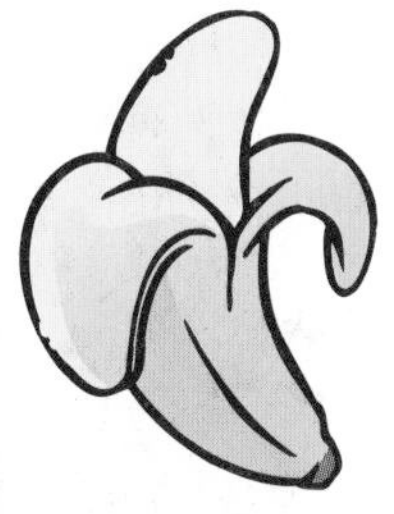

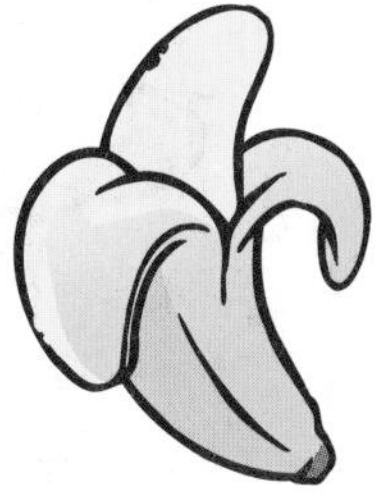

Parents: (Top) Ask your child, "Is there a bone for each dog?" Have him or her trace the line from each dog to each bone. (Bottom) Ask, "Is there a banana for each monkey?" Have your child draw a line from each monkey to a banana.

Counting to 1

Count and color 1.

1

Count and circle 1.

**Parents: (Top) Point to the number 1 and say, "This is the number 1." Ask your child to count the birds in the picture. Have him or her color the bird.
(Bottom) Ask your child to count and circle one bird.**

For the Birds

Count and color 1 in each group.

Parents: **Ask your child to count and color one picture in each group.**

Counting to 2

2

Count and color 2.

Count and circle 2.

Parents: (Top) Point to the number 2 and say, "This is the number 2." Ask your child to count the gingerbread houses in the picture. Have him or her color the gingerbread houses. (Bottom) Ask your child to count and circle two gingerbread men.

Sweet Treats

Count and color 2 in each group.

Parents: **Ask your child to count and color two pictures in each group.**

MATH

Counting to 3

Count and color 3.

3

Count and circle 3.

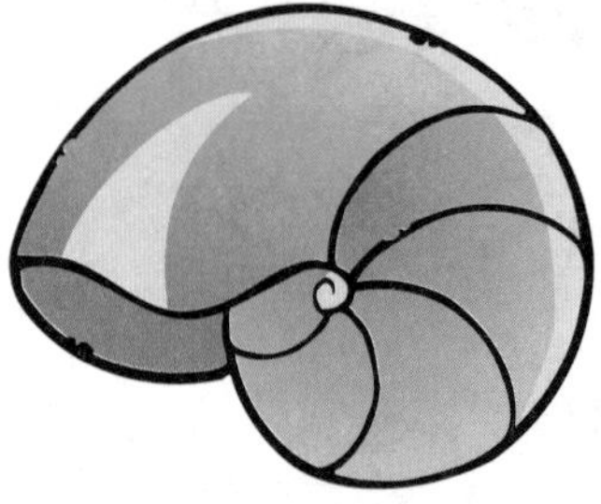 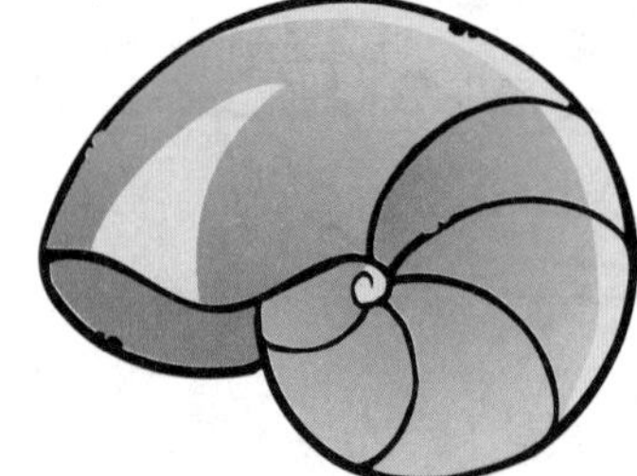

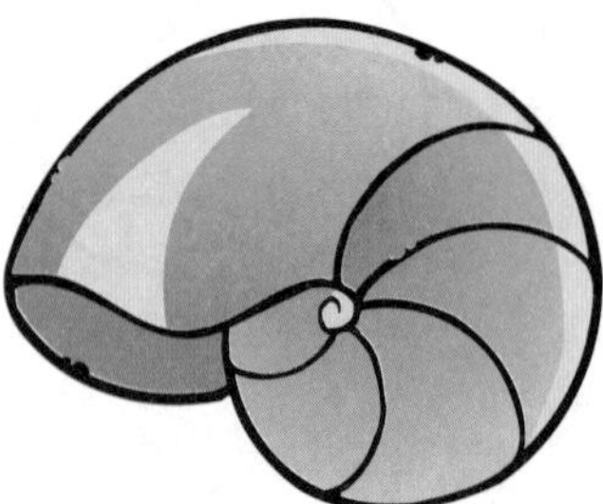 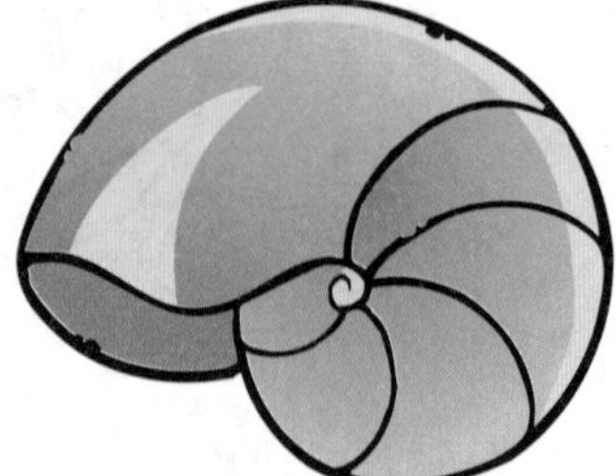 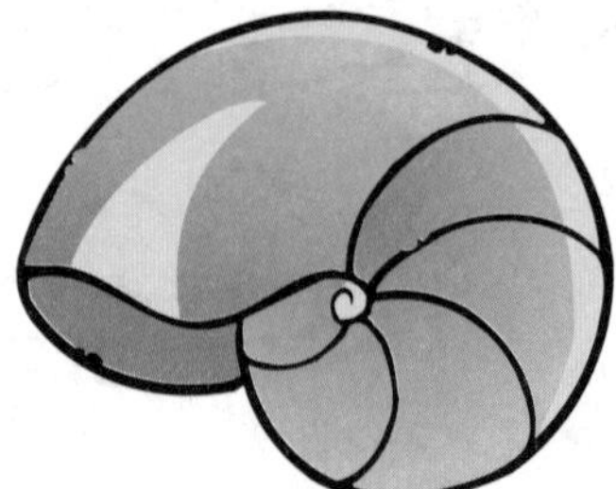

Parents: (Top) Point to the number 3 and say, "This is the number 3." Ask your child to count the shells in the picture. Have him or her color the shells.
(Bottom) Ask your child to count and circle three shells.

Beach Fun

Count and color 3 in each group.

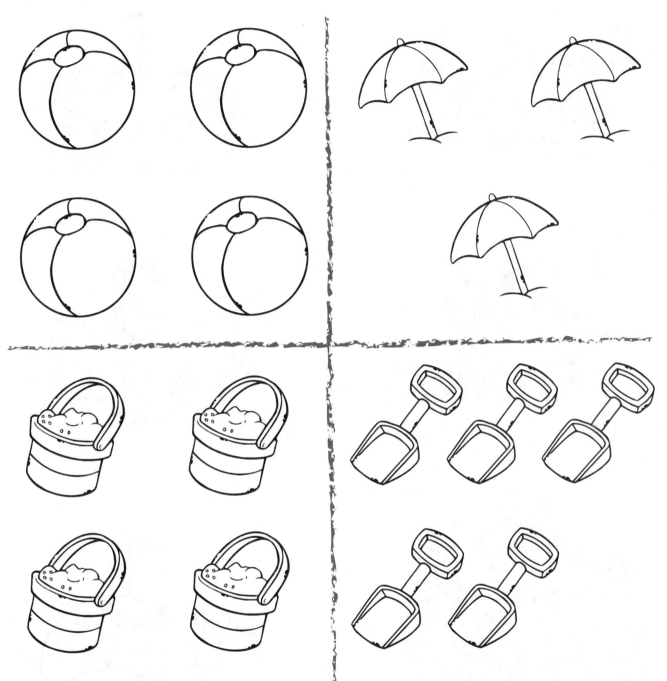

Parents: Ask your child to count and color three pictures in each group.

Circus Fun

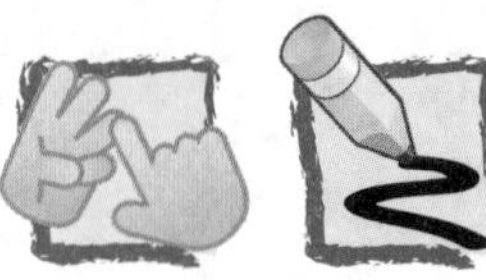

Draw a line to the correct number.

1

3

2

Parents: Ask your child to count the number of clowns in each group. Have him or her draw a line to connect the clowns to the number that shows how many there are.

Music Fun

Circle the correct number.

1 2

3 2

2 3

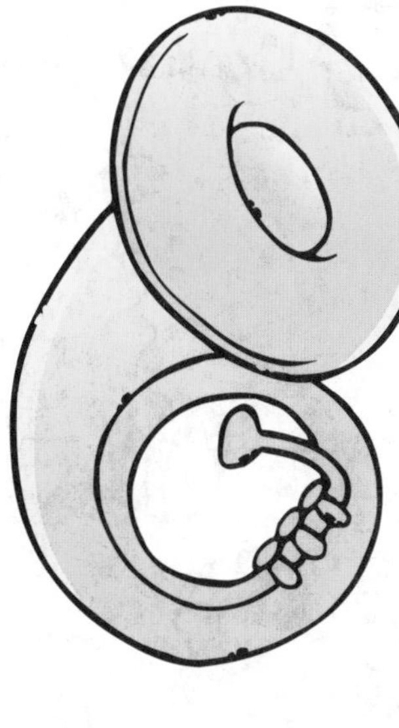

3 1

Parents: **Ask your child to count the number of instruments in each group. Have him or her circle the number that shows how many there are.**

Counting to 4

4

Count and color 4.

Count and circle 4.

Parents: (Top) Point to the number 4 and say, "This is the number 4." Ask your child to count the teddy bears in the picture. Have him or her color the teddy bears. (Bottom) Ask your child to count and circle four dolls.

Toy Time

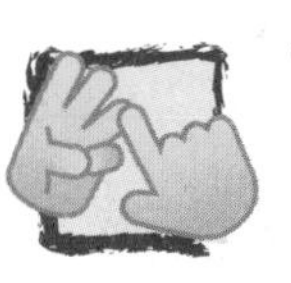

Count and color 4 in each group.

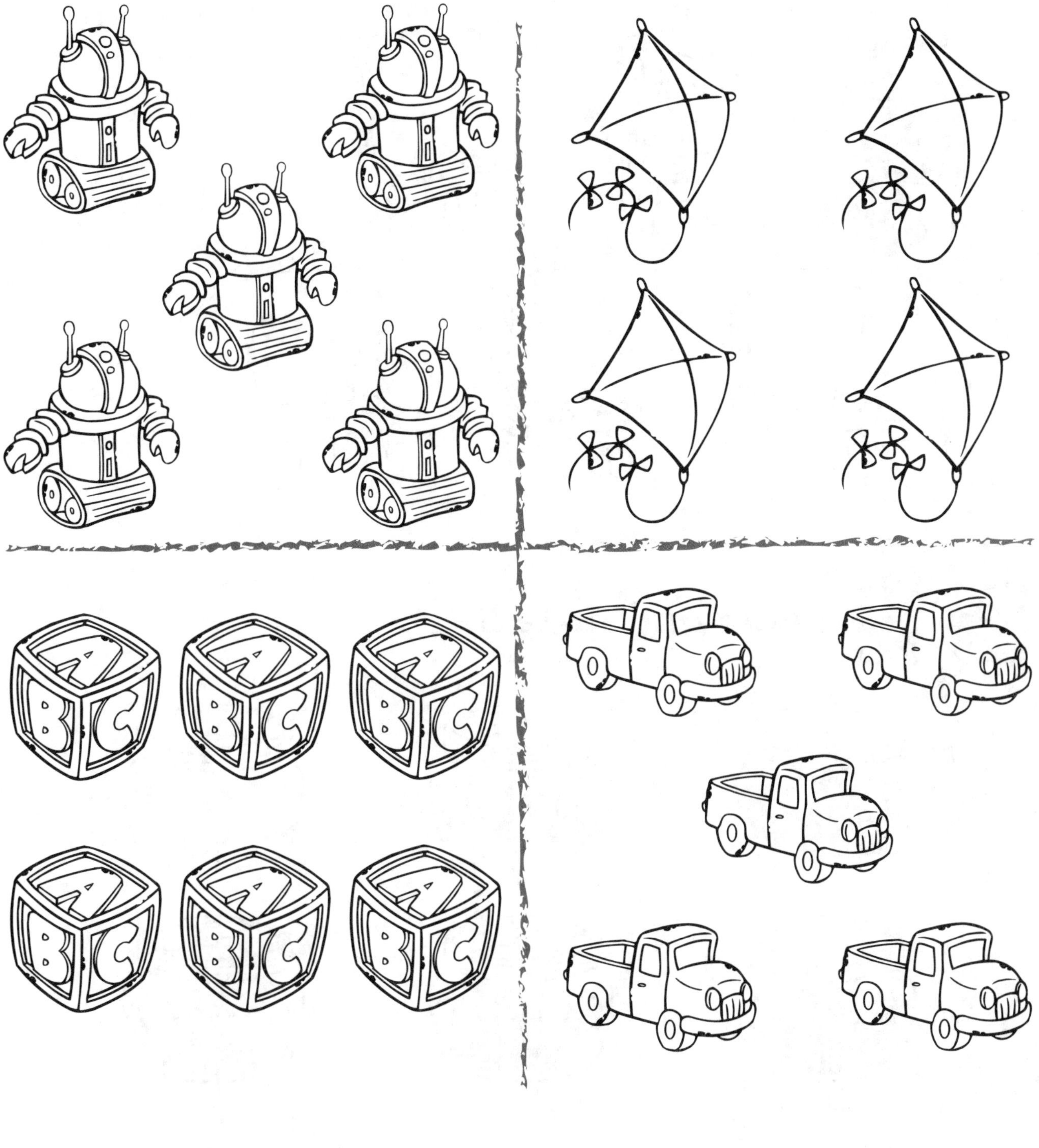

Parents: **Ask your child to count and color four pictures in each group.**

Counting to 5

5

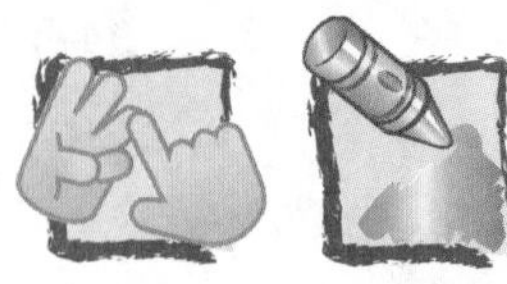

Count and color 5.

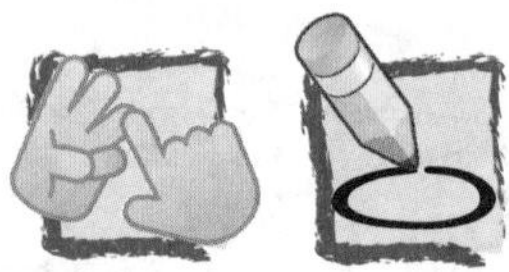

Count and circle 5.

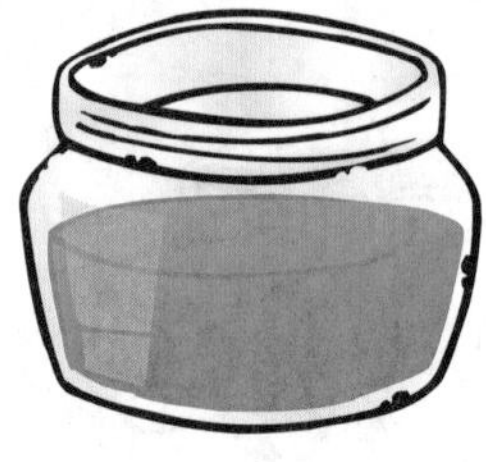

Parents: (Top) Point to the number 5 and say, "This is the number 5." Ask your child to count the easels in the picture. Have him or her color the easels.
(Bottom) Ask your child to count and circle five jars of paint.

Art Smarts

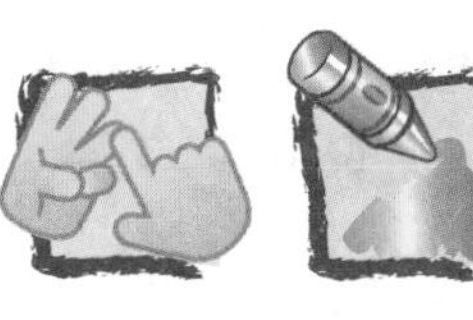

Count and color 5 in each group.

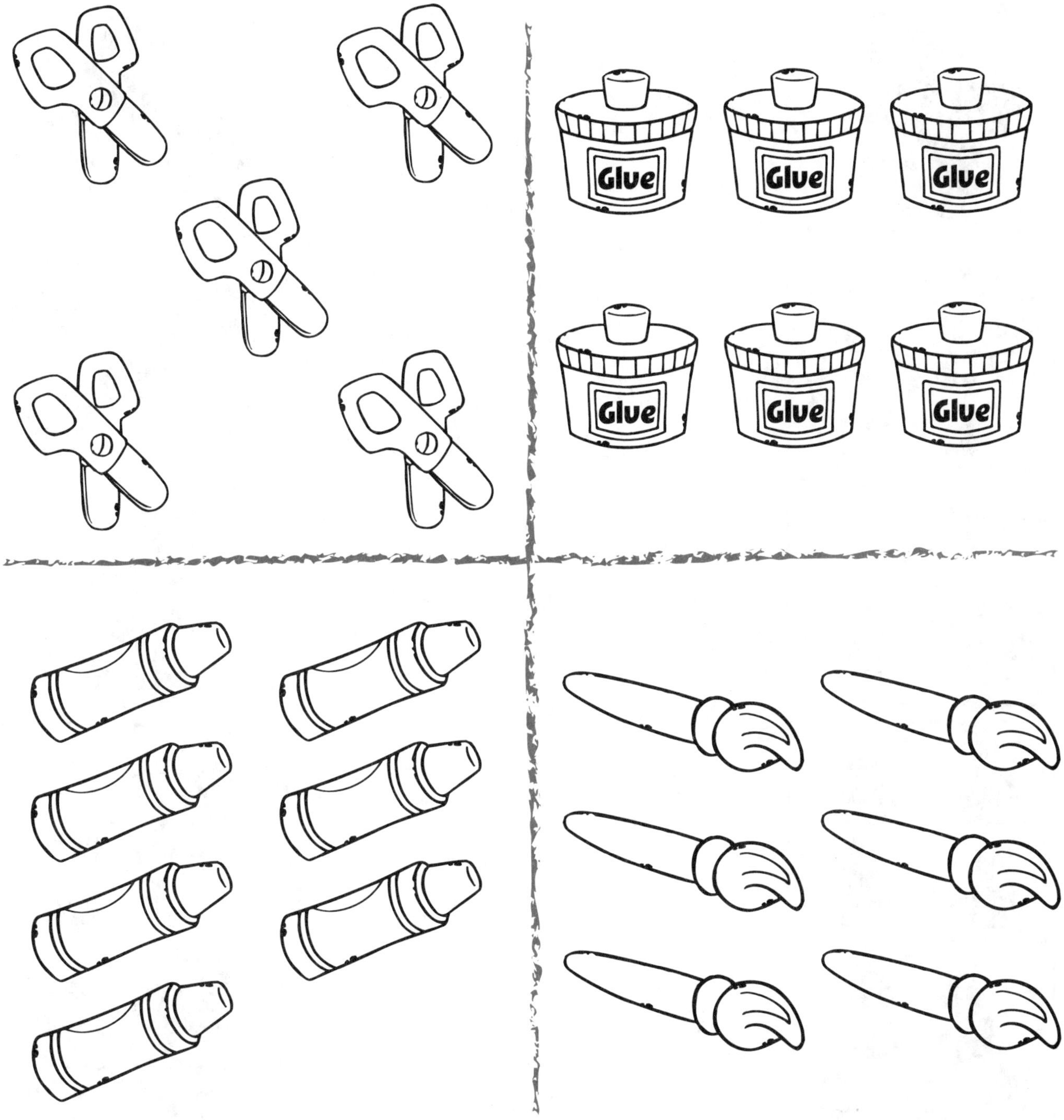

Glue

Glue

Glue

Glue

Glue

Glue

Parents: Ask your child to count and color five pictures in each group.

On the Farm

Match the ones with the same number.

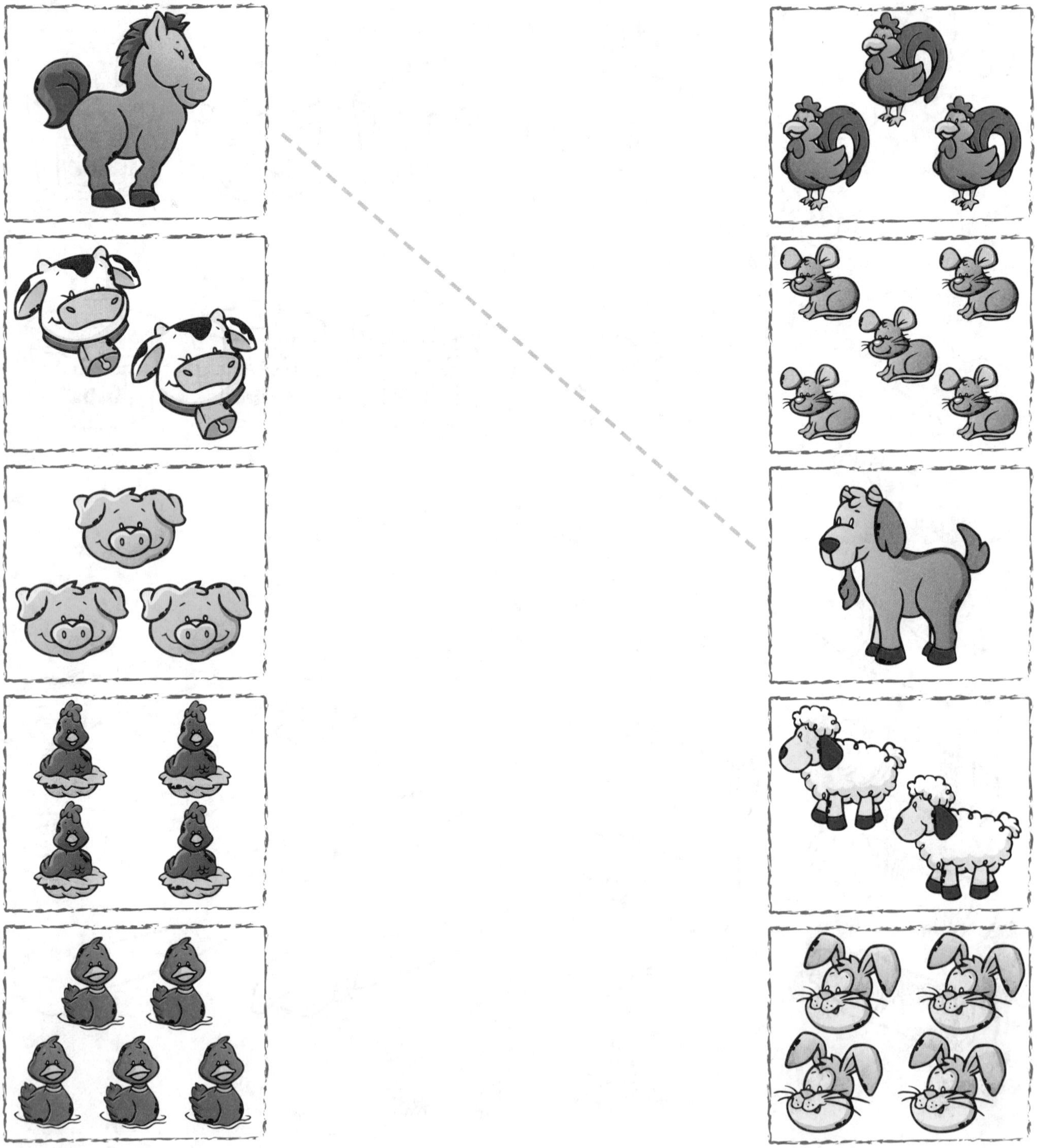

Parents: **Have your child draw a line from the horse to the goat. Ask, "Why do the horse and goat go together?" (There is one horse and one goat.) Then ask your child to match the other groups with the same number of animals.**

At the Zoo

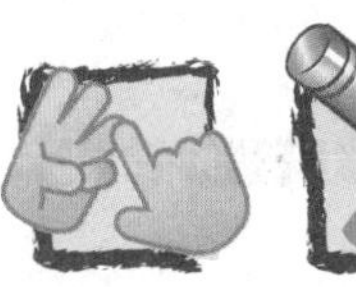

Count and color to show the correct number.

1	
2	
3	
4	
5	

Parents: Have your child read the number at the beginning of each row and color that many animals in the row.

MATH

Gone Fishing

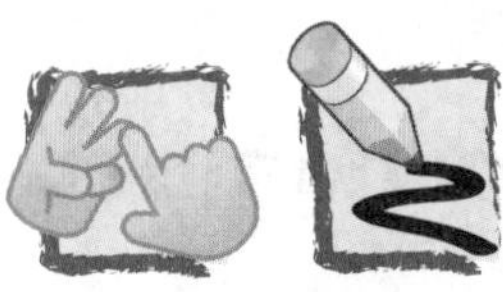

Count. Draw a line to the correct numbers.

1

2

3

4

5

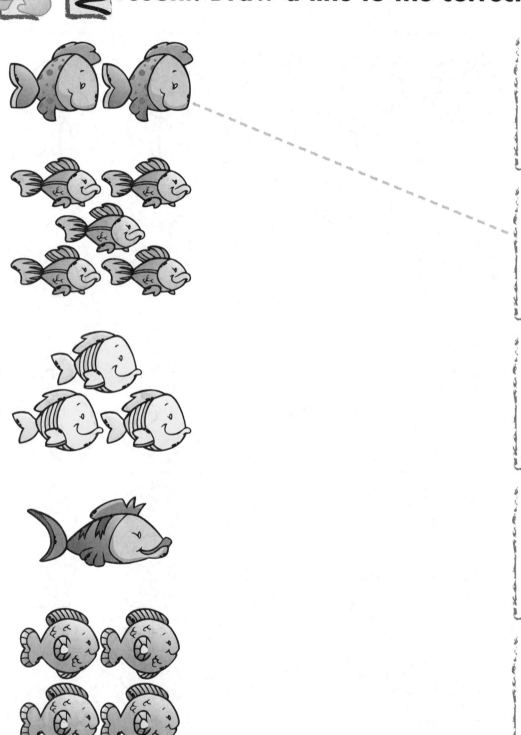

Parents: Have your child count the fish in each group and draw a line to that number on the right.

Under the Sea

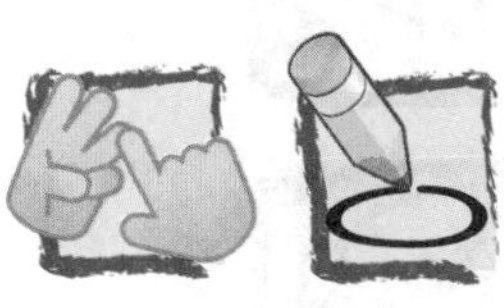

Count. Circle the correct number.

2 4 1

3 2 5

1 3 5

3 2 1

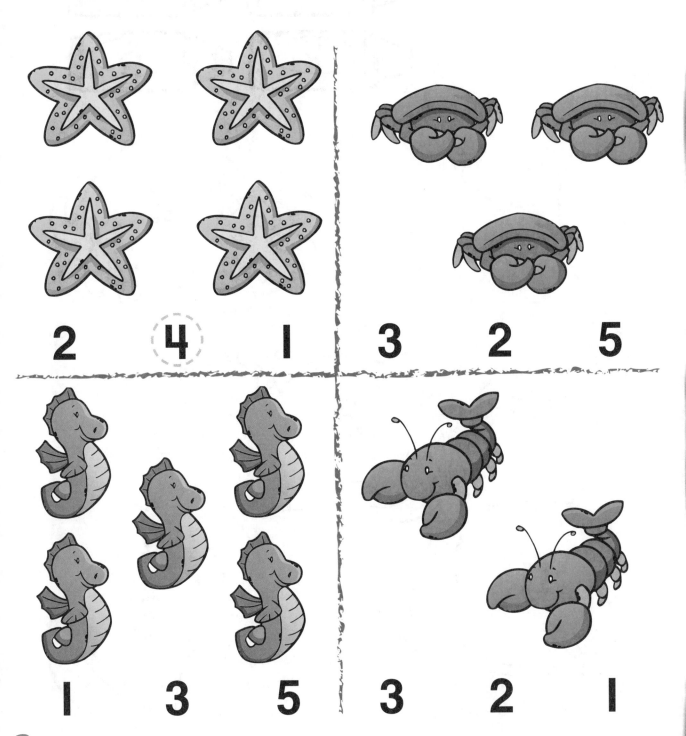

Parents: **Ask your child to count the number of sea creatures in each group. Have him or her circle the number that shows how many there are.**

Color by Number

Color.

Parents: Have your child point to and read the numeral on each crayon and identify the color of the crayon. Then ask your child to color the dinosaurs using the crayon code.

Recognizing numerals; identifying colors; following directions

The Cats' Picnic

Look closely.

Count and circle how many.

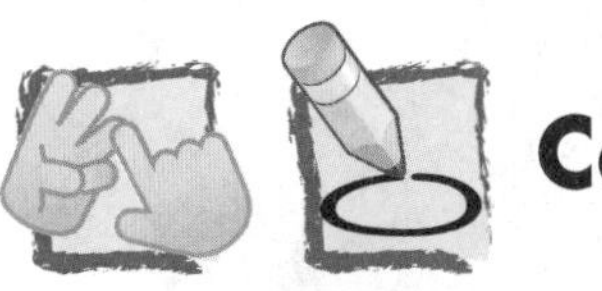

Parents: Ask your child to count the number of picnic baskets, cats, clouds, ants, and trees in the picture. Have him or her circle the number that he or she counted for each.

MATH

Apple Trees

Draw 🍎s on the 🌳.

1 2 3 4 5

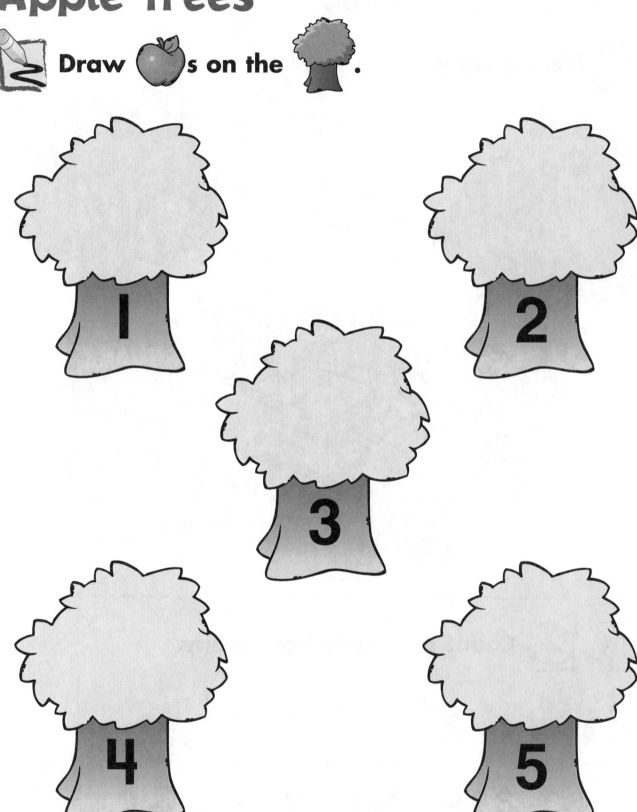

Parents: Have your child read the number on each tree trunk and draw that many apples on the tree.

The Same Amount

Match the ones with the same number.

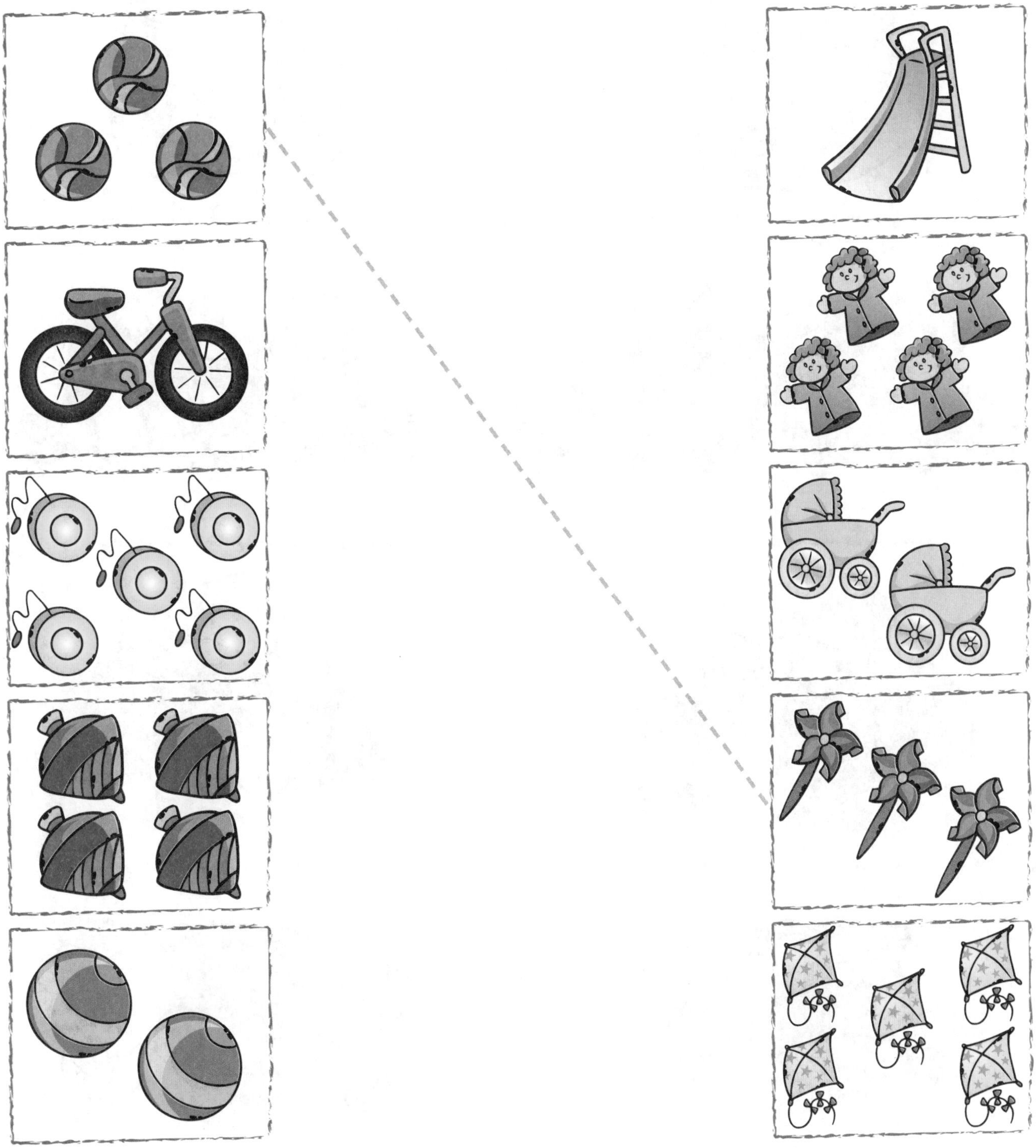

Parents: Have your child draw a line from the marbles to the pinwheels. Ask, "Why do the marbles and pinwheels go together?" (There are three marbles and three pinwheels.) Then ask your child to match the other groups with the same number of toys.

More

Circle the group with more.

Parents: Help your child count the number of fish in each bowl. Have him or her circle the bowl that has more fish. Repeat for each row, discussing the number of birds, bears, and bees.

Fewer

Circle the group with fewer.

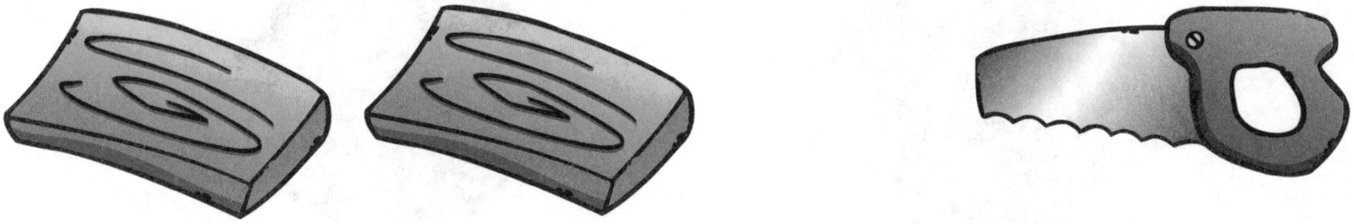

Parents: Help your child identify the objects pictured in each row. Then have him or her count the number of objects in each group and circle the one that has fewer.

Same Size

Look closely.

Circle the cows that are the same size.

Circle the sheep that are the same size.

Parents: **Have your child point to the two turkeys and compare them. Ask, "How are they the same?" Help your child see that the turkeys are the same size. Then have him or her circle the cows and sheep that are the same size.**

Big and Little

Look closely.

Color the big animal.
Circle the little animal.

Parents: Ask your child to point to the big lion and then to the little lion. Then have him or her color the big animal and circle the little animal in each row.

Littlest and Biggest

Look closely.

Color the biggest.
Circle the littlest.

Parents: Ask your child to point to the biggest boat and then to the littlest boat. Then have him or her color the biggest vehicle and circle the littlest vehicle in each row.

Long and Short

Look closely.

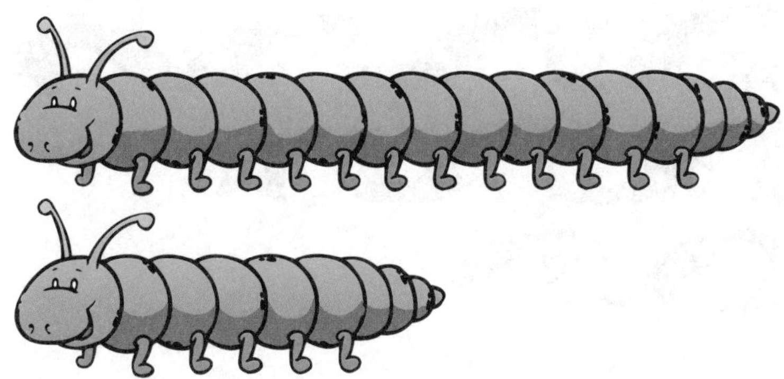

Color the long ones red.
Color the short ones blue.

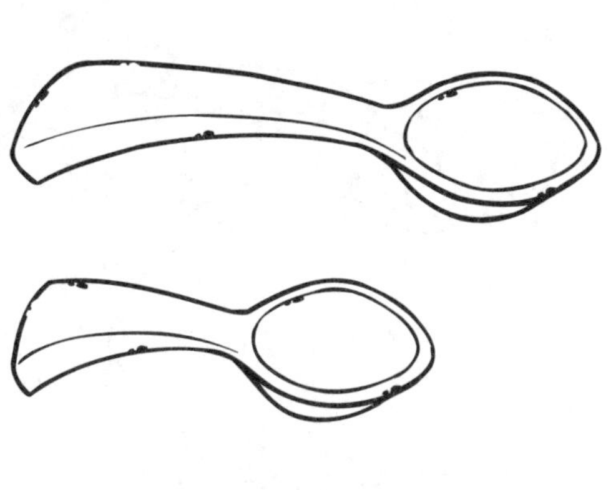

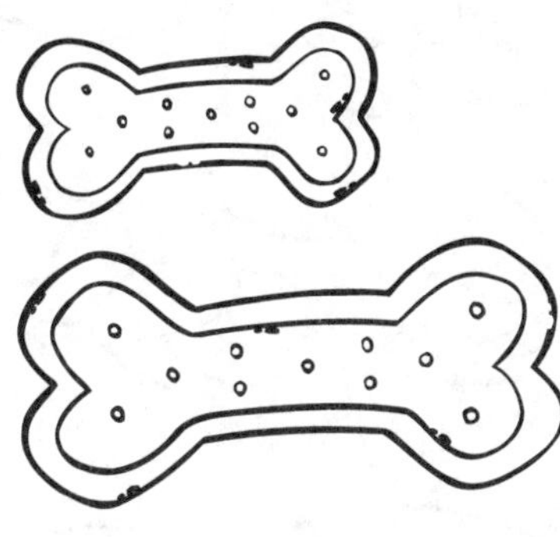

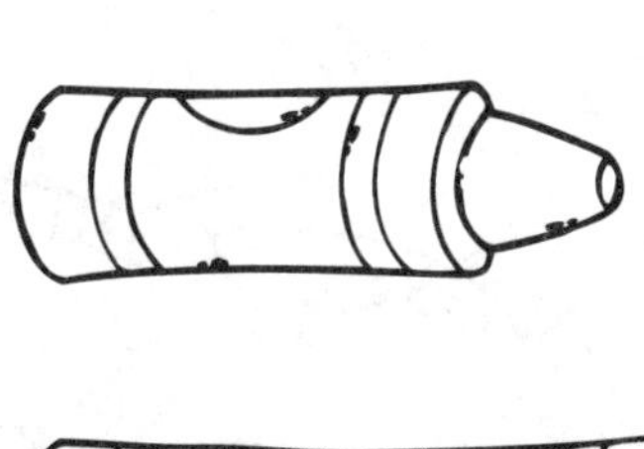

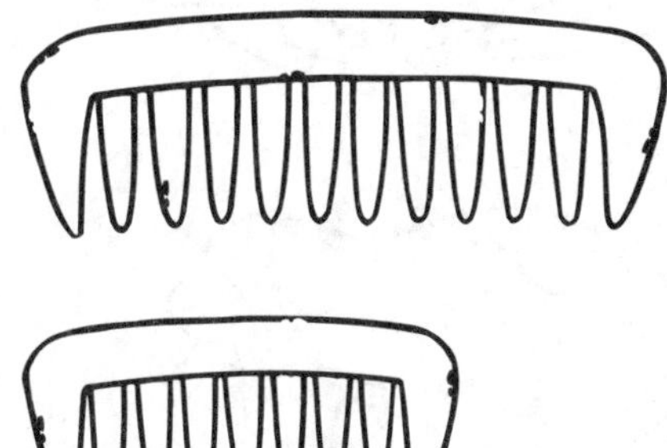

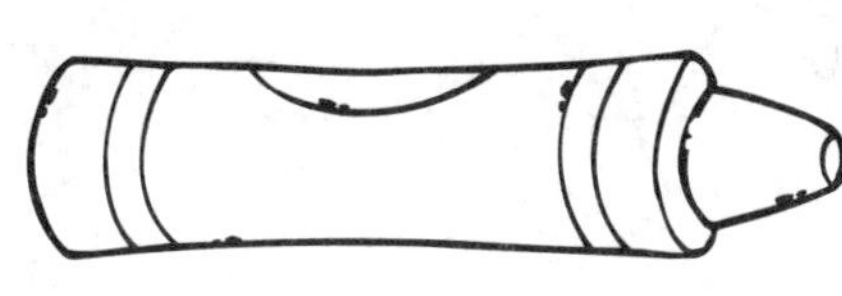

Parents: Ask your child to point to the long caterpillar and then to the short caterpillar. Then have him or her color the long object in each group red and the short object in each group blue.

Longest and Shortest

Look closely.

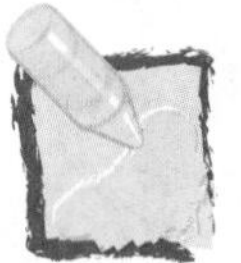

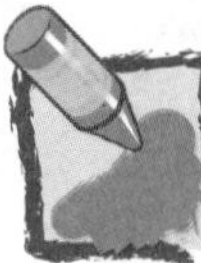

Color the longest yellow.
Color the shortest green.

Parents: Ask your child to point to the longest ribbon and then to the shortest ribbon. Then have him or her color the longest animal in each column yellow and the shortest animal in each column green.

Cut out the cards.

Parents: Help your child cut out the playing cards. Mix the cards and ask your child to match them by putting together the cards that show the same number of objects. Mix the cards again and place them face down. Take turns flipping over two cards. If the cards show the same amount, the player keeps the cards and goes again. If not, turn the cards face down and place them back in their original places. Continue taking turns until all the cards are matched.

Month 4 Checklist

Hands-on activities to help prepare your child for school!

LANGUAGE

Rhyming Words: pages 99-109, 125-128

Some of the worksheets for this month focus on rhyming words. Learning rhyming words helps children listen for specific sounds at the end of a word—a necessary skill for beginning readers.

- ❑ Complete the worksheets.
- ❑ Read rhyming stories and nursery rhymes to your child and ask which words rhyme. Try this with songs, too.
- ❑ Ask your child to change a favorite nursery rhyme by replacing key words with rhyming words. For example, "Twinkle, Twinkle, Little Star" may become "Twinkle, Twinkle, Little Car."
- ❑ Make up riddles to help your child practice rhyming words. For example, "I say quack, quack. My name rhymes with truck. What am I?"
- ❑ Invite everyone in the family to play a silly rhyming game at the dinner table. When asking for an item of food, use a word that rhymes with it instead. For example, you might say "please pass the horn" when you want some corn. See how long you can play before someone starts laughing!
- ❑ Go on a scavenger hunt in your home to find pairs of objects that rhyme.
- ❑ Make new playing cards with pairs of rhyming pictures. Add them to the cards from pages 107 and 108 so you can make even more matches!

LANGUAGE

Opposites: pages 110-120

Understanding opposites is a prerequisite for many academic tasks—following directions, thinking, and reading. The activities here will help you make opposites more tangible for your child.

- ❑ Complete the worksheets.
- ❑ Try to use words that name opposites in everyday conversations.
- ❑ After your child completes each worksheet on opposites, find hands-on ways to reinforce the meaning of the words. For example, help your child sort clean clothes from dirty ones.
- ❑ Play "I Spy" using opposites. For example, you can say "I spy something little" when you really mean big.
- ❑ Say nursery rhymes together that use opposites, such as "Hickory, Dickory, Dock," "Jack and Jill," and "Pease Porridge Hot."
- ❑ Make new playing cards for *long* and *short, hot* and *cold, old* and *new, clean* and *dirty,* and *day* and *night.* Add them to the cards from pages 119 and 120 so you can make even more matches!
- ❑ Have your child use a toy car or truck to demonstrate push and pull.
- ❑ Have your child stretch a rubber band to demonstrate long and short.

Naming Words: pages 121-124

"Mama" and "Dada" are often the first words babies say. The names of family members and pets are among the most frequently used words in early vocabulary. Use the following activities to encourage vocabulary development with names for people and animals.

- ❑ Complete the worksheets.
- ❑ Make a scrapbook of family pictures. Label the pictures using words like mother, father, brother, and sister.
- ❑ Have your child draw a picture of each family member and help him or her label each picture—e.g., "my little sister." Make the pictures into a book and read the book together.
- ❑ Sing the song "Old MacDonald."
- ❑ Visit a farm or pet store. Have your child ask the farmer or storeowner to talk about his or her favorite animal.
- ❑ Read Brown Bear, Brown Bear, by Bill Martin, Jr. Invite your child to join in as you read the names of the animals.
- ❑ Go outside and look at the clouds. Share ideas about the shapes of the clouds and the animals they resemble.

Pizza Rhymes

Color the ones with rhyming names.

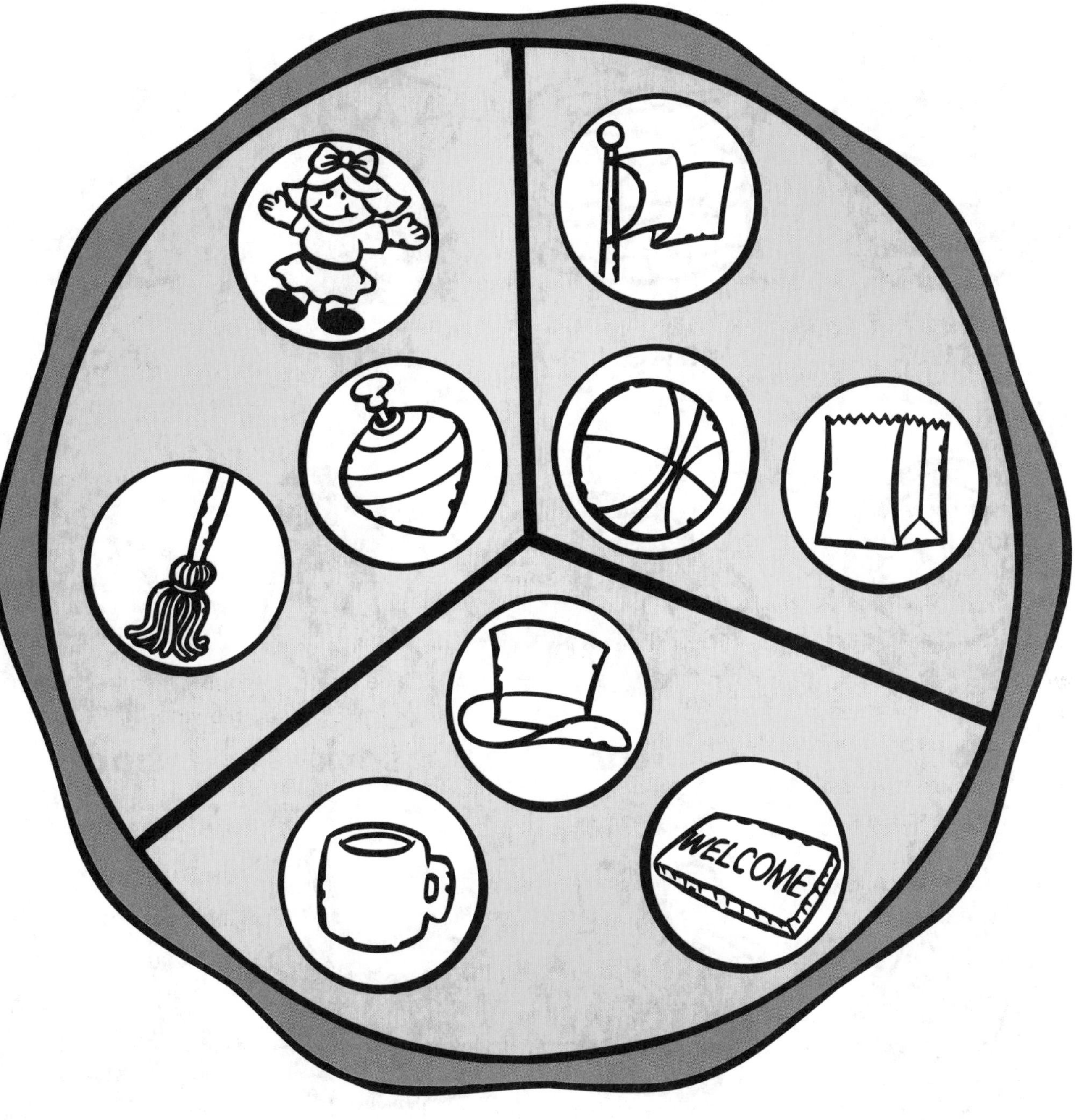

Parents: Point to each picture on the first slice of pizza and say its name. Have your child do the same. Explain that *mop* and *top* rhyme because they both have the -op sound at the end. Have your child color the mop and top. Then help him or her complete the rest of the page.

Identifying words that rhyme

Rows of Rhymes

Circle the one that rhymes with the first picture in each row.

snake	cake	dog	snail
clock	car	sock	boat
king	bee	drum	swing

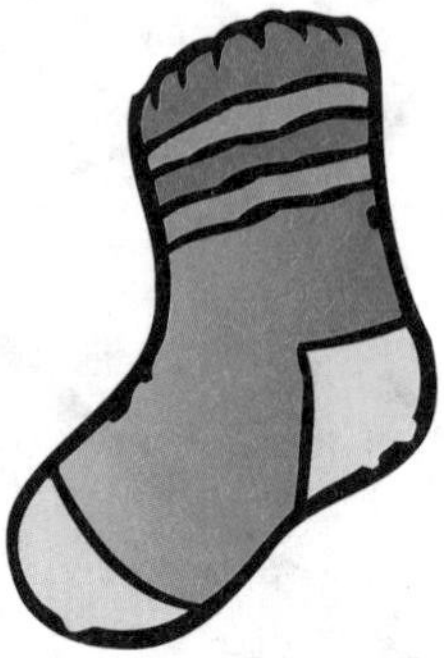

Parents: Point to the snake and say its name. Have your child do the same. Help him or her name the other pictures in the row. Explain that *snake* and *cake* rhyme because they both have the -ake sound at the end. Have your child cirlce the cake. Then help him or her complete the rest of the page.

Heart Rhymes

Color the ones with rhyming names.

Parents: Point to each picture in the first section of the heart and say its name. Have your child do the same. Explain that *pie* and *tie* rhyme because they both have the -ie sound at the end. Have your child color the pie and tie. Then help him or her complete the rest of the page.

LANGUAGE

Fan-cy Rhymes

Color the ones that rhyme with the first picture in each row.

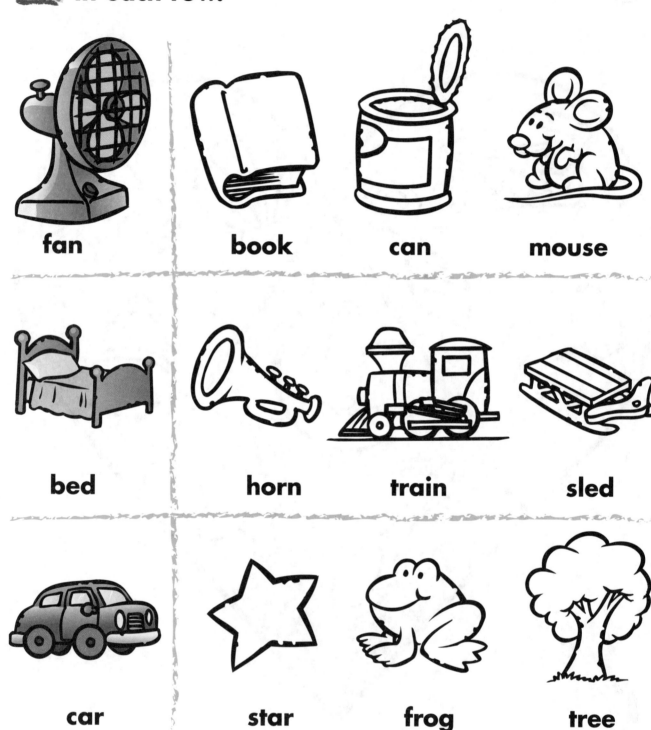

fan	**book**	**can**	**mouse**
bed	**horn**	**train**	**sled**
car	**star**	**frog**	**tree**

Parents: Point to the fan and say its name. Have your child do the same. Help him or her name the other pictures in the row. Explain that *fan* and *can* rhyme because they both have the -an sound at the end. Have your child color the can. Then help him or her complete the rest of the page.

Identifying words that rhyme

Train Load of Rhymes

train

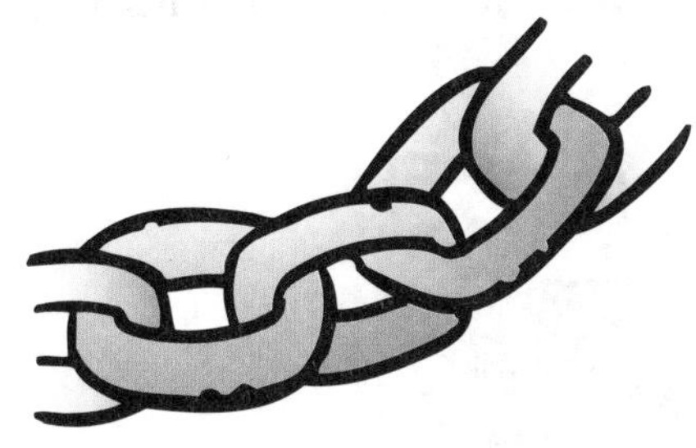

chain

Color the one that rhymes with  **.**

Circle the ones with rhyming names.

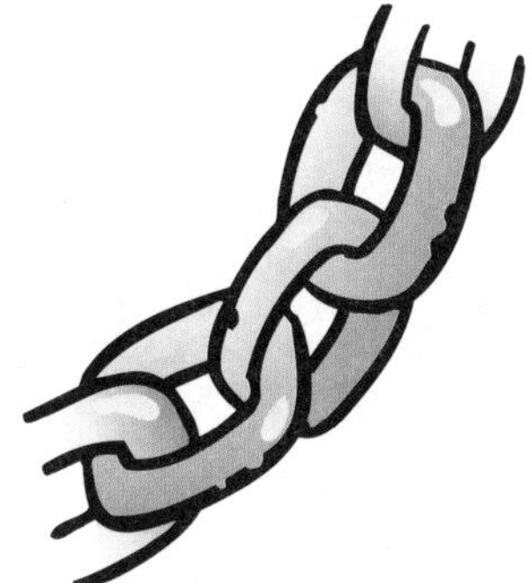

Parents: Point to each picture at the top of the page and say its name. Have your child do the same. Explain that *train* and *chain* rhyme because they both have the -ain sound at the end. Then help your child complete the rest of the page.

Animal Rhymes

Match the ones that rhyme.

Parents: Point to the cat and say its name. Have your child trace the line from the cat to the hat. Explain that *cat* and *hat* rhyme because they both have the -at sound at the end. Then help your child complete the rest of the page.

More Animal Rhymes

Match the ones that rhyme.

Parents: Point to the duck and say its name. Have your child trace the line from the duck to the truck. Explain that *duck* and *truck* rhyme because they both have the *-uck* sound at the end. Then help your child complete the rest of the page.

Pail of Rhymes

pail

nail

Color the one that rhymes with (nail).

Color the ones with rhyming names.

Parents: Point to each picture at the top of the page and say its name. Have your child do the same. Explain that *pail* and *nail* rhyme because they both have the *-ail* sound at the end. Then help your child complete the rest of the page.

Rhyming Game

Cut out the cards.

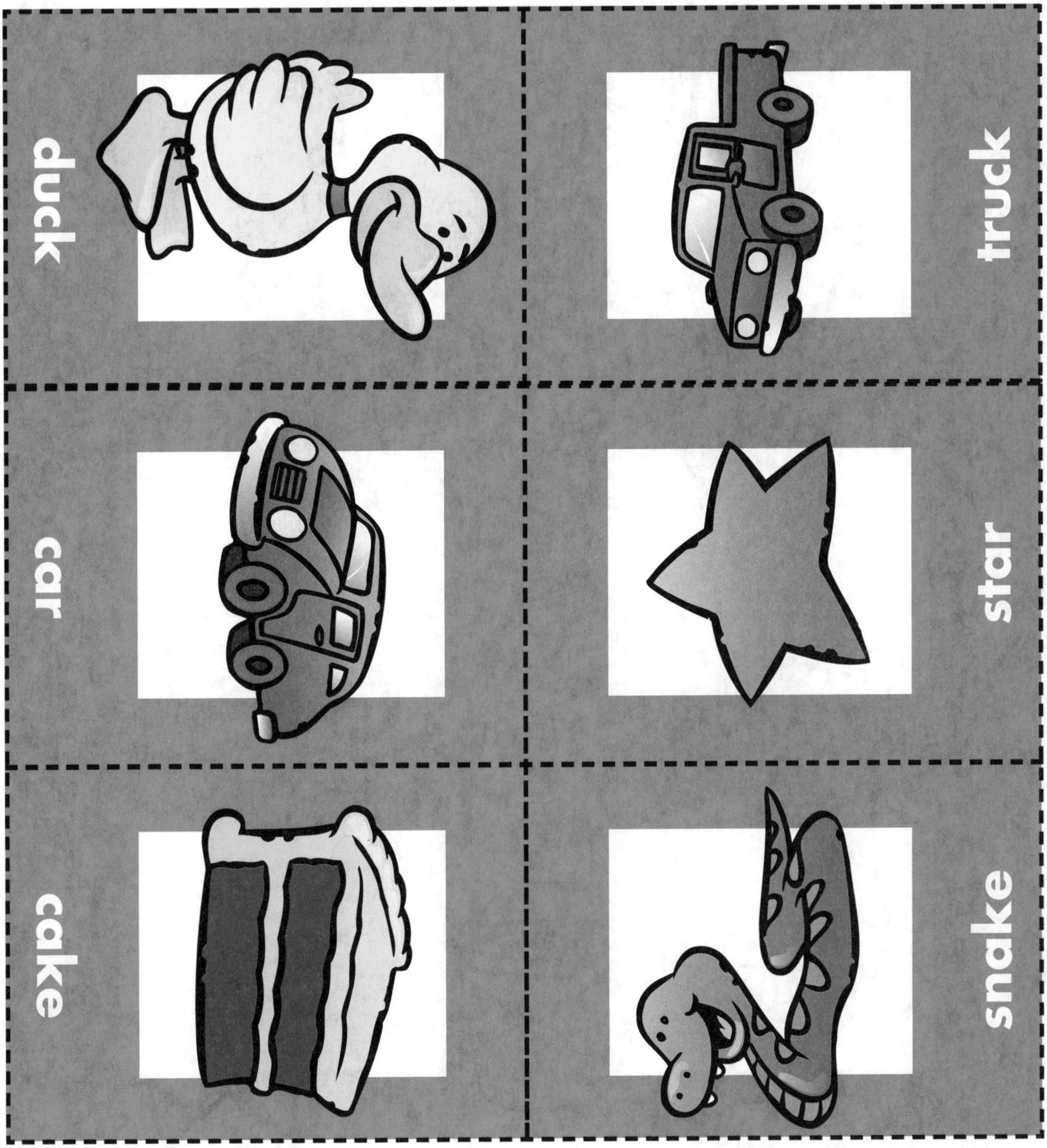

duck	truck
car	star
cake	snake

Parents: **Help your child cut along the lines to make six cards. Place the cards with the red border face up on a table. Have your child say the name of each picture and find the rhyming pairs.**

LANGUAGE

Rhyming Game

Cut out the cards.

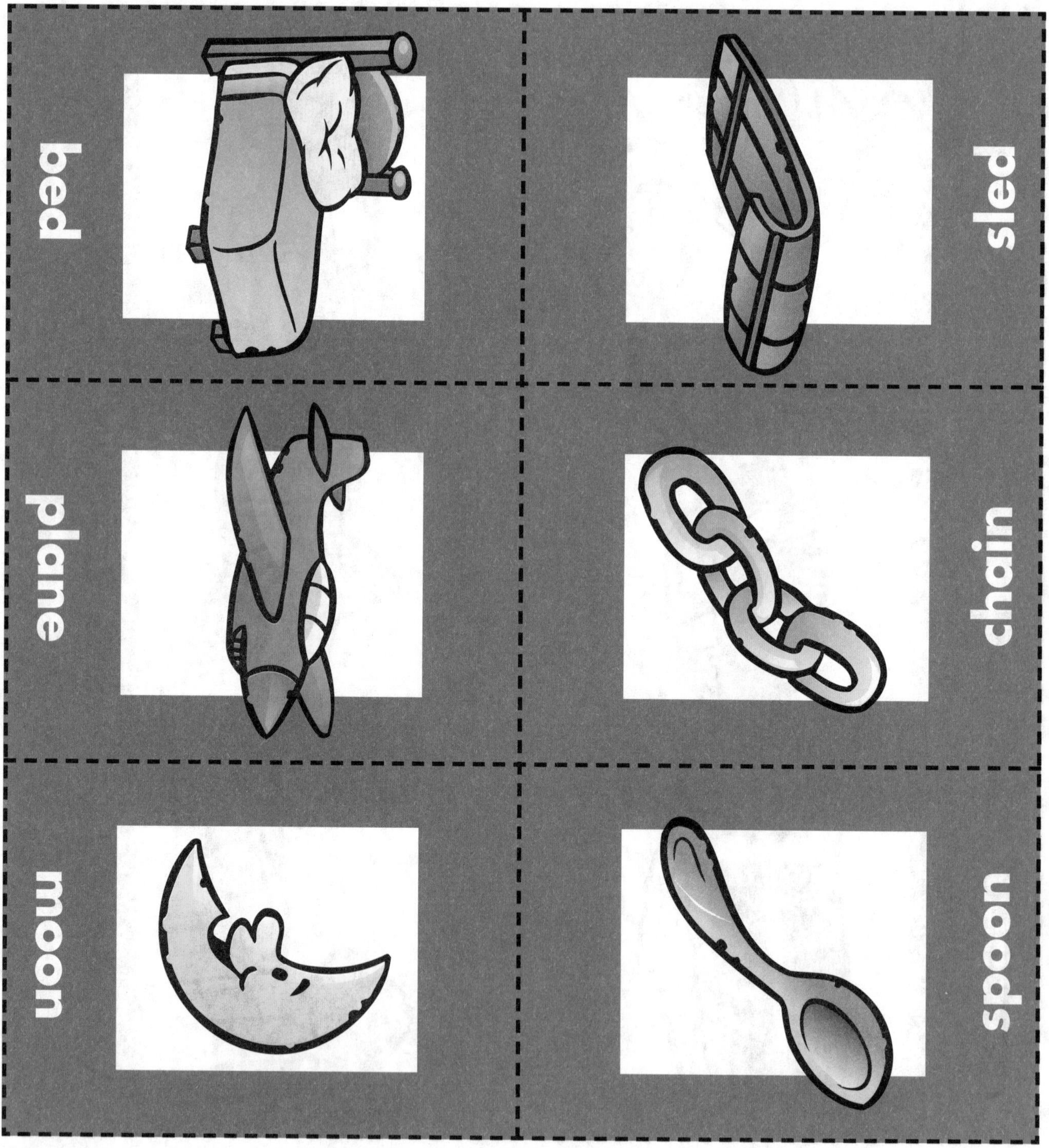

bed

sled

plane

chain

moon

spoon

Parents: Help your child cut along the lines to make six cards. Place the cards with the blue border face up on a table. Have your child say the name of each picture and find the rhyming pairs.

Bear Rhymes

bear **pear**

Color the one that rhymes with .

Color the ones with rhyming names.

Parents: Point to each picture at the top of the page and say its name. Have your child do the same. Explain that *bear* and *pear* rhyme because they both have the -ear sound at the end. Then help your child complete the rest of the page.

Long and Short

Look closely.

long

short

Color the long fish blue.

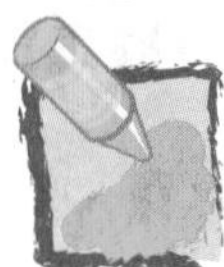

Color the short fish orange.

Parents: Ask your child to point to the bear with the *long* fishing rod and then to the bear with the *short* fishing rod. Point to the words *long* and *short*. Explain that they are called opposites. Then say, "Find the *long* fish and color it blue. Color the *short* fish orange."

Hot and Cold

Look closely.

hot

cold

Color the snowman that is hot yellow.

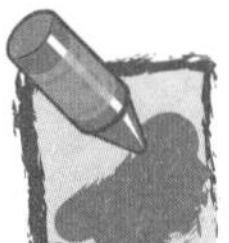

Color the snowman that is cold blue.

Parents: **Ask your child to point to the *hot* drink and then to the *cold* drink. Point to the words *hot* and *cold*. Explain that they are called opposites. Then say, "Find the snowman that is *hot* and color it yellow. Color the *cold* snowman blue."**

Opposites Attract

Match the opposites.

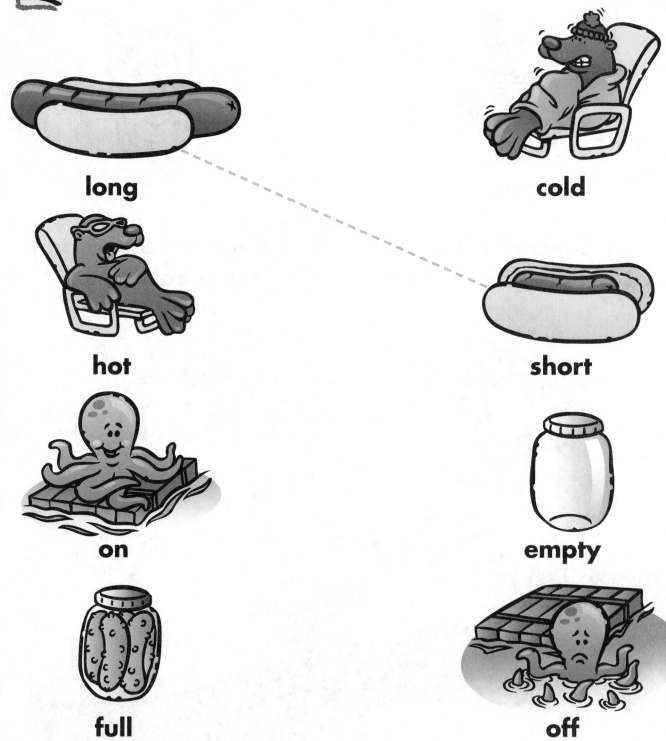

long

cold

hot

short

on

empty

full

off

Parents: Point to the picture at the top left and explain that the hot dog is *long*. Ask your child what the opposite of *long* is. Have him or her draw a line to the picture that shows the *short* hot dog. Repeat for each picture in the left-hand column.

Push and Pull

Look closely.

push

pull

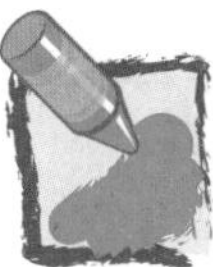

Color the truck being pushed red.

Color the truck being pulled green.

Parents: Ask your child to point to the raccoon that is *pushing* a wagon and then to the raccoon that is *pulling* a wagon. Point to the words *push* and *pull*. Explain that they are called opposites. Then say, "Find the truck that the raccoon is *pushing* and color it red. Color the truck that the raccoon is *pulling* green."

Old and New

Look closely.

old

new

Color the old toy lion green.

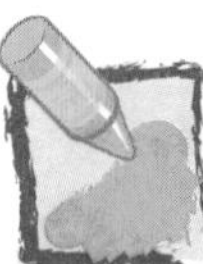

Color the new toy lion orange.

Parents: Ask your child to point to the *new* bike and then to the *old* bike. Point to the words *old* and *new*. Explain that they are called opposites. Then say, "Find the toy lion that is *old* and color it green. Color the *new* toy lion orange."

Clean and Dirty

Look closely.

clean

dirty

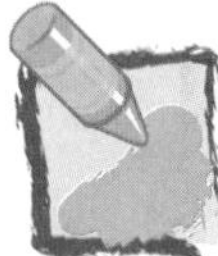

Color the clean bunny pink.

Color the dirty bunny brown.

Parents: Ask your child to point to the bunny with the *clean* vest and then to the bunny with the *dirty* vest. Point to the words *clean* and *dirty*. Explain that they are called opposites. Then say, "Find the *clean* bunny and color it pink. Color the *dirty* bunny brown."

Day and Night

Look closely.

day **night**

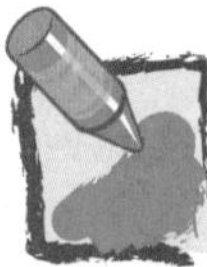

Color the penguin that is fishing during the day red.

Color the penguin that is fishing at night purple.

Parents: **Ask your child to point to the sky during the *day* and then to the sky at *night*. Point to the words *day* and *night*. Explain that they are called opposites. Then say, "Find the penguin that is fishing during the *day* and color it red. Color the penguin that is fishing at *night* purple."**

Opposites Review

Look at the first picture in each row. Circle its opposite.

wet

dirty

night

Parents: Have your child tell about the first picture in each row. Point out and read the word under each picture. Then have your child circle the picture that shows its opposite.

Practice Opposites

Match the opposites.

clean

short

long

sad

on

dirty

happy

off

Parents: **Point to the picture at the top left and explain that the turtle is *clean*. Ask your child what the opposite of *clean* is. Have him or her draw a line to the picture that shows the *dirty* turtle. Repeat for each picture in the left-hand column.**

Opposites Game

Cut out the cards.

open

closed

full

empty

big

little

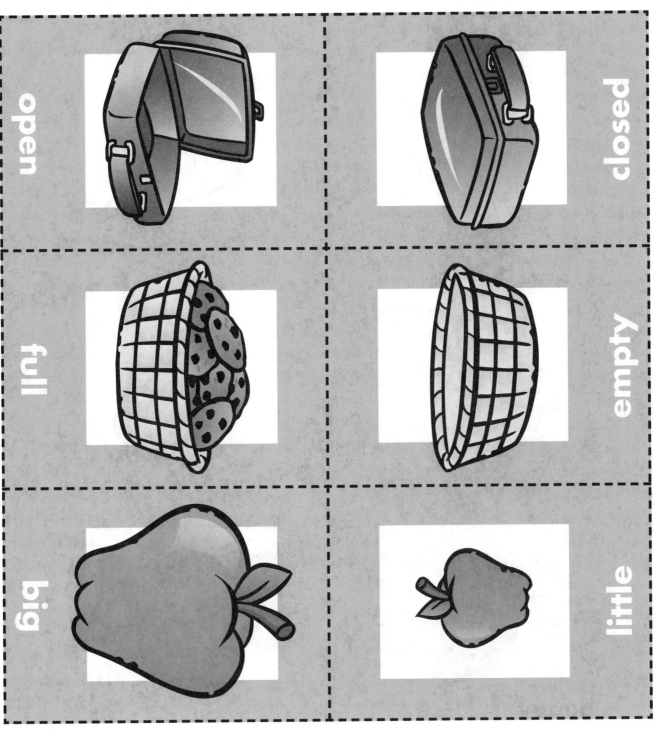

Parents: Help your child cut along the lines to make six cards. Place the cards with the orange border face up on a table. Talk about the pictures with your child and read each label. Then play a game to match the opposites.

Opposites Game

Cut out the cards.

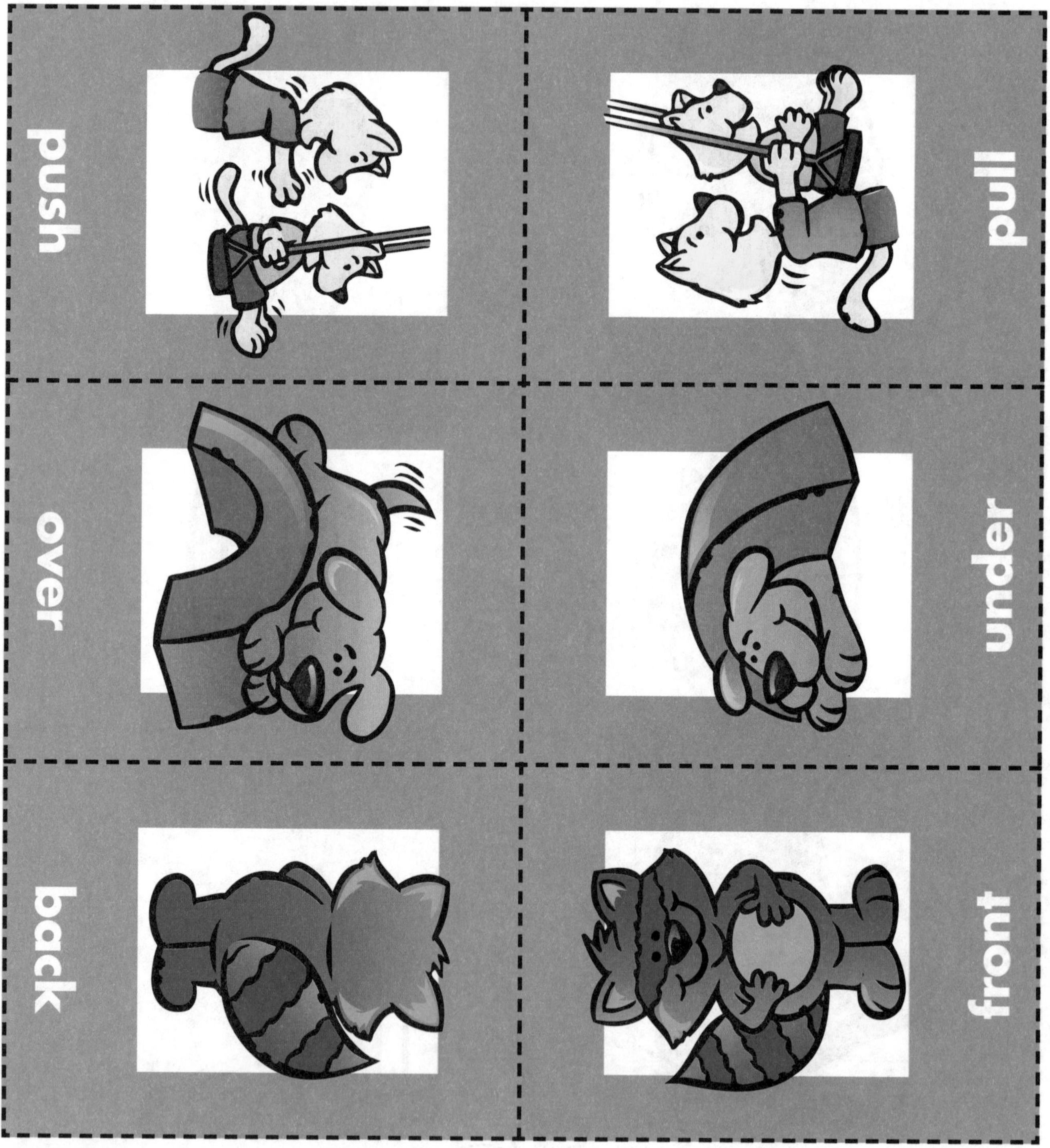

push

pull

over

under

back

front

Parents: Help your child cut along the lines to make six cards. Place the cards with the green border face up on a table. Talk about the pictures with your child and read each label. Then play a game to match the opposites.

Names for People

Look closely.

mother **father**

Color the mother's clothes red.

Color the father's clothes blue.

Parents: Help your child name each person at the top of the page. Point to the words *mother* and *father* and explain that they are names for people. Then say, "Find the mother in the picture and color her clothes red. Color the father's clothes blue."

More Names for People

Look closely.

sister

brother

Color the sisters' clothes green.

Color the brother's clothes yellow.

Parents: Help your child name each person at the top of the page. Point to the words *sister* and *brother* and explain that they are names for people. Encourage your child to tell about the people in his or her family. Then say, "Find the two sisters in the picture and color their clothes green. Color the brother's clothes yellow."

Pets

Look closely.

cat **dog**

Color the cat yellow.

Color the dog red.

Parents: Ask your child to point to the picture of the cat and then to the picture of the dog. Point to the words *cat* and *dog* and explain that they are names of animals that make good pets. Encourage your child to tell about other pets people could have. Then say, "Find the cat in the picture and color it yellow. Color the dog red."

Farm Animals

Look closely.

cow

pig

Color the pig pink.

Color the cow brown.

Parents: Ask your child to point to the picture of the pig and then to the picture of the cow. Point to the words *pig* and *cow* and explain that they are names of animals that live on a farm. Encourage your child to tell about other farm animals he or she has seen. Then say, "Find the pig in the picture and color it pink. Color the cow brown."

RHYMING RIDDLES

Answer: It turns into a WET PET.

What happens when a kitten eats too much?

Answer: It turns into a FAT CAT.

What happens when a curious puppy jumps into a swimming pool?

Answer: He turns into a
GLAD DAD.

What happens when an
elephant sits on a cap?

Answer: It turns into a FLAT HAT.

What happens when you give your father a hug?

Month 5 Checklist

Hands-on activities to help prepare your child for school!

READING

Beginning Letters and Sounds, Consonants: pages 131-153, 159-160

One of the first steps in learning to read is being able to recognize and distinguish letter sounds. Later, your child will learn that sounds can be blended together to say and read words. You can help your child by starting with the sounds at the beginning of words. Use these activities to focus on consonants with your child:

- ❑ Complete the worksheets.
- ❑ Invite your child to watch in a mirror as he or she says the words *bee, dog, cat, mouse, goat, lion, rock, sock,* and *pig*. Have your child say each word again, repeating and drawing out the first sound of the word—e.g., for *bee,* have them say "bbb-bee." Point out the way the lips or tongue move to make the sound.
- ❑ Look around your home for things that start with a specific consonant sound. Take turns identifying items with that sound. Examples: *sink, soap,* and *sandwich* for the sound of s, *pajamas, pillow,* and *puppet* for the sound of p, and *toothbrush, toothpaste, tube,* and *towel* for the sound of t. Try this outside, too!
- ❑ Ask your child to draw an animal that he or she likes. Have him or her say the animal's name. Then say two words and ask your child to choose the one that begins with the same sound. Help your child draw a picture of the word with the matching sound.
- ❑ Play "I Spy." Say an object's name by pausing after the initial consonant sound. For example, say, "I spy with my little eye a b [pause] all." Have your child blend together the beginning sound with the rest of the word to name the item.
- ❑ Read books to your child that contain alliterations (repeating beginning consonant sounds). Some examples are All About Arthur, by Eric Carle, Busy Buzzing Bumblebees and Other Tongue Twisters, by Alvin Schwartz, and Six Sick Sheep: 101 Tongue Twisters, by Joanna Cole and Stephanie Calmenson. Invite your child to find and say words that have the same beginning sound.

READING

Beginning Letters and Sounds, Vowels: pages 154-158, 159-160

Vowel sounds differ from consonant sounds. Consonants are closed sounds. The lips or the tongue help say them. Vowels are open sounds. You only need to open your mouth to say them. Help your child learn the short vowel sounds with these activities:

- ❑ Complete the worksheets.
- ❑ Ask your child to listen as you make a series of three vowel sounds. Have him or her repeat the sounds in the same order. Repeat with different sounds. Then invite your child to make up his or her own series of vowel sounds.
- ❑ Play "What Am I?" Ask riddles for words that begin with vowel letters. For example, say, "I am red. I am a fruit. What am I?" (Possible answer: an apple)
- ❑ Read the classic Green Eggs and Ham, by Dr. Seuss. Have your child listen for the *a* and other vowel sounds.
- ❑ Make two stick puppets and name them "Ollie, the Octopus" and "Oscar, the Otter." Have your child choose one of the characters and have a pretend conversation between them. Be sure to use their names in the conversation to reinforce the sound of short *o*. Repeat this activity for other vowel letters.
- ❑ Play "What Goes Up?" to reinforce the sound of short *u*. Take turns thinking of things that go up. Start each turn by saying, "(blank) goes up." For example, "A balloon goes up."

Animal Match

Match the ones with the same beginning sound.

Parents: Point to the bee and say its name. Then name the pictures in the right-hand column. Ask your child to draw a line to the one that begins with the same sound. Repeat for *cat, dog,* and *mouse*.

Sounds Like . . .

Circle the ones with the same beginning sound.

Parents: Ask your child to point to and name each picture in the first row. Then say, "Listen closely to the words. Which picture has the same beginning sound as the first one? Circle the picture." Help your child complete the rest of the page.

Put It Away

Draw a line to the ones with the same beginning sound.

Parents: Point to the box and say, "Box begins with the letter *B*. Listen for the sound *B* makes at the beginning of bbb-box. Say it!" Help your child say the names of the other pictures and then ask him or her to draw a line from the box to the other pictures with the same beginning sound. Repeat for *can* and *pail*.

Beginning Sound Tt

Color if its name begins like turtle.

Parents: Point to the turtle and say, "Turtle begins with the letter *T*. Listen for the sound *T* makes at the beginning of ttt-turtle. Say it!" Help your child say the names of the other pictures and then ask him or her to color the ones with the same beginning sound as turtle.

Beginning Sound Mm

Circle if its name begins like monkey.

Mm

Parents: Point to the monkey and say, "Monkey begins with the letter *M*. Listen for the sound *M* makes at the beginning of mmm-monkey. Say it!" Help your child say the names of the other pictures and then ask him or her to circle the ones with the same beginning sound as monkey.

Beginning Sound Bb

Circle if its name begins like bear.

Bb

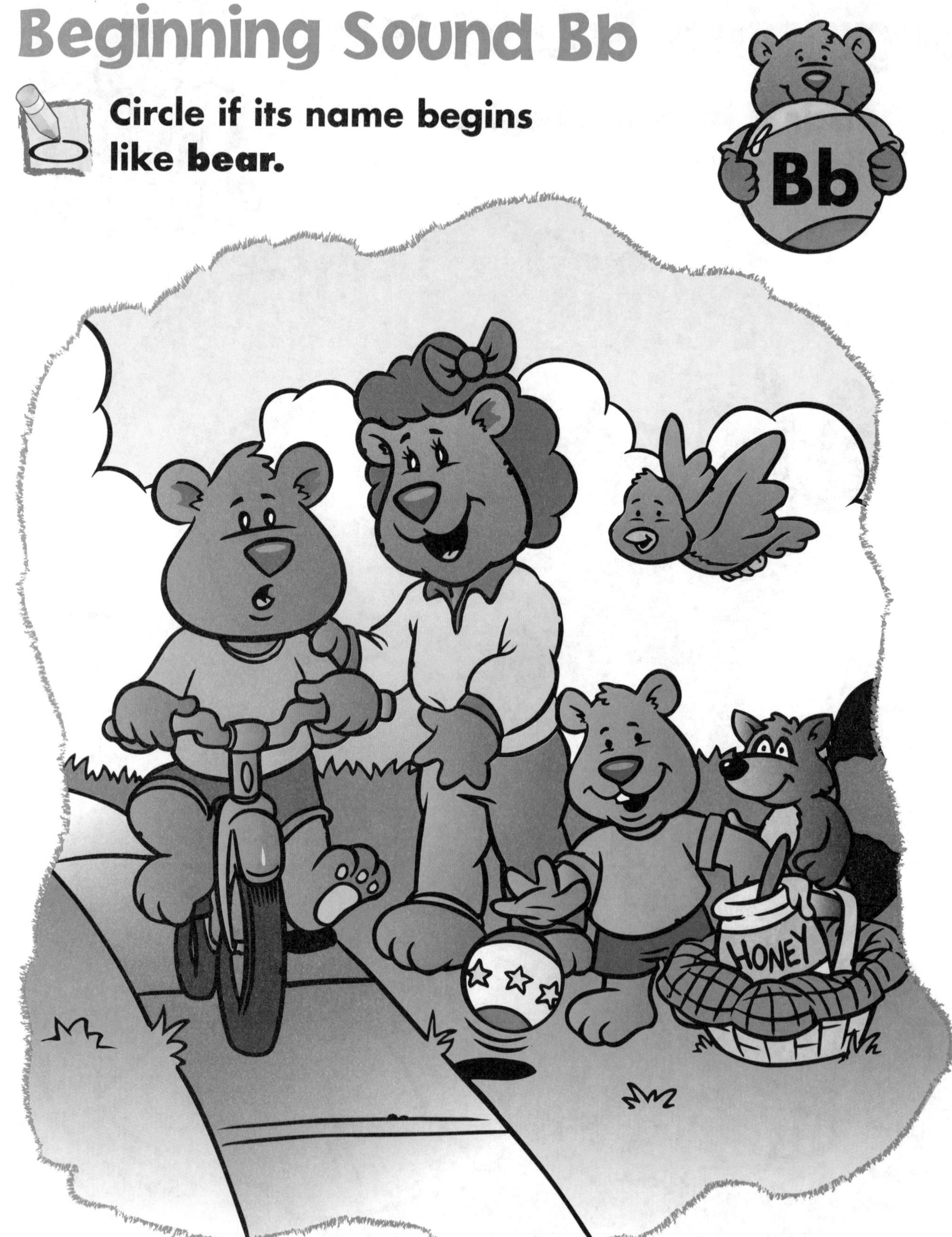

Parents: Point to the bear and say, "Bear begins with the letter *B*. Listen for the sound *B* makes at the beginning of bbb-bear. Say it!" Help your child say the names of the other pictures and then ask him or her to circle the ones with the same beginning sound as bear.

Beginning Sound Ss

Color if its name begins like seal.

Parents: Point to the seal and say, "Seal begins with the letter *S*. Listen for the sound *S* makes at the beginning of sss-seal. Say it!" Help your child say the names of the other pictures and then ask him or her to color the ones with the same beginning sound as seal.

READING

Beginning Sound Pp

Circle if its name begins like pig.

Parents: Point to the pig and say, "Pig begins with the letter *P*. Listen for the sound *P* makes at the beginning of ppp-pig. Say it!" Help your child say the names of the other pictures and then ask him or her to circle the ones with the same beginning sound as pig.

Beginning Sound Cc

Color if its name begins like cat.

Parents: Point to the cat and say, "Cat begins with the letter *C*. Listen for the sound *C* makes at the beginning of ccc-cat. Say it!" Help your child say the names of the other pictures and then ask him or her to color the ones with the same beginning sound as cat.

READING

Beginning Sound Ll

Circle if its name begins like lion.

Parents: Point to the lion and say, "Lion begins with the letter *L*. Listen for the sound *L* makes at the beginning of lll-lion. Say it!" Help your child say the names of the other pictures and then ask him or her to circle the ones with the same beginning sound as lion.

Beginning Sound Nn

Circle if its name begins like nest.

Nn

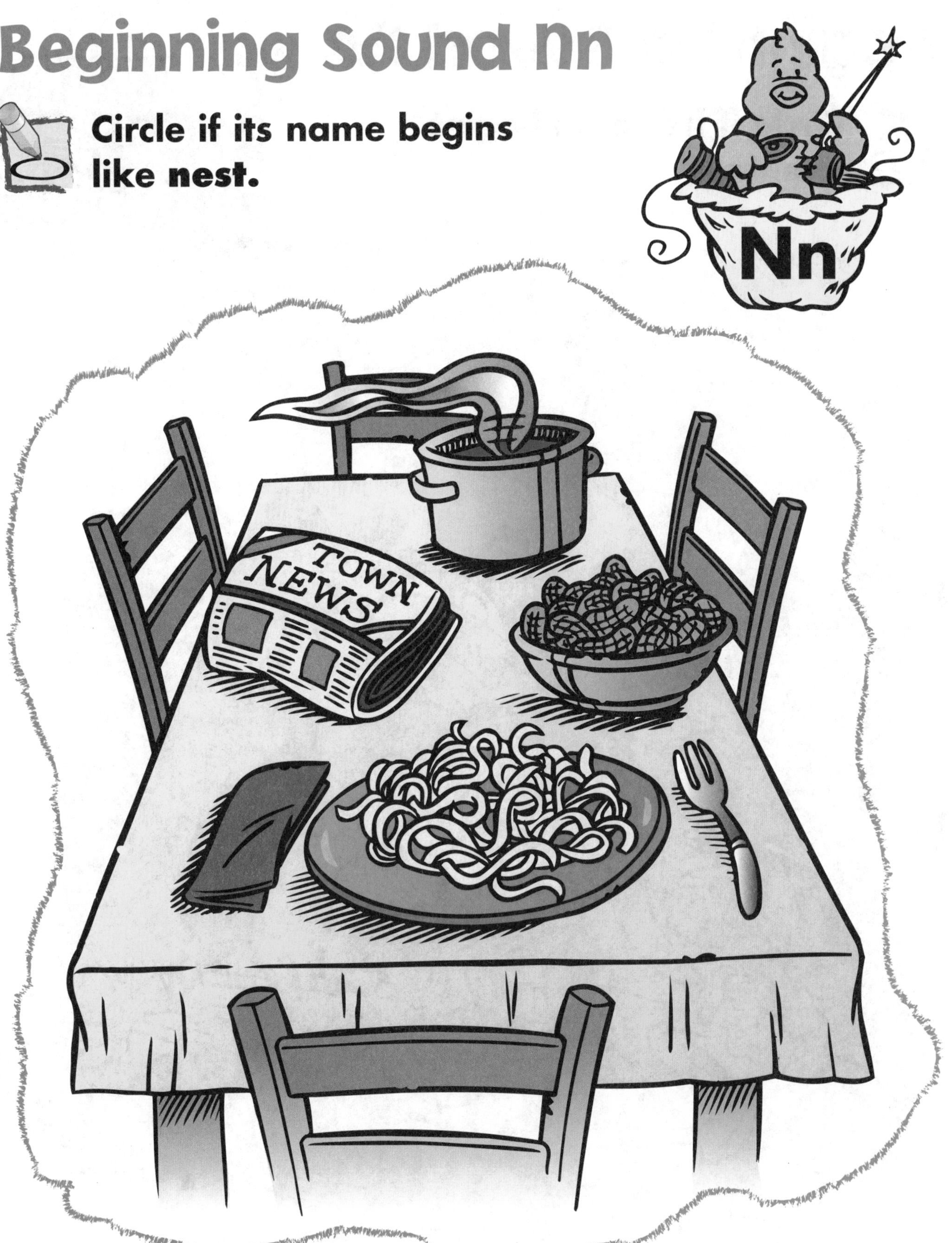

Parents: Point to the nest and say, "Nest begins with the letter *N*. Listen for the sound *N* makes at the beginning of nnn-nest. Say it!" Help your child say the names of the other pictures and then ask him or her to circle the ones with the same beginning sound as nest.

READING

Beginning Sound Dd

Circle if its name begins like dog.

Dd

Parents: Point to the dog and say, "Dog begins with the letter *D*. Listen for the sound *D* makes at the beginning of ddd-dog. Say it!" Help your child say the names of the other pictures and then ask him or her to circle the ones with the same beginning sound as dog.

Beginning Sound Ff

Color the picture if its name begins like (fox).

Parents: Point to the fox and say, "Fox begins with the letter *F*. Listen for the sound *F* makes at the beginning of fff-fox. Say it!" Help your child say the names of the pictures in the footprints and then ask him or her to color the ones with the same beginning sound as fox.

Beginning Sound Hh

Circle if its name begins like hippo.

Hh

Parents: Point to the hippo and say, "Hippo begins with the letter *H*. Listen for the sound *H* makes at the beginning of hhh-hippo. Say it!" Help your child say the names of the other pictures and then ask him or her to circle the ones with the same beginning sound as hippo.

Beginning Sound Rr

Color if its name begins like rooster.

Parents: Point to the rooster weather vane in the first row and say, "Rooster begins with the letter *R*. Listen for the sound *R* makes at the beginning of rrr-rooster. Say it!" Help your child say the names of the other pictures in the first row and then ask him or her to color the one with the same beginning sound as rooster. Repeat for the other rows.

Beginning Sound Jj

Circle if its name begins like jack-in-the-box.

Parents: **Point to the jack-in-the-box and say, "Jack-in-the-box begins with the letter *J*. Listen for the sound *J* makes at the beginning of jjj-jack-in-the-box. Say it!" Help your child say the names of the other pictures and then ask him or her to circle the ones with the same beginning sound as jack-in-the-box.**

Beginning Sound Gg

Circle if its name begins like gorilla.

Parents: Point to the gorilla and say, "Gorilla begins with the letter *G*. Listen for the sound *G* makes at the beginning of ggg-gorilla. Say it!" Help your child say the names of he other pictures and then ask him or her to circle the ones with the same beginning sound as gorilla.

Beginning Sound Kk

Kk

Circle if its name begins like koala.

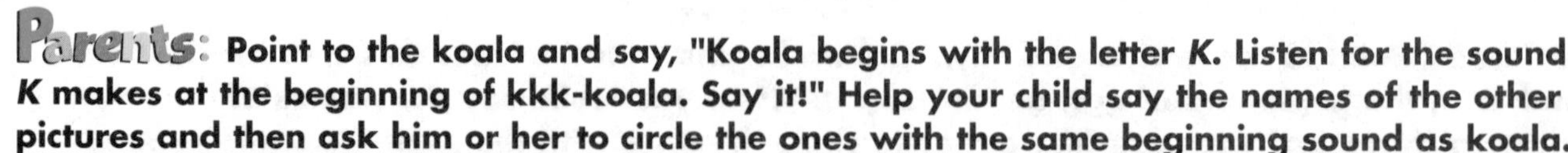

Parents: Point to the koala and say, "Koala begins with the letter *K*. Listen for the sound *K* makes at the beginning of kkk-koala. Say it!" Help your child say the names of the other pictures and then ask him or her to circle the ones with the same beginning sound as koala.

Beginning Sound Ww

Circle if its name begins like **weasel.**

Ww

Parents: Point to the weasel and say, "Weasel begins with the letter *W*. Listen for the sound *W* makes at the beginning of www-weasel. Say it!" Help your child say the names of the other pictures and then ask him or her to circle the ones with the same beginning sound as weasel.

Beginning Sound Yy

Circle (yellow yo-yo) if its name begins like yo-yo.
Circle (blue yo-yo) if its name has a different beginning sound.

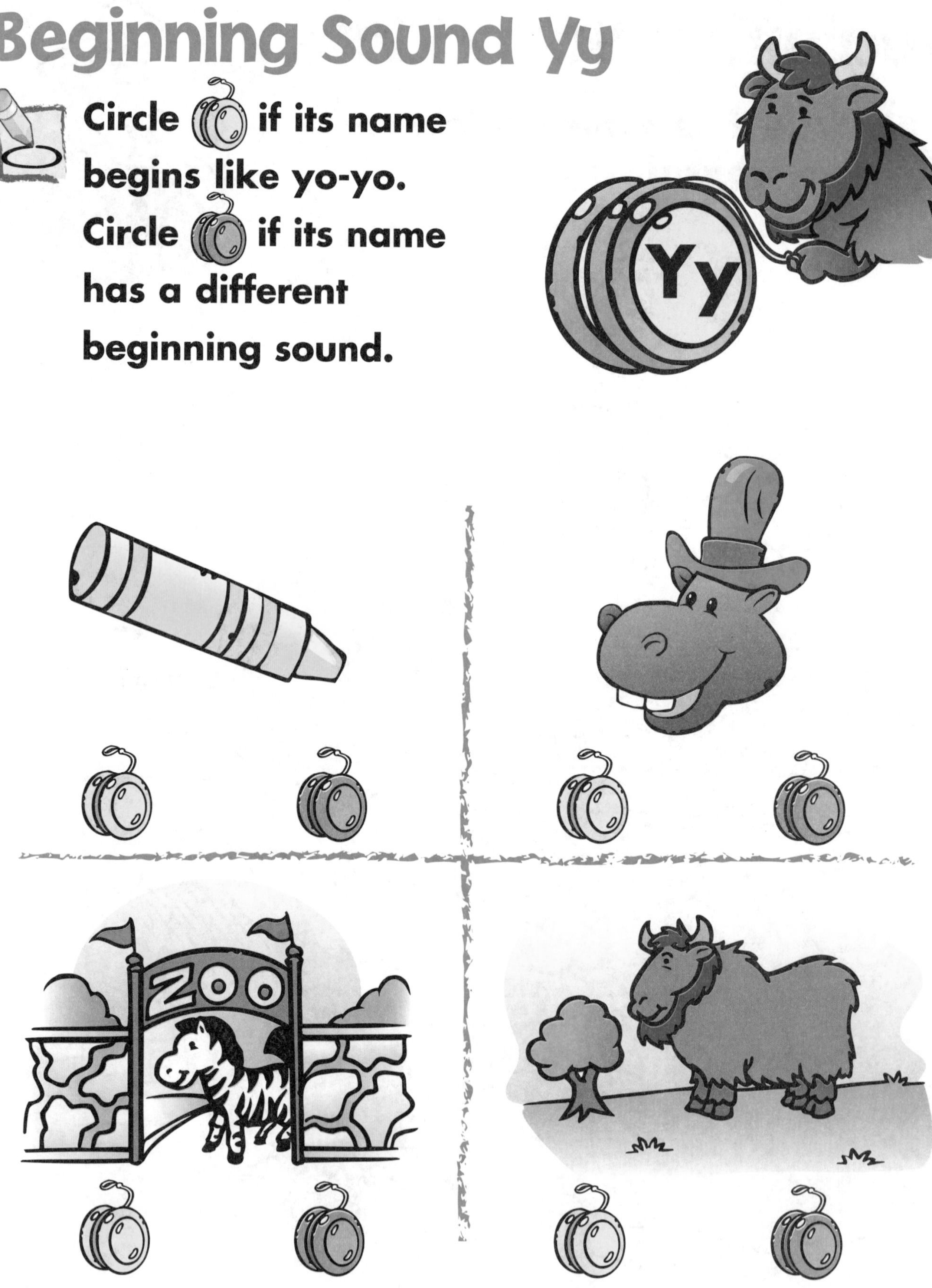

Parents: Point to the yo-yo and say, "Yo-yo begins with the letter *Y*. Listen for the sound *Y* makes at the beginning of yyy-yo-yo. Say it!" Help your child say the names of the pictures in each box. Then ask him or her to circle the yellow yo-yo under the pictures that have the same beginning sound as yo-yo and the blue yo-yo under the ones with a different sound.

Beginning Sound Vv

Color the spaces red if the picture's name begins like violin.

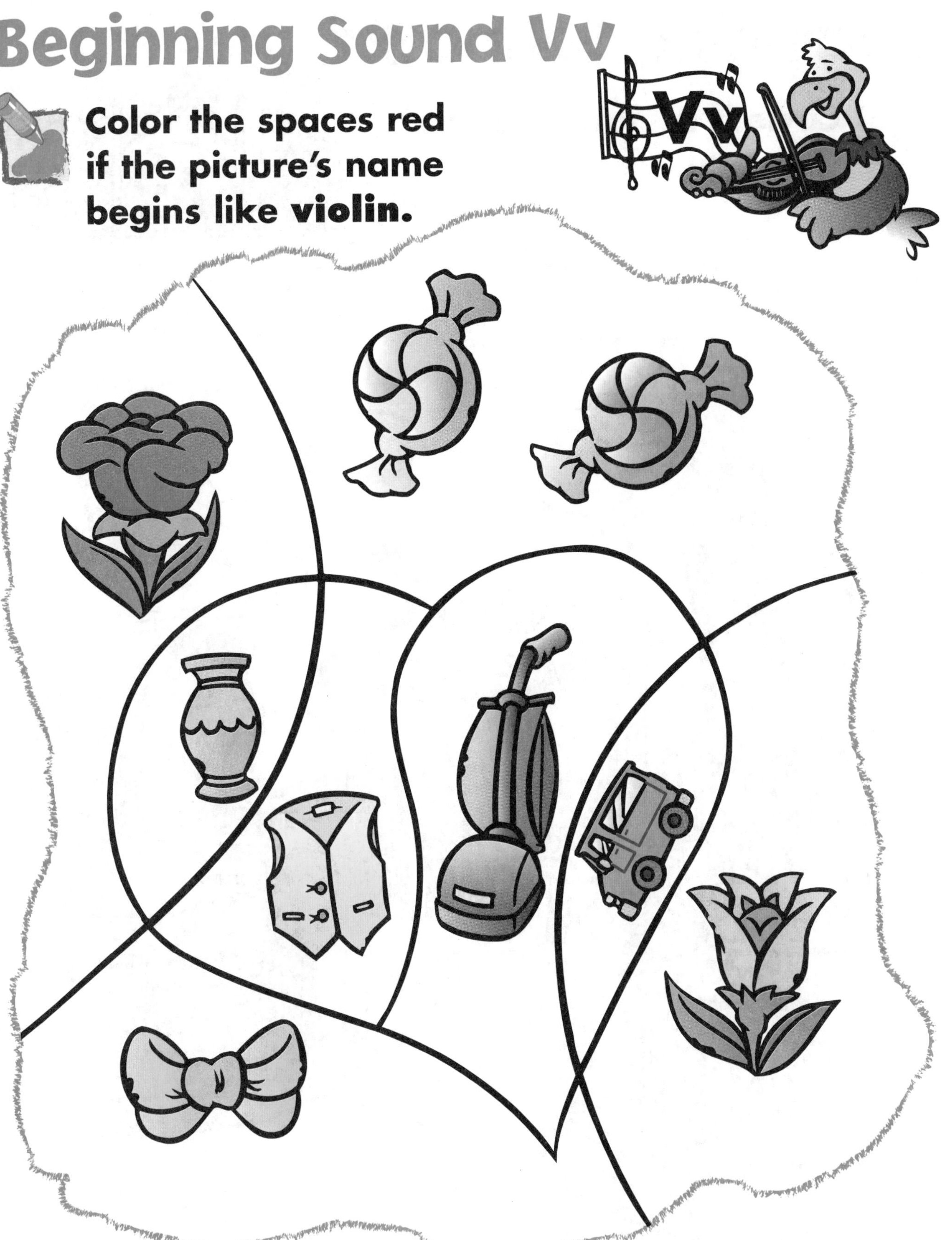

Parents: Point to the violin and say, "Violin begins with the letter *V*. Listen for the sound *V* makes at the beginning of vvv-violin. Say it!" Help your child say the names of the other pictures and then ask him or her to color the spaces that have pictures with the same beginning sound as violin red. When completed, the red spaces will form a valentine!

Beginning Sound Zz

Circle if its name begins like zoo.

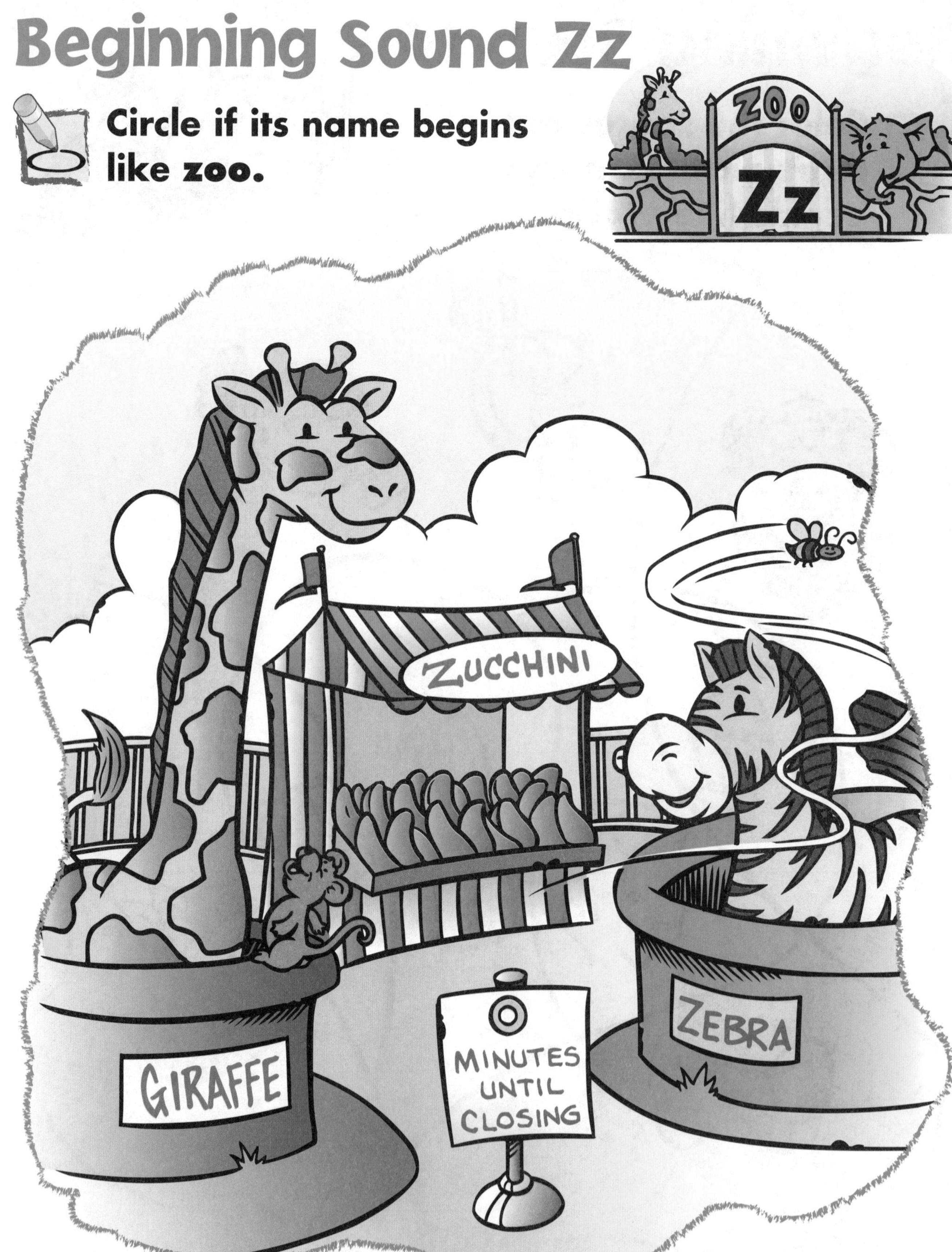

Parents: Point to the zoo and say, "Zoo begins with the letter Z. Listen for the sound Z makes at the beginning of zzz-zoo. Say it!" Help your child say the names of the other pictures and then ask him or her to circle the ones with the same beginning sound as zoo.

Beginning Sound Qq

Circle if its name begins like quail.

Parents: Point to the quail and say, "Quail begins with the letter Q. Listen for the sound Q makes at the beginning of qqq-quail. Say it!" Help your child say the names of the other pictures and then ask him or her to circle the ones with the same beginning sound as quail.

Beginning Sound Aa

Circle if its name begins like apple.

Aa

Parents: Point to the apple and say, "Apple begins with the letter *A*. Listen for the sound *A* makes at the beginning of aaa-apple. Say it!" Help your child say the names of the other pictures and then ask him or her to circle the ones with the same beginning sound as apple.

Beginning Sound Ee

Circle if its name begins like elephant.

Parents: Point to the elephant and say, "Elephant begins with the letter *E.* Listen for the sound *E* makes at the beginning of eee-elephant. Say it!" Help your child say the names of the other pictures and then ask him or her to circle the ones with the same beginning sound as elephant.

Beginning Sound Oo

Circle if its name begins like octopus.

Parents: Point to the octopus and say, "Octopus begins with the letter *O.* Listen for the sound *O* makes at the beginning of ooo-octopus. Say it!" Help your child say the names of the other pictures and then ask him or her to circle the ones with the same beginning sound as octopus.

Beginning Sound Ii

Circle if its name begins like igloo.

Ii

INK

Parents: Point to the igloo and say, "Igloo begins with the letter *I*. Listen for the sound *I* makes at the beginning of iii-igloo. Say it!" Help your child say the names of the other pictures and then ask him or her to circle the ones with the same beginning sound as igloo.

READING

Beginning Sound Uu

Circle if its name begins like umpire.

Parents: Point to the umpire and say, "Umpire begins with the letter *U*. Listen for the sound *U* makes at the beginning of uuu-umpire. Say it!" Help your child say the names of the pictures in each row and then ask him or her to circle the ones with the same beginning sound as umpire.

Sound Match

Match the ones with the same beginning sound.

SOAP

Parents: Point to the tiger and say, "Tiger begins with the letter *T*. Listen for the sound *T* makes at the beginning of ttt-tiger. Say it!" Help your child say the names of the other pictures and then ask him or her to draw a line to connect the pictures with the matching beginning sounds.

More Sound Match

Match the ones with the same beginning sound.

Parents: Point to the fox and say, "Fox begins with the letter *F*. Listen for the sound *F* makes at the beginning of fff-fox. Say it!" Help your child say the names of the other pictures and then ask him or her to draw a line to connect the pictures with the matching beginning sounds.

Month 6 Checklist

Hands-on activities to help prepare your child for school!

PREWRITING

Learning to manipulate a pencil or crayon to trace, draw, and color paths and lines helps children build fine motor skills. This will help them when they begin to write letters.

Tracing and Drawing Lines: pages 163-180

- ❑ Complete the worksheets.
- ❑ Play "Simon Says." Be sure to use directions that involve left and right. For example, you might say, "Simon says raise your right hand." or "Simon says, take one step to the left."
- ❑ Take your child to the playground. Ask him or her to draw the seesaw, slide, and other objects with slanted lines.
- ❑ Use a finger to trace circular objects in your home, such as clocks, dinner plates, and coasters. Have your child begin at the top and move his or her hand in a counterclockwise direction.
- ❑ Make circles in the air.
- ❑ Have your child practice brushing his or her teeth up and down.
- ❑ Gently press basic shapes into rolled out cookie dough without cutting completely through. Have your child use a plastic knife to trace the shapes and cut through the dough. Bake and eat the cookie shapes!

Dot-to-Dots and Mazes: pages 181-188

- ❑ Complete the worksheets.
- ❑ In addition to the mazes in this section, you can help your child with prewriting skills by drawing several simple zigzag or curved lines on a piece of paper and having him or her trace over them in different colors. Learning to stay on a line is a prerequisite for writing.
- ❑ Draw a simple picture of a kite on poster board. Punch out five holes—one at each corner and one at the end of the kite's tail. Number the holes in order from 1-5. Cut a long strand of yarn and glue one end from the 4 hole to the 1 hole. Have your child continue gluing around the outline of the kite in number order.

More Fine Motor Activities: pages 189-192

- ❑ Complete the mini-book.
- ❑ Draw other simple pictures and shapes and ask your child to copy them.
- ❑ Have your child practice lacing and tying shoes and buttoning shirts or jackets.
- ❑ Find zippers of different sizes, such as zippers for coin purses, clothing, and upholstery. Have your child practice zipping and unzipping them.
- ❑ Ask your child to paint pictures that have basic shapes.
- ❑ Have your child string yarn through noodles and buttons to make necklaces.
- ❑ Weave paper placemats. Set out paper with precut slits one inch apart and a box of colorful paper strips. Help your child weave the paper strips in and out of the spaces across the paper. Glue down the ends of the paper strips.
- ❑ Encourage your child to make pictures with an assortment of stickers.
- ❑ Help your child cut a banana lengthwise with a plastic knife. Ask him or her to spread peanut butter on the banana. Point out the left-to-right or top-to-bottom strokes your child uses. Then eat the banana!
- ❑ Have your child finger paint pictures of frogs on large paper.

Left to Right Frogs

Trace each line from the  to the .

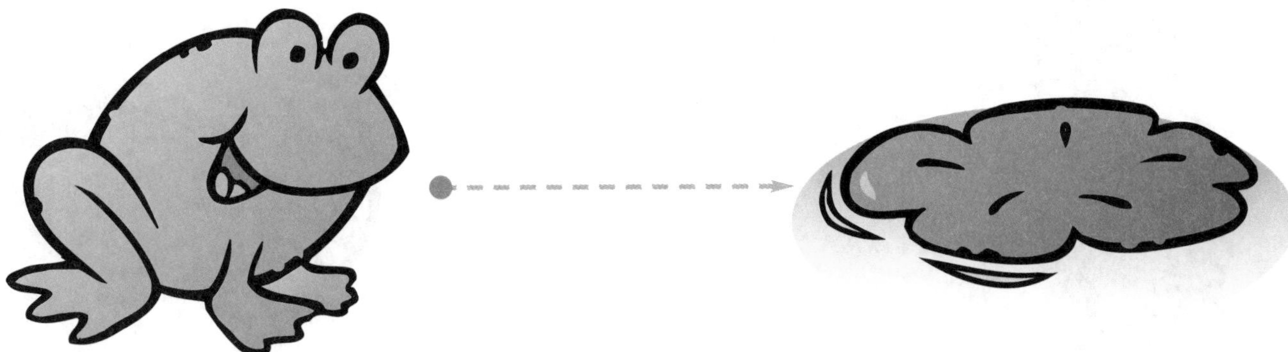

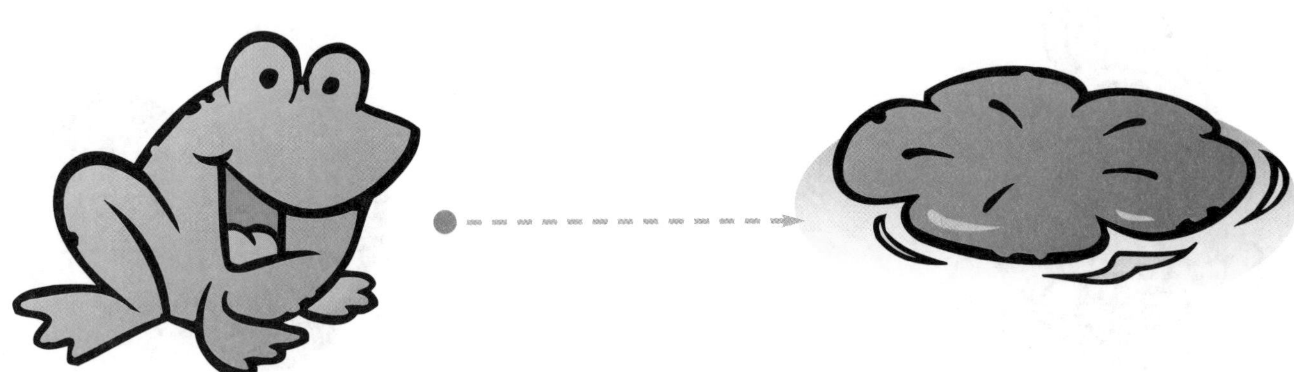

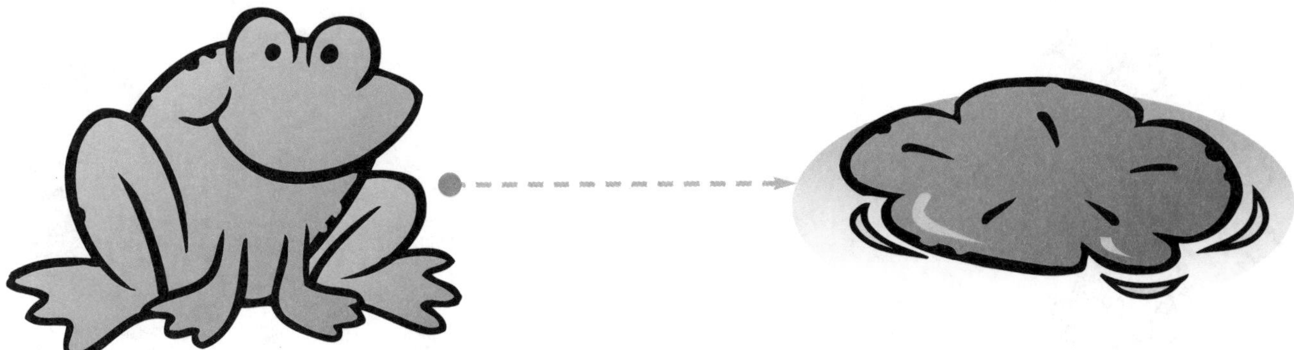

Parents: Have your child use his or her finger to trace the line from each frog on the *left* to the lily pad on the *right*. Then have your child use a crayon to trace the lines.

PREWRITING

Left to Right Kittens

 **Trace each line from the  to the .**

Parents: Recite the nursery rhyme "Three Little Kittens" with your child. Have your child use his or her finger to trace the line from each kitten on the *left* to the pair of mittens on the *right*. Then have your child use a crayon to trace the lines.

Left to Right Magicians

Trace each line from the  **to the**  **.**

Parents: Have your child use his or her finger to trace the line from each magician on the *left* to the hat on the *right*. Then have your child use a crayon to trace the lines.

Top to Bottom Basketball

Trace each line from the top to the bottom.

Parents: **Have your child use his or her finger to trace the line from the *top* of each pole to the *bottom*. Then have your child use a crayon to trace the lines.**

Top to Bottom Beanstalks

Trace each line from the top to the bottom.

Parents: **Ask your child to help you retell the fairytale of "Jack and the Beanstalk." Have your child use his or her finger to trace the line from the *top* of each beanstalk to the *bottom*. Then have your child use a crayon to trace the lines.**

Slanted Hotdogs

Trace the line on each 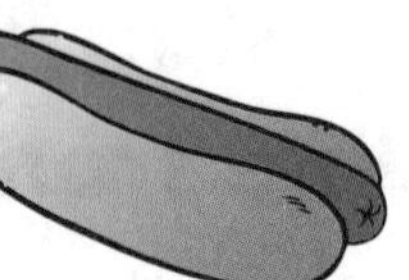 **.**

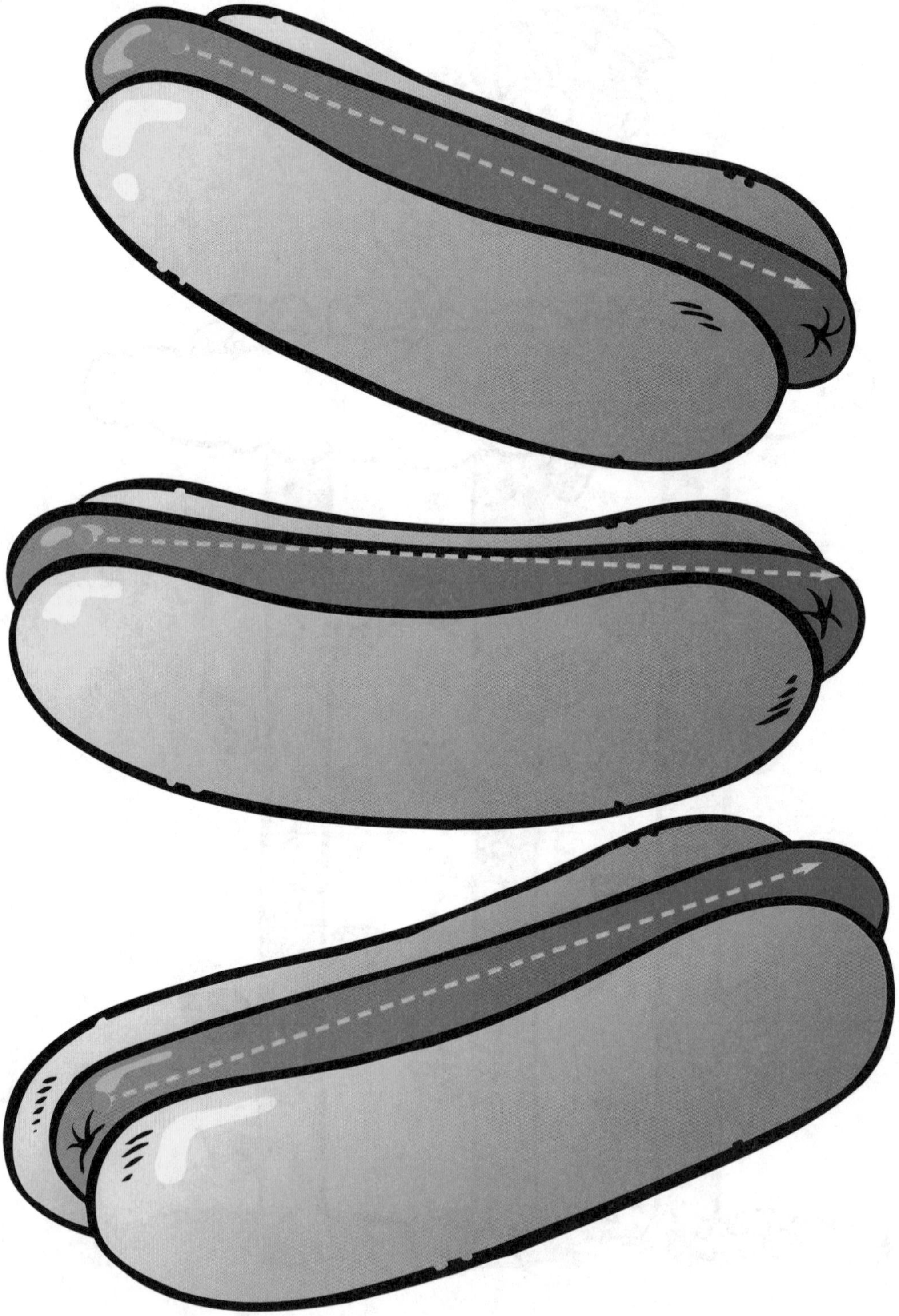

Parents: **Have your child use his or her finger to trace the line across each hot dog from the *left* to the *right*. Then have your child use a red crayon (for ketchup) or yellow crayon (for mustard) to trace the lines.**

Curved Jumps

Trace the lines over the **.**

Parents: Recite the nursery rhyme "Jack Be Nimble" with your child. Have your child use his or her finger to trace the *curved* line that the bee, spider, and Jack should follow to jump over the candlestick. Then have your child use a crayon to trace the lines.

PREWRITING

Paths for Mother Hubbard

Trace each line from [Mother Hubbard] to the [cupboard].

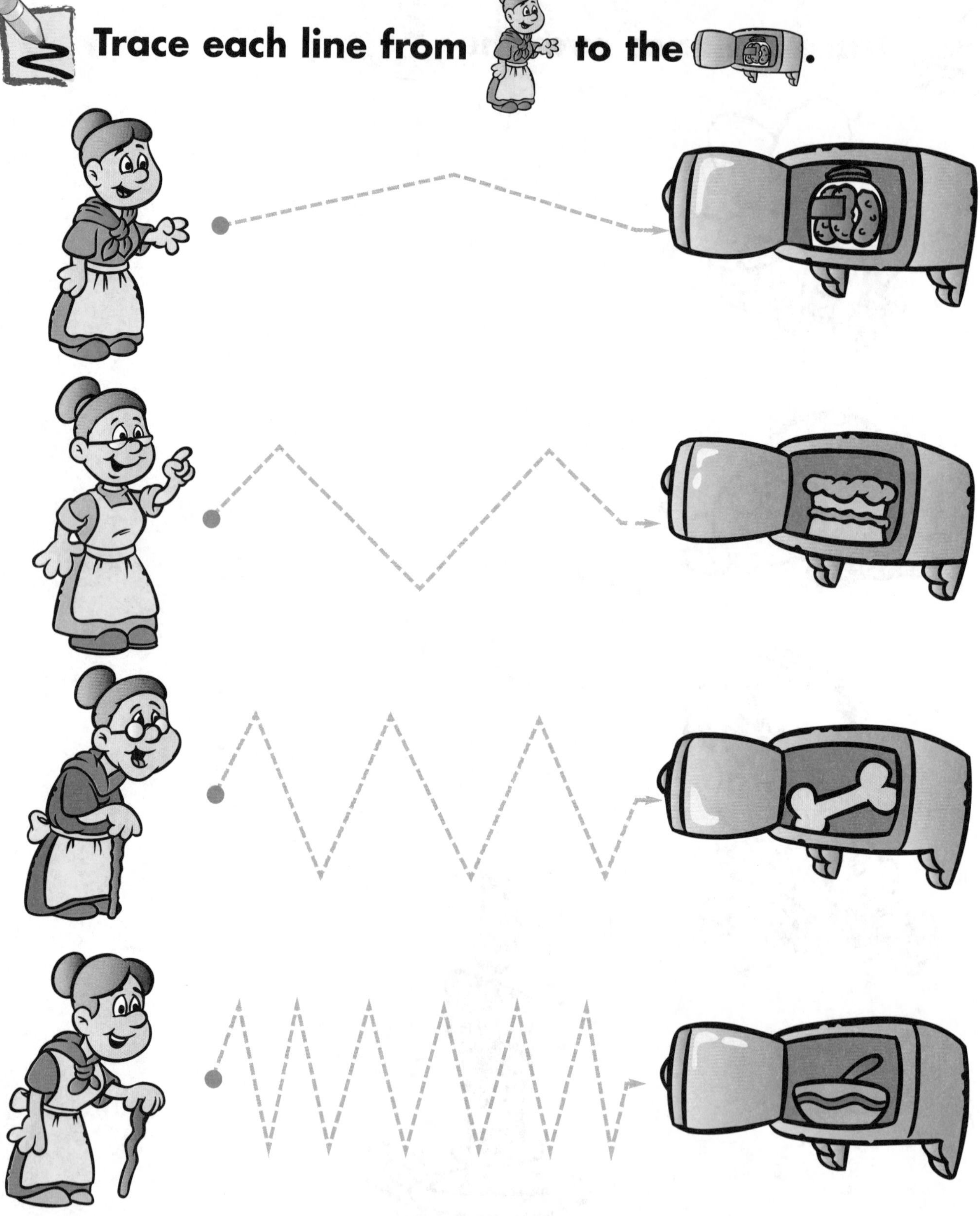

Parents: **Recite the nursery rhyme "Old Mother Hubbard" with your child. Have your child use his or her finger to trace the line from each picture of Mother Hubbard on the *left* to the cupboard on the *right*. Then have your child use a crayon to trace the paths.**

Paths for Little Piggies

Trace each  **'s path.**

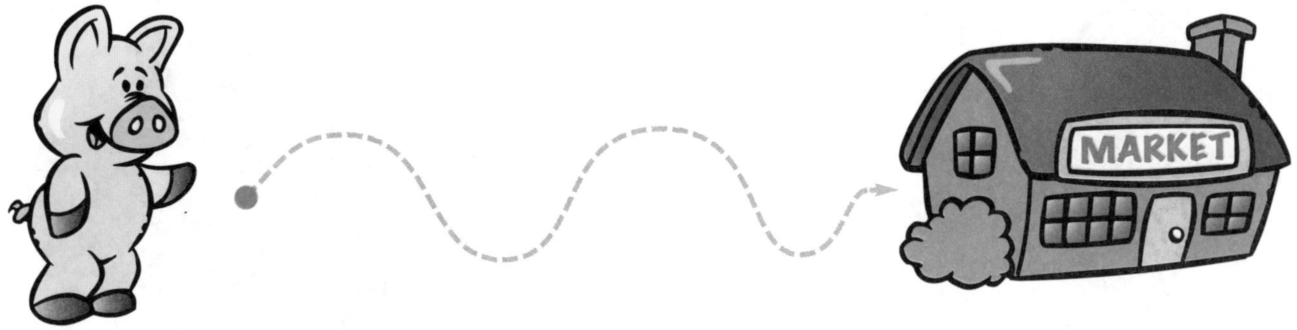

MARKET

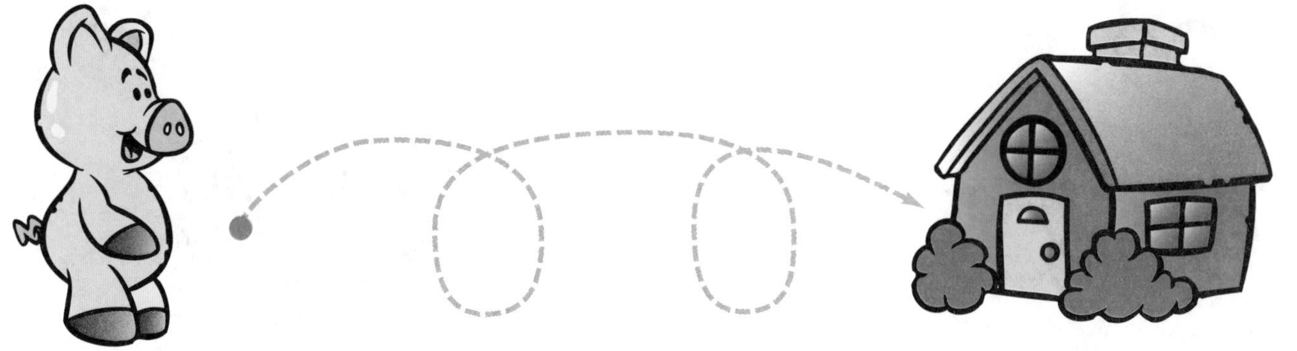

Parents: **Recite the nursery rhyme "This Little Piggy Went to Market" with your child. Have your child use his or her finger to trace the line from each piggy on the *left* to the scene on the *right*. Then have your child use a crayon to trace the paths.**

Paths for Baby Animals

Trace each path.

Parents: **Have your child use his or her finger to trace the line from each baby animal on the *left* to its mother on the *right*. Then have your child use a crayon to trace the paths.**

Trace a Treat

Trace the lines.

Parents: Have your child use his or her finger to trace the dashed lines on the ice cream cone. Then have your child use a crayon to trace the lines.

Trace a Boat

Trace the lines.

Parents: **Have your child use his or her finger to trace the dashed lines on the boat. Then have your child use a crayon to trace the lines.**

Trace a Funny Face

Trace the lines.

Parents: **Have your child use his or her finger to trace the dashed lines on the monkey. Then have your child use a crayon to trace the lines.**

Trace a Valentine

Trace the lines.

Parents: Have your child use his or her finger to trace the dashed lines on the valentine. Then have your child use a crayon to trace the lines.

Trace Circles

Trace the circles.

Parents: Have your child use his or her finger to trace the circles on the caterpillar. Then have your child use a crayon to trace the circles.

Trace Squares

Trace the squares.

Parents: **Have your child use his or her finger to trace the squares on the fire truck. Then have your child use a crayon to trace the squares.**

Trace Rectangles

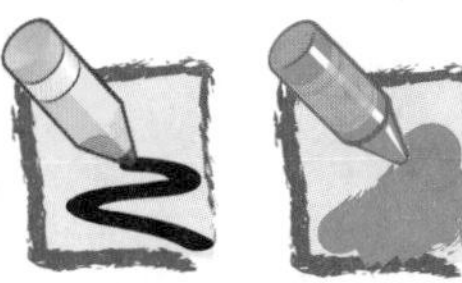

Trace the rectangles. Color the stripes.

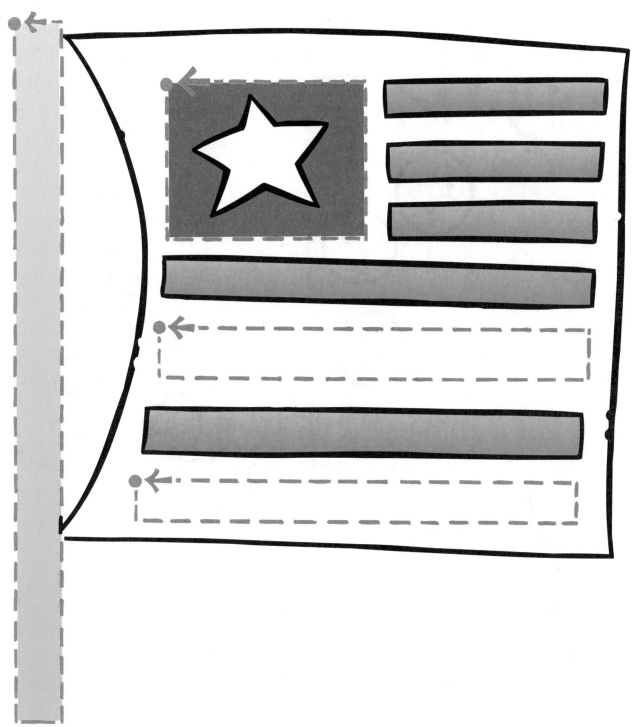

Parents: Have your child use his or her finger to trace the rectangles on the flag. Then have your child use a crayon to trace the rectangles and ask him or her to color the two new stripes red.

Trace Triangles

Trace the triangles. Color the pizza.

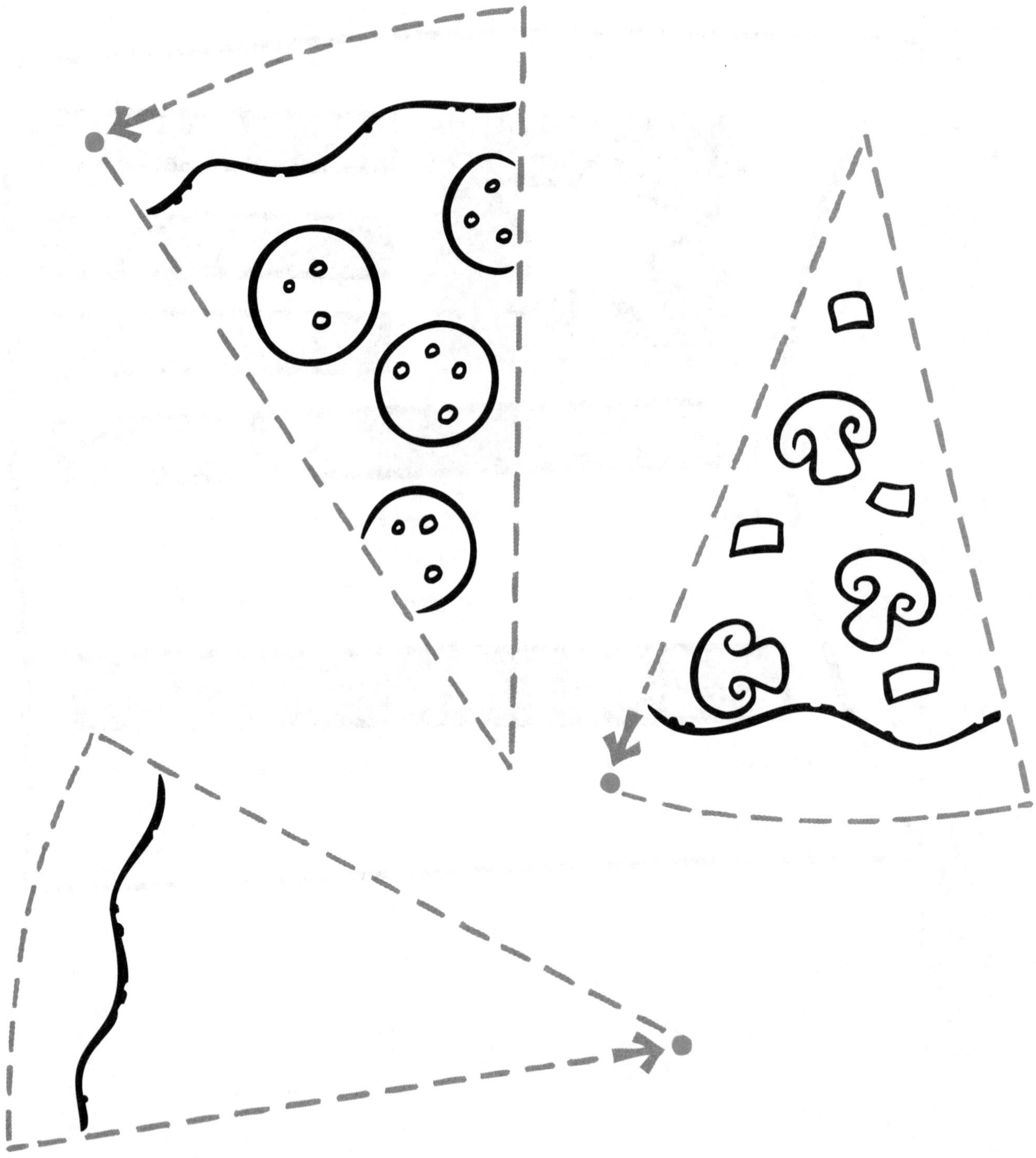

Parents: Have your child use his or her finger to trace the triangles. Then have your child use a crayon to trace the triangles and to color his or her favorite kind of pizza.

Bubble Bath Dot-to-Dot

Connect the dots. Color the picture.

1

2

3

4

5

Parents: **Ask your child to predict what the dot-to-dot picture will show. Then have him or her connect the dots in numeric order. Let your child color the completed picture.**

High Wire Dot-to-Dot

Connect the dots. Color the picture.

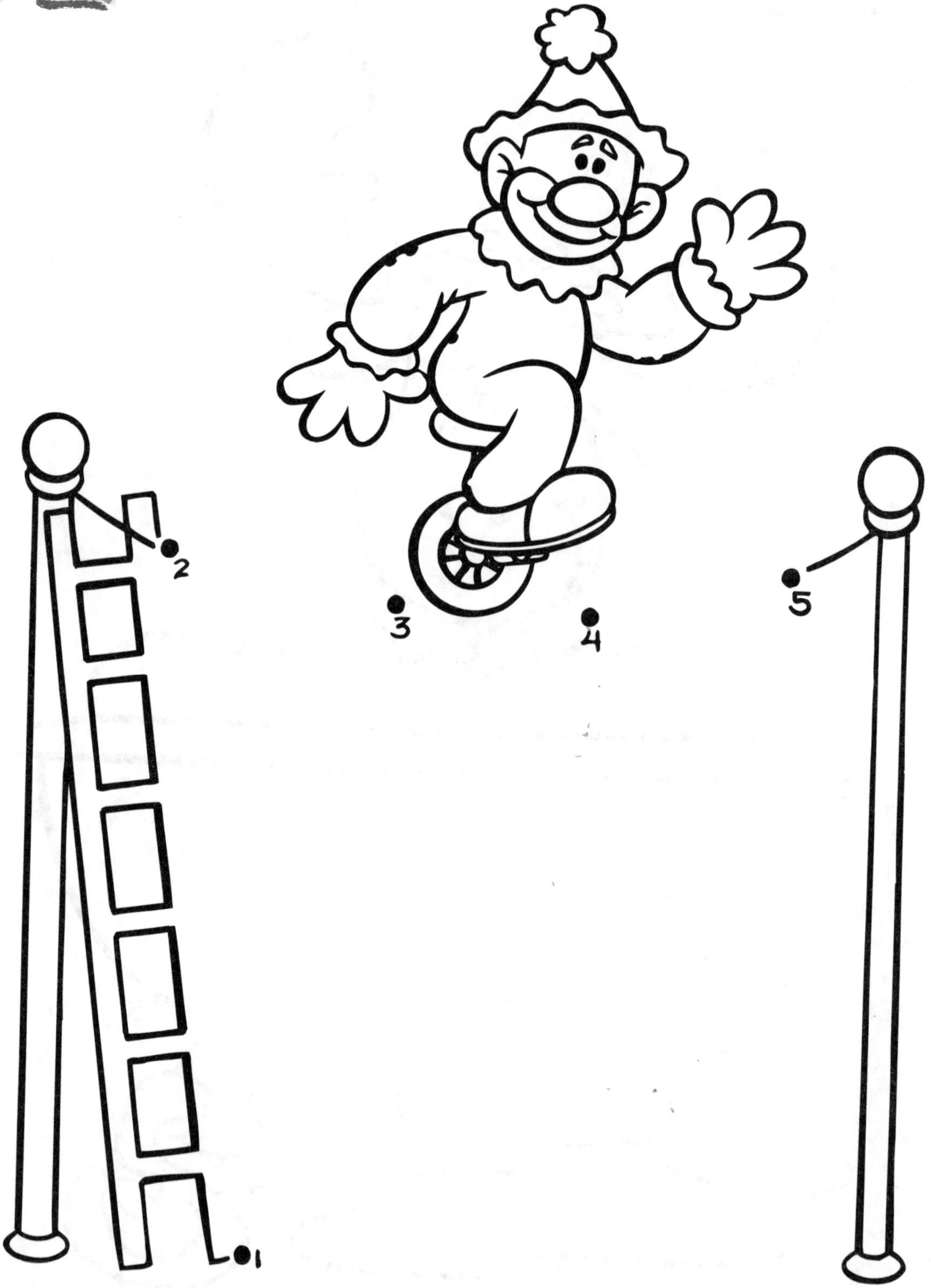

2

3

4

5

1

Parents: Ask your child to predict what the dot-to-dot picture will show. Then have him or her connect the dots in numeric order. Let your child color the completed picture.

Raccoon Dot-to-Dot

Connect the dots. Color the picture.

1

2

5

3

4

Parents: **Ask your child to predict what the dot-to-dot picture will show. Then have him or her connect the dots in numeric order. Let your child color the completed picture.**

Hickory Dickory Dock

Draw the path to the cheese.

Parents: Recite the nursery rhyme "Hickory Dickory Dock" with your child. Ask him or her to use a finger to follow the path from the mouse to the cheese. Then have your child use a pencil or crayon to draw the path the mouse should take.

Developing fine motor control; drawing a path to complete a maze

Hey Diddle Diddle

Draw the path to the spoon.

Parents: **Recite the nursery rhyme "Hey Diddle Diddle" with your child. Ask him or her to use a finger to follow the path from the dish to the spoon. Then have your child use a pencil or crayon to draw the path the spoon should take.**

Race to the Finish

Draw the path to the finish line.

FINISH

Parents: Ask your child to use his or her finger to follow the path from the racecar to the finish line. Then have your child use a pencil or crayon to draw the path the racecar should take.

River Crossing

Draw the path to the dam.

Parents: Ask your child to use his or her finger to follow the logs from the beaver to the dam. Then have your child use a pencil or crayon to draw the path the beaver should take.

Lost Bunny

Draw the path to the baby bunny.

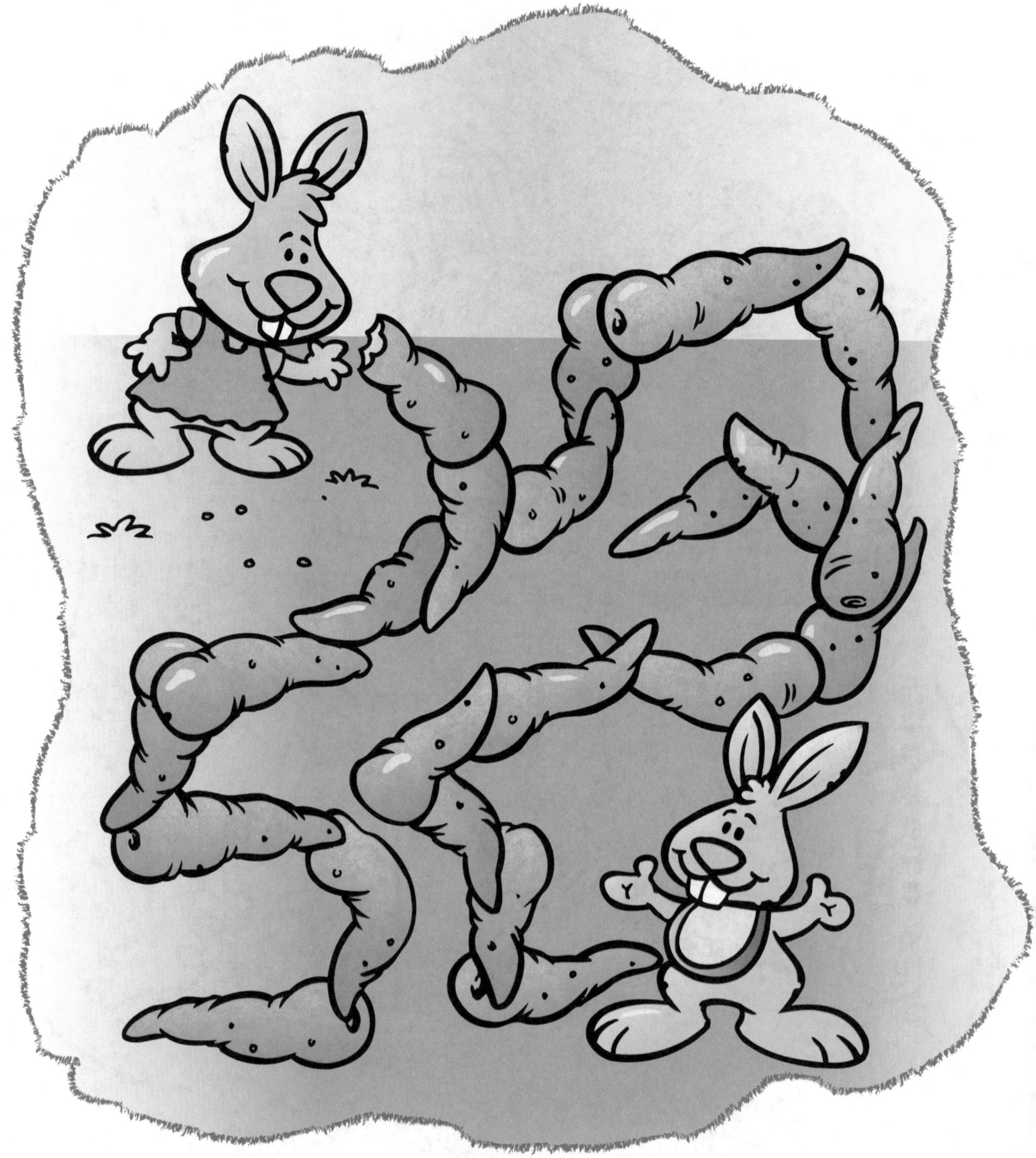

Parents: **Ask your child to use his or her finger to follow the carrots from the mother rabbit to the baby bunny. Then have your child use a pencil or crayon to draw the path the mother rabbit should take.**

How To Draw A Frog

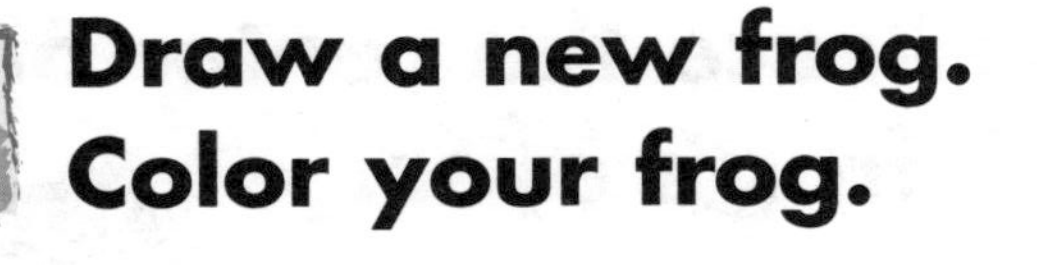

Draw a new frog.
Color your frog.

Trace the frog's body.

Trace the center of the frog's eyes.

Trace the frog's eyes.

Trace the frog's smile.

Trace the frog's front legs.

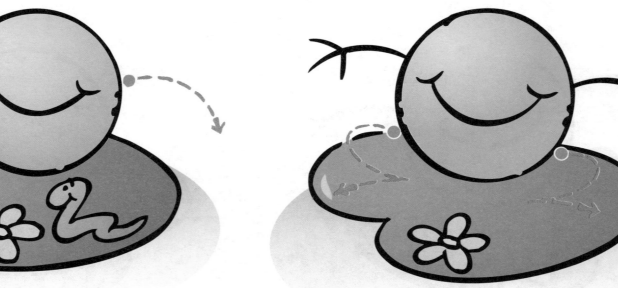

Trace the frog's back legs.

Month 7 Checklist

Hands-on activities to help prepare your child for school!

PREREADING

Same and Different: pages 195-197
Matching Shapes: pages 198-199
Direction: pages 200-203

Continue to help your child notice similarities and differences among objects as his or her abilities progress. Matching shapes with objects will help your child recognize the shapes of letters in words. Observing different directions of objects will help him or her identify letters in different positions within words. You can help your child with these skills through the following activities:

- ❑ Complete the worksheets.
- ❑ Decorate a cookie or cupcake with different colors of icing. Ask your child to decorate his or her own to look the same as yours.
- ❑ Cut squares from patterned wallpaper or cloth samples. Have your child match the squares to the samples.
- ❑ Give your child an assortment of bottles, jars, pots, pans, and plastic containers with lids. Separate and mix up the lids and containers and have your child match the ones that go together.
- ❑ Also, the next time you have a gift to wrap or mail, set out several boxes to choose from and ask your child to find the best fit.
- ❑ Place small household items, such as a key, comb, crayon, paper clip, and spoon, on a large sheet of paper. Trace around each item. Then give the items to your child and ask him or her to match them with the shape outlines.
- ❑ Place a light so that you and your child can make shadows on a wall. Take turns making shadow shapes with your hands. Identify the shapes.
- ❑ Line up four socks in a row with one facing a different direction from the others. Have your child find the one that is facing the different direction. Try this with fish-shaped crackers. Invite your child to eat the fish that are facing the same direction.

PREREADING

Visual Discrimination: pages 204-215

Some of the worksheets for this month challenge your child to look closely at pictures to notice details. Your child will be asked to find an object, identify what's missing, and recognize what's wrong with a picture. This type of visual discrimination is a building block for reading that improves with practice. You can give your child this all-important practice through the following activities:

- ❑ Complete the worksheets.
- ❑ Play "I Spy" using small objects in one room, such as a bathroom. For example, say, "I spy with my little eye ... a bar of soap." Have your child find the soap.
- ❑ Place several items on a table. Have your child look closely at the items. Cover his or her eyes and remove one item. Then ask your child to open his or her eyes and name the missing item.
- ❑ Find pictures in magazines that show distinct parts—e.g., a house with a roof, a table with legs, and a bike with a seat. Cut out the pictures and cut off the part. Tape or glue each picture to a sheet of paper and ask your child to draw the missing parts.
- ❑ Ask your to child draw a picture of the park or playground where he or she likes to play. Have him or her add one thing to the picture that is wrong. Draw your own picture and do the same. Exchange drawings and circle the things that are wrong.

Draw Conclusions: pages 216-217
Make Predictions: pages 218-219
Sequence: pages 220-224

Drawing conclusions, making predictions, and sequencing or putting events in time order are critical thinking skills that your child will use to comprehend what he or she reads. You can help your child build these skills through the following activities:

- ❑ Complete the worksheets.
- ❑ Give your child examples of situations that require him or her to draw a conclusion. Use family members in your examples. For instance, grandma has on her pajamas and is brushing her teeth. Do you think she will go to the library or go to bed? Dad has a hose and a bucket. Do you think he will wash the car or mow the lawn?
- ❑ Show a new storybook to your child. Read the first page aloud. Ask your child to predict what might happen next.
- ❑ Have your child select a favorite page from a familiar story, such as "The Three Little Pigs." Have him or her choose an event and tell what happens next. Then ask your child to change the event that happens next. For example, the wolf huffs and puffs, but the house of sticks is not blown over. How does that change the story?
- ❑ Fill a glass with water and take a drink from it. Ask your child to describe what you did using the words *first, next,* and *last.*
- ❑ Help your child think of three things that he or she does most days—e.g., eat breakfast, get dressed, and go to preschool. Have your child draw what he or she does first, next, and last. Encourage him or her to talk about the pictures using the words *first, next,* and *last.*

Two Colorful Clowns

  **Look closely. Color the clown to match.**

Parents: Have your child identify each color in the picture of the clown at the top of the page. Then ask him or her to color the clown at the bottom to look the same as the clown at the top.

Jack-in-the-Box

Cut out and paste the matching halves.

Parents: **Help your child cut out the box halves on the left of the page. Then have him or her paste each one in the box next to the matching pattern.**

Sweet Treats

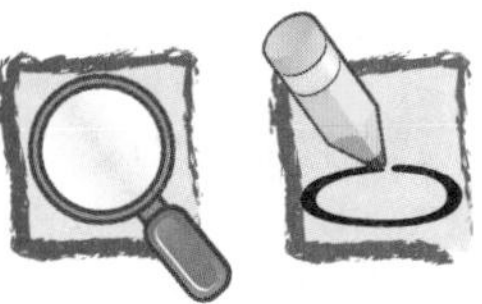

Circle the one that's different in each group.

Parents: Have your child identify the sweet treats in each row. Then have him or her circle the one that is different. Talk about what makes it different.

Fruit Bowl

Match the ones with the same shape.

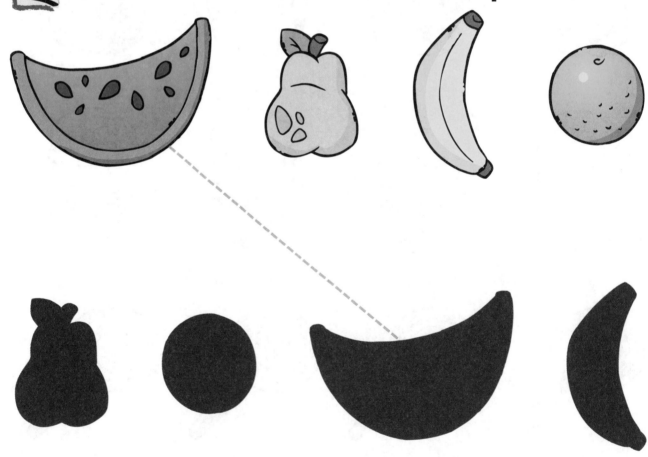

Parents: Ask your child to look closely at the fruit and trace the shape of each picture with his or her finger. Then have your child draw a line from each fruit to its matching shape.

A Present for You

Match the ones with the same shape.

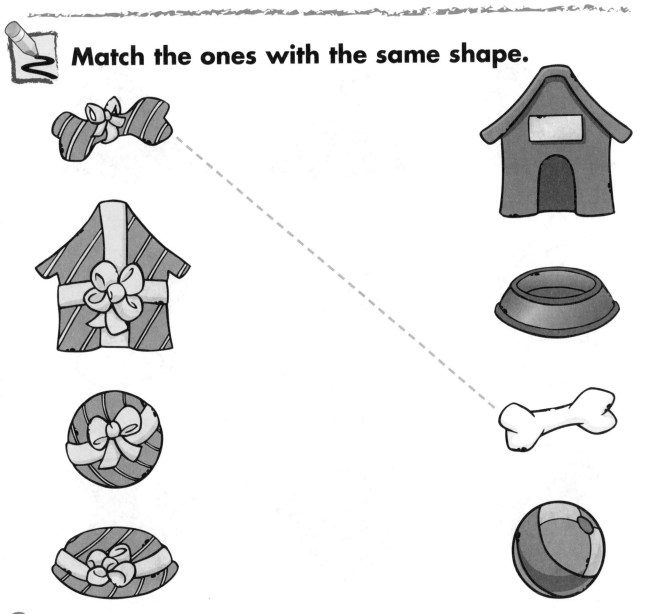

Parents: **Ask your child to figure out what presents the puppy received. First, have him or her trace the shape of each present with a finger. Then ask your child to draw a line from each present to the object that has the same shape.**

Turn-Around on Ice

Circle the ones that face the same way.

Parents: Ask your child to look closely at each row of animals and circle the two that face the same direction.

Bugging Out

Circle the ones that face the same way.

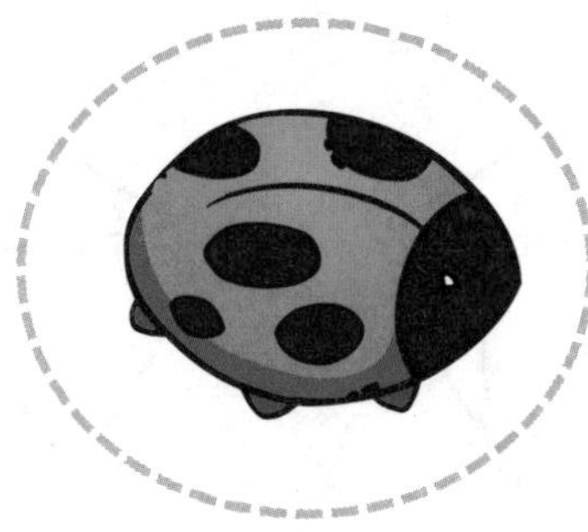
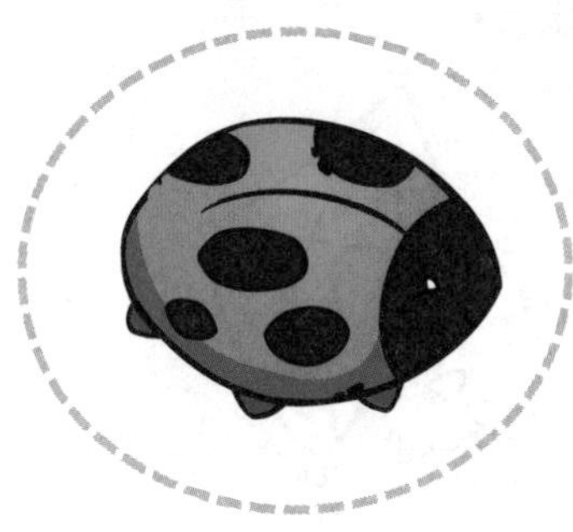

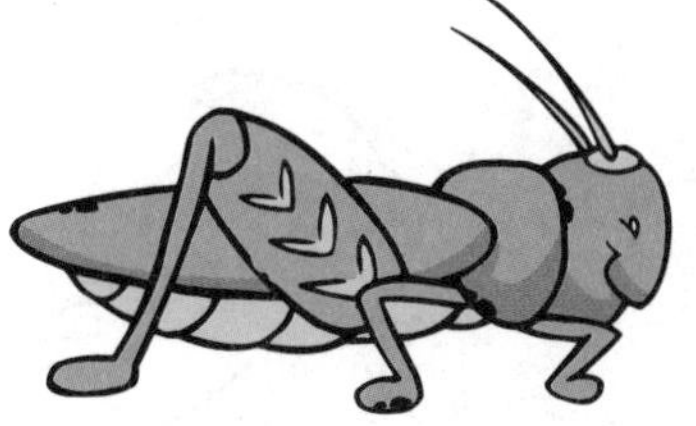

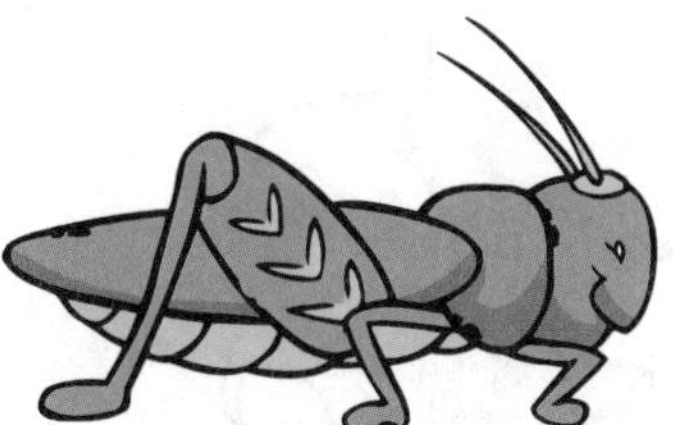

Parents: Ask your child to look closely at each row of insects and circle the two that face the same direction.

High in the Sky

Color the one that faces a different way.

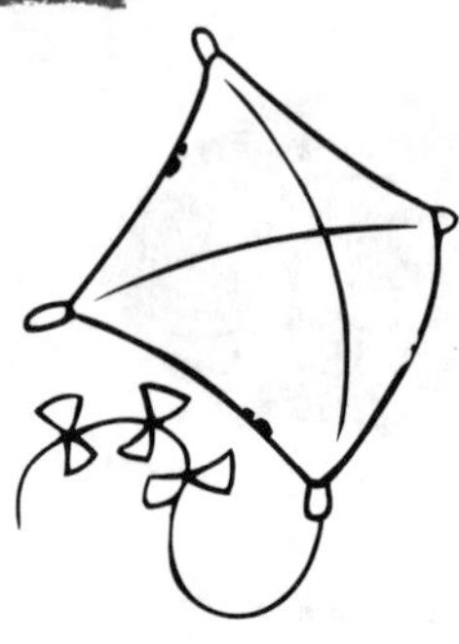

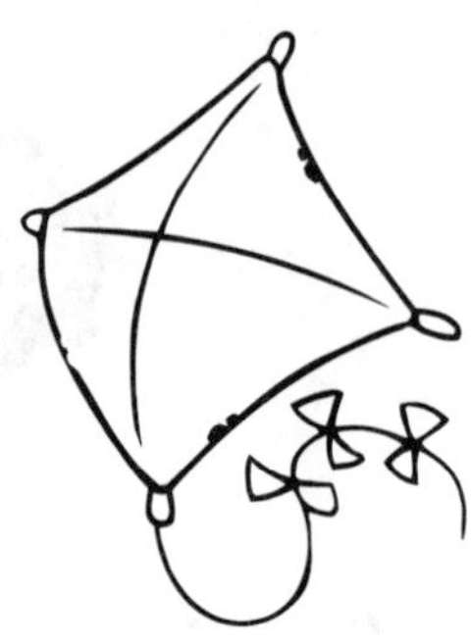
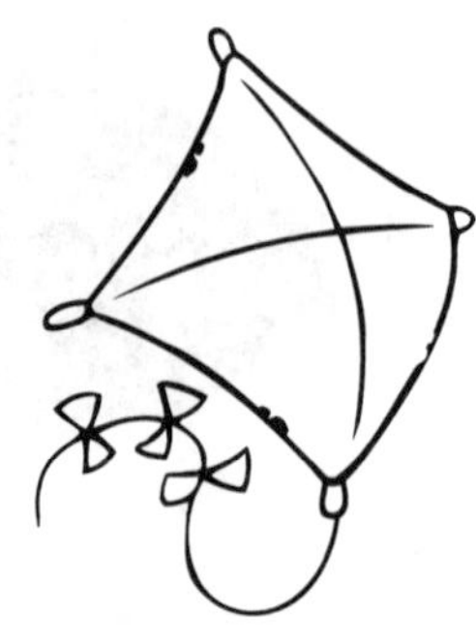

Parents: Ask your child to look closely at each row of things that fly and color the one that faces a different direction from the others.

Under the Sea

Color the one that faces a different way.

Parents: **Ask your child to look closely at each row of sea creatures and color the one that faces a different direction from the others.**

PREREADING

Finding Frogs

Circle [frogs].

Parents: Help your child find and circle the four frogs.

Going Batty

Color [bat pictures] **.**

Parents: **Help your child find and color the four bats.**

PREREADING

Batter Up!

Circle .

Parents: Help your child find and circle the five baseball bats.

Tea for Two

Color ☐☐☐☐☐.

Parents: Help your child find and color the five teacups.

Nursery Rhyme Pictures

Look closely.

Parents: Have your child look closely at the objects and find them in the picture on page 209.

Nursery Rhyme Find

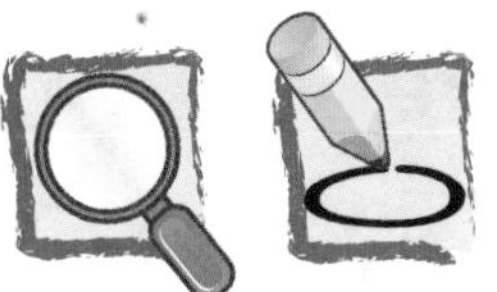

Look closely. Circle the objects in the picture.

Parents: Have your child look closely at the picture and circle the objects from page 208.

What's Missing at the Bus Stop?

  **Circle what's missing in the picture and draw it.**

BUS STOP

BUS STOP

Parents: Have your child look closely at the objects at the top of the page and circle the one that is missing in the picture. Ask him or her to draw the missing object in the picture.

Rain Forest Animals

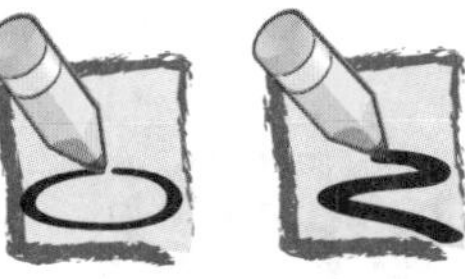

Circle the one that has something missing and draw the missing part.

Parents: **Have your child look closely at each animal pair and circle the one that has something missing. Then, ask him or her to draw the missing part.**

PREREADING

Beaver Band

Draw the missing part.

Parents: Have your child look closely at the picture at the top of the page. Then ask him or her to look at each musical instrument below and draw the missing part.

Dinosaur Dance

Circle the one that has something missing and draw the missing part.

Parents: Have your child look closely at the pictures in each row and circle the one that is missing a part. Then ask him or her to draw the missing part.

What's Wrong at the Beach?

  **Circle what's wrong.**

Parents: **Have your child look closely at the picture and circle four things that are wrong.**

What's Wrong in the Yard?

Color what's wrong.

Fido

Parents: **Have your child look closely at the picture and color four things that are wrong.**

Where Are They Going?

Draw a line to where they are going.

Parents: Have your child draw a line from the turtles to the picture that shows where they are going.

What Are They Making?

Color what they made.

Parents: Have your child color the picture at the bottom of the page that shows what the mother and daughter tigers made.

What Will Happen Next?

Draw a line to what will happen next.

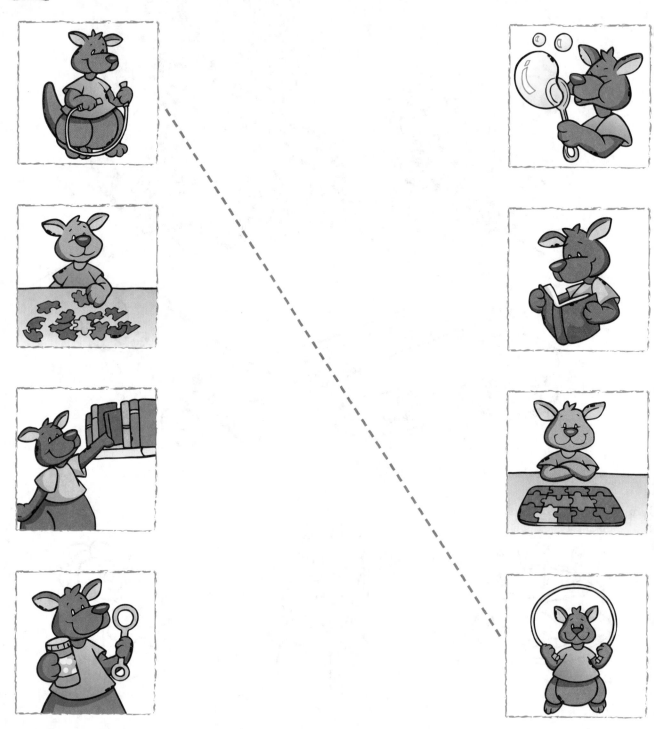

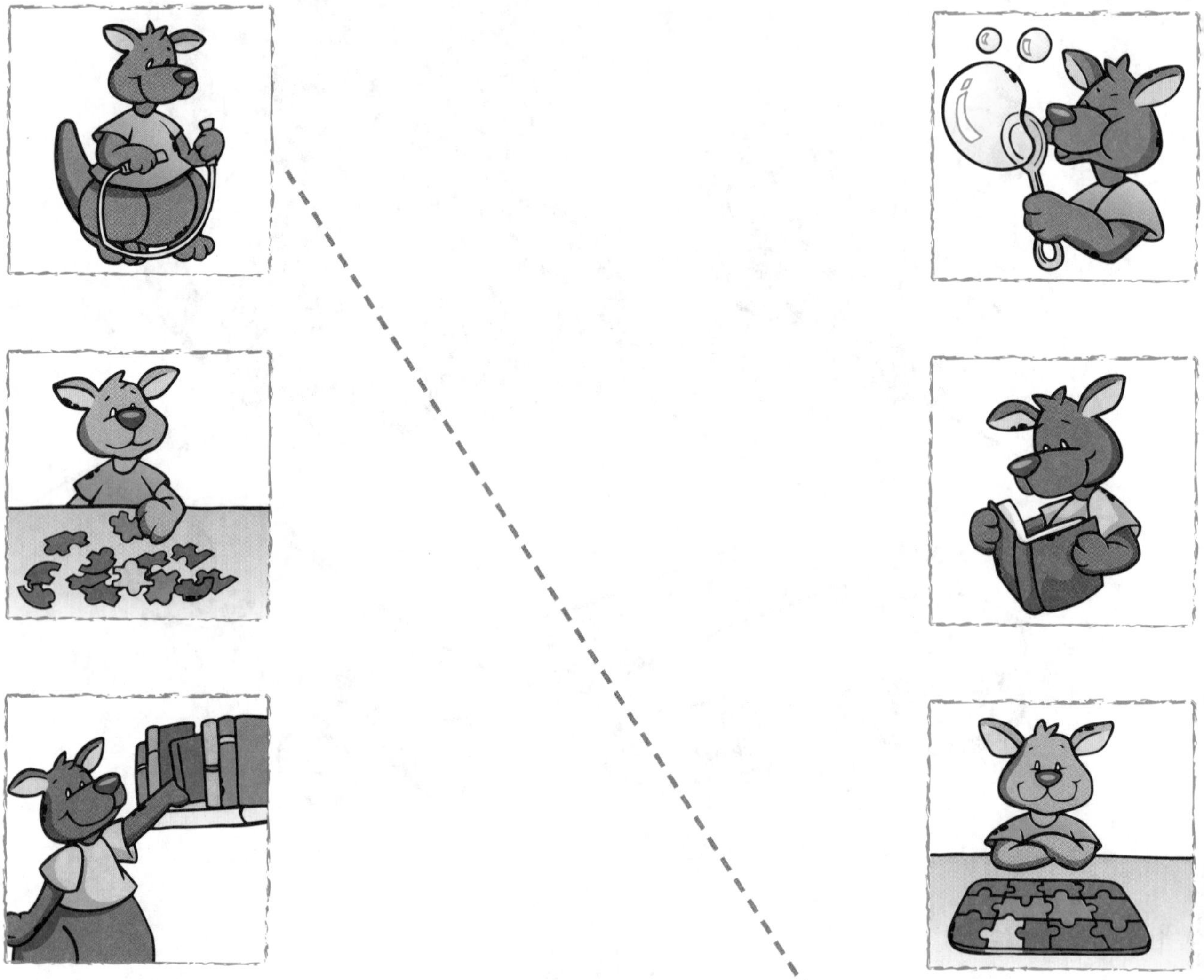

Parents: **Point to the picture at the top left and ask, "What is happening here?" Have your child draw a line to the picture that shows what will happen next. Repeat for each picture. Encourage your child to tell a story about each set of pictures using the words *first* and *next*.**

Next, Please!

Circle what will happen next.

Parents: Have your child look closely at the first picture in each row and circle the picture in that row that shows what will happen next.

Robins in Spring

Draw lines to show the correct order.

1

2

3

Parents: Mention to your child that spring is a time of birth, and explain to him or her that the pictures show three baby robins being born. Have your child draw a line from each number to a picture to show the correct order of the robins hatching from the eggs.

Let's Build a Snowman

Draw lines to show the correct order.

1

2

3

Parents: Have your child draw a line from each number to a picture to show the correct order of the snowman being built. Encourage your child to tell a story from the pictures using the words *first, next,* and *last*.

Recognizing the order of events; identifying what comes first, next, and last

Puppy Love

Write 1, 2, and 3 to show the order of what happened.

Parents: **Have your child write 1, 2, and 3 in the boxes in each row to show what happened first, next, and last. Encourage your child to tell a story about each row of pictures using the words first, next, and last.**

Month 8 Checklist

Hands-on activities to help prepare your child for school!

MATH

Counting: pages 227-244, 248-249, 252-255
This month, your child will expand his or her understanding of number concepts to identify sets of six to 10 objects. Help your child with these skills through the following activities:

- ❑ Complete the worksheets.
- ❑ Give your child a bag of small objects. Show a card with a number from 6 to 10. Ask your child to take the same number of objects out of the bag and count them aloud. You can also show your child a group of six to 10 objects and ask him or her to tell you how many there are.
- ❑ Make fun, healthy snacks that call for ingredients to be counted. For example, to make "ants on a log," help your child spread cream cheese or peanut butter on celery sticks. Then have him or her add a certain number of raisins on each one.
- ❑ Place a plastic container or box on the floor and give your child 10 small, unbreakable objects, such as buttons or paper clips. Have your child stand a few feet away from the container or box and try to toss the objects into it. Then have him or her count how many landed inside and how many did not.

Recognizing Numerals: pages 241-247

This month, your child will also practice recognizing the numerals that represent sets of six to 10 objects. To do this, have him or her try the following activities:

- ❑ Complete the worksheets.
- ❑ Point out numbers in your daily activities. Examples include numbers in the supermarket, on signs, and on license plates.
- ❑ Help your child cut out pictures of objects and sort them into groups of one to 10. Label pieces of construction paper 1 to 10 and have your child paste the picture groups onto the appropriate page. Bind the pages together and add a cover to create a counting book.
- ❑ Play "Simon Says" using number cards to accompany the directions you give. For example, hold up a card with the number 6 and say, "Simon says touch your nose this many times."

MATH

Number Order: pages 250-251, 256

As children learn to identify sets of six to 10 objects and recognize the numerals that represent each set, they are introduced to the concept of number order. They begin to recognize the idea of numbers being *one more.*

- ❑ Complete the worksheets.
- ❑ Write the numbers 1 to 10 on large index cards or pieces of construction paper. Arrange the cards in order in front of your child. Then give him or her small stickers or sticky notes. Have your child place one sticker on the card with the number 1, two stickers on the card with the number 2, and so on. When all the stickers are in place, ask your child to mix up the cards and put them back in order. Have your child read the numbers in order. Also try having your child close his or her eyes while you remove one of the cards. Then ask your child to open his or her eyes and say what number is missing. Encourage your child to say how he or she knows.
- ❑ Give your child several small objects, such as buttons, pennies, or beans. Ask him or her to make groups of one to 10 objects and arrange the groups in order.
- ❑ Write a number from 2 to 9 on a piece of paper. Ask your child to read it and say what number comes before or after. Repeat with other numbers.

Writing Numerals: pages 252-256

As children develop the skill of counting groups of one to 10 objects, they are introduced to writing the corresponding numbers. You can help your child with these skills through the following activities:

- ❑ Complete the worksheets.
- ❑ Print a numeral from 1 to 10 on an index card or construction paper. Help your child outline the number with glue. Then sprinkle glitter or rice over the glue and shake off the excess to make a raised number. When the glue is dry, your child can trace the shape of the number with a finger.
- ❑ Give your child many opportunities to practice writing large-scale numbers. Have him or her use a paintbrush dipped in water to write numbers on the sidewalk or driveway. Spread salt in a shallow tray (or box lid) and let your child practice writing the numbers with a finger in the salt. If finger paint is available, let your child practice forming the numbers using finger paint on paper.
- ❑ Show your child how to roll a piece of clay into a snake and bend it to form the numbers 1 to 10. Have him or her use clay to make the numbers and display them on pieces of cardboard. Then have your child make clay shapes and place them next to the numbers to illustrate how many the numbers represent.

Brrrr! It's Cold Out!

Draw a line to the correct number.

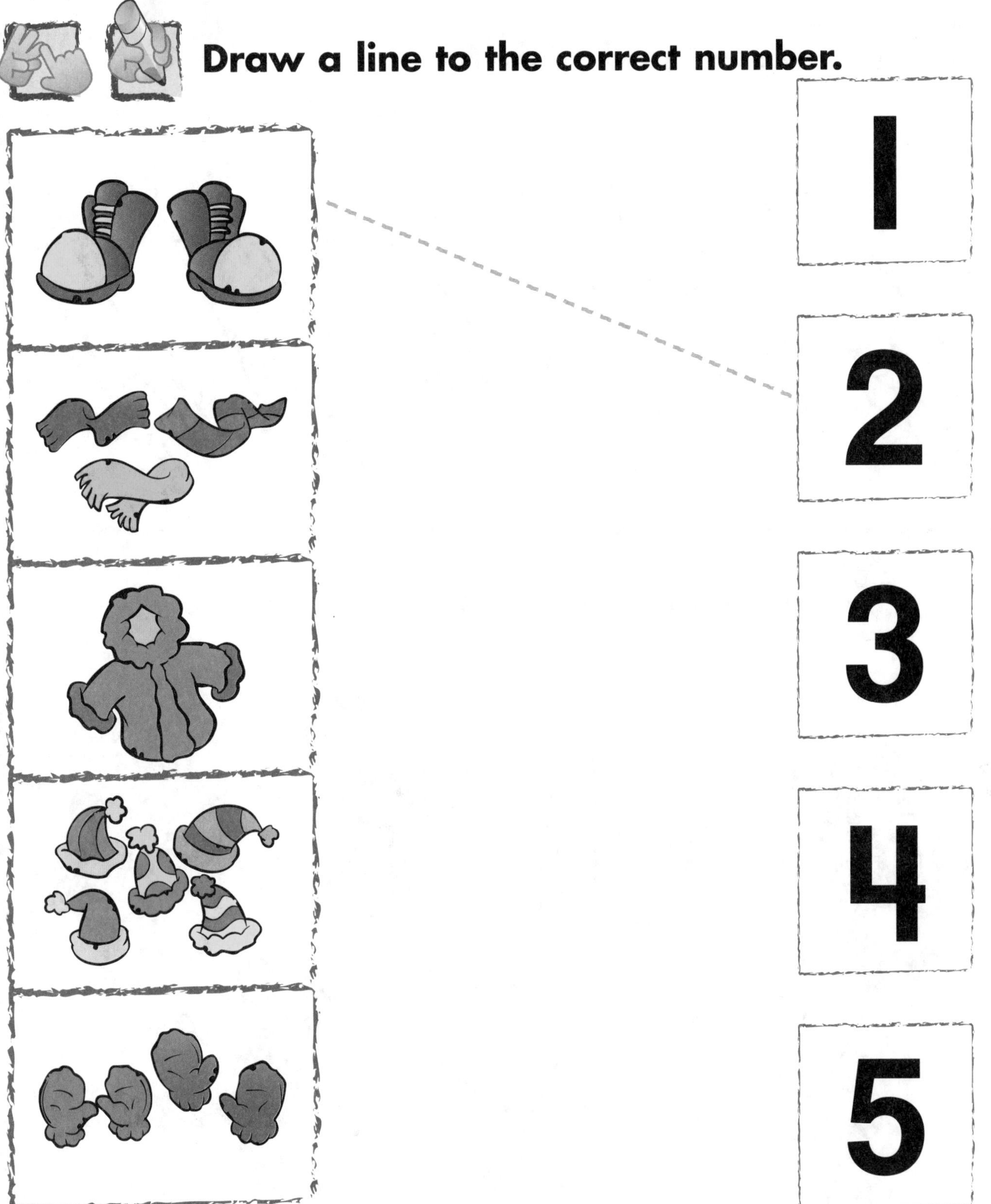

Parents: Have your child count the items in each set and draw a line to the correct number.

Counting to 6

6

Count and color 6.

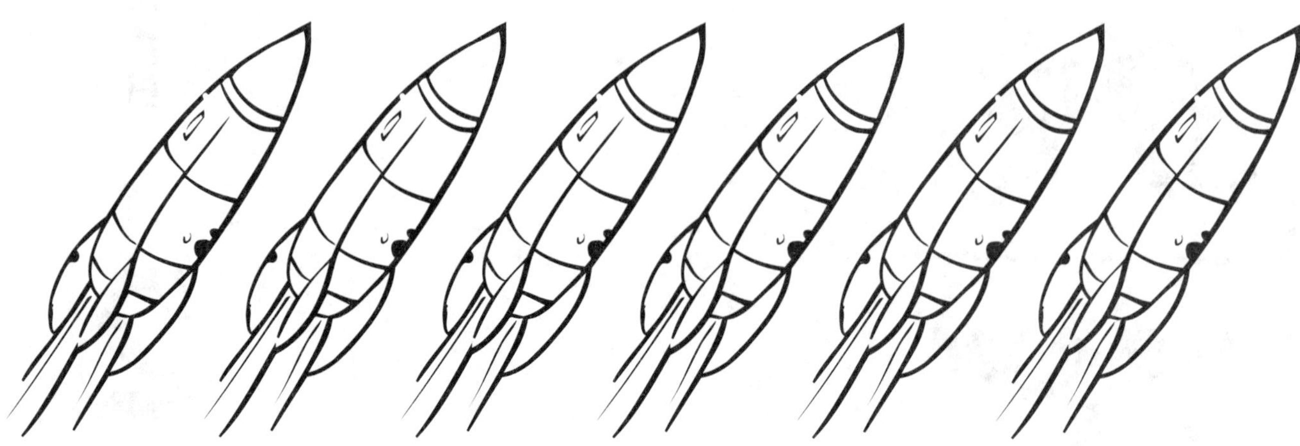

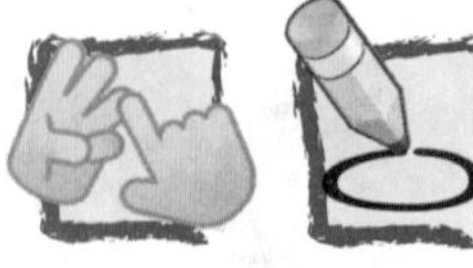

Count and circle 6.

Parents: (Top) Point to the number 6 and say, "This is the number 6." Ask your child to count the six rockets and color them. (Bottom) Ask him or her to count and circle six astronauts.

Up in the Sky

  **Count and color 6 in each group.**

Parents: Ask your child to color six pictures in each group.

Counting to 7

7

Count and color 7.

Count and circle 7.

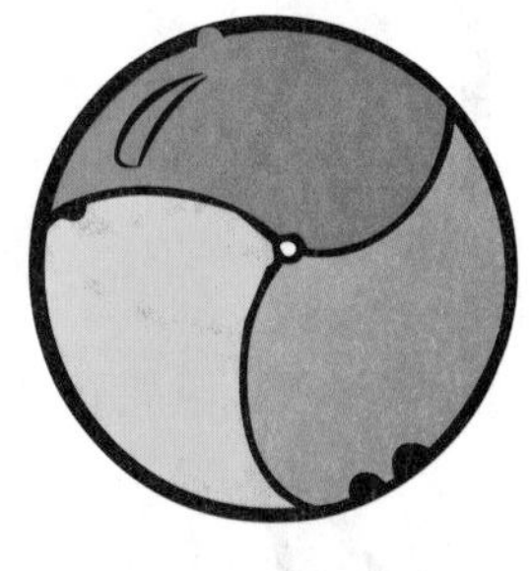
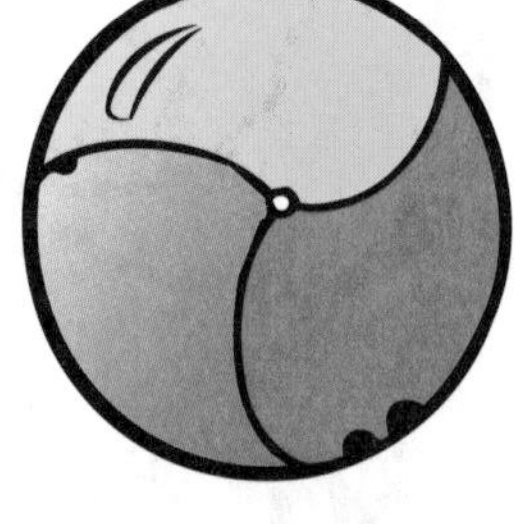
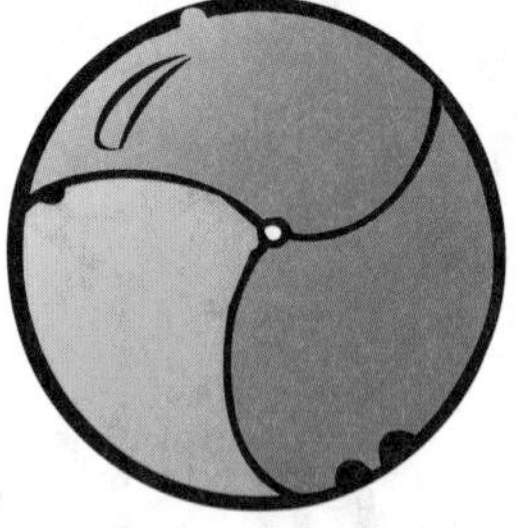
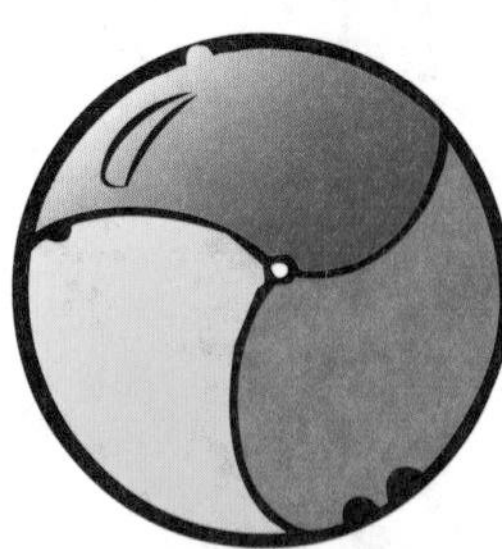
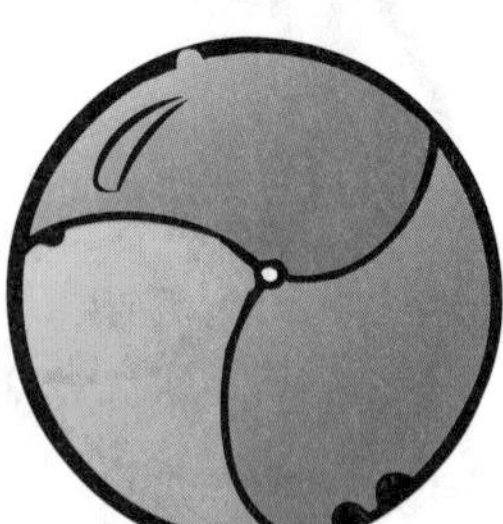
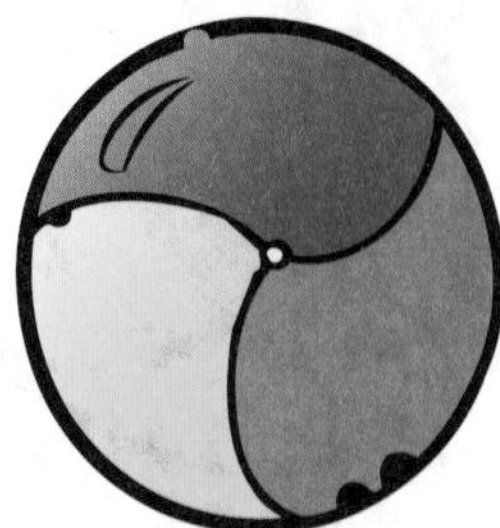
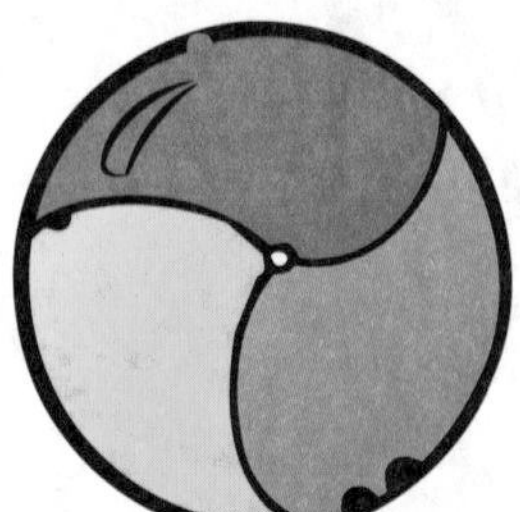
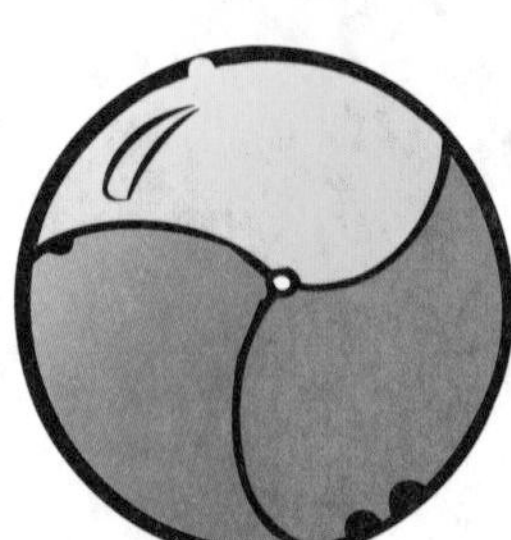

Parents: **(Top) Point to the number 7 and say, "This is the number 7." Ask your child to count the seven tubes and color them. (Bottom) Ask him or her to count and circle seven balls.**

Fun in the Sand

Count and color 7 in each group.

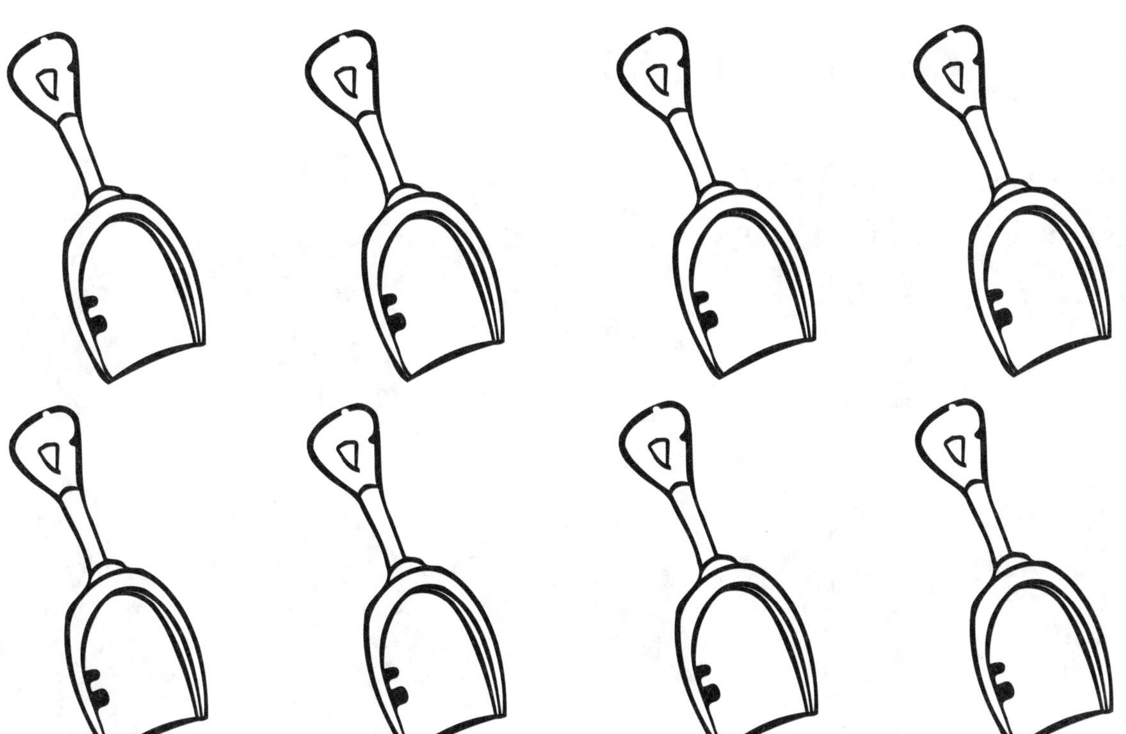

Parents: Ask your child to color seven pictures in each group.

Counting to 8

8

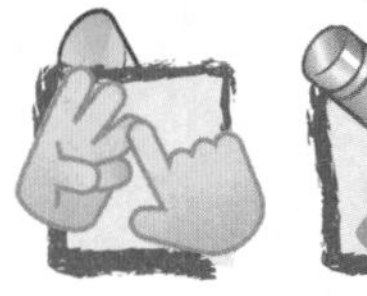

Count and color 8.

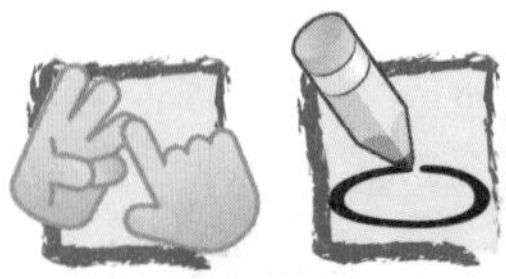

Count and circle 8.

Parents: (Top) Point to the number 8 and say, "This is the number 8." Ask your child to count the eight bees and color them. (Bottom) Ask him or her to count and circle eight butterflies.

Insects All Around

Count and color 8 in each group.

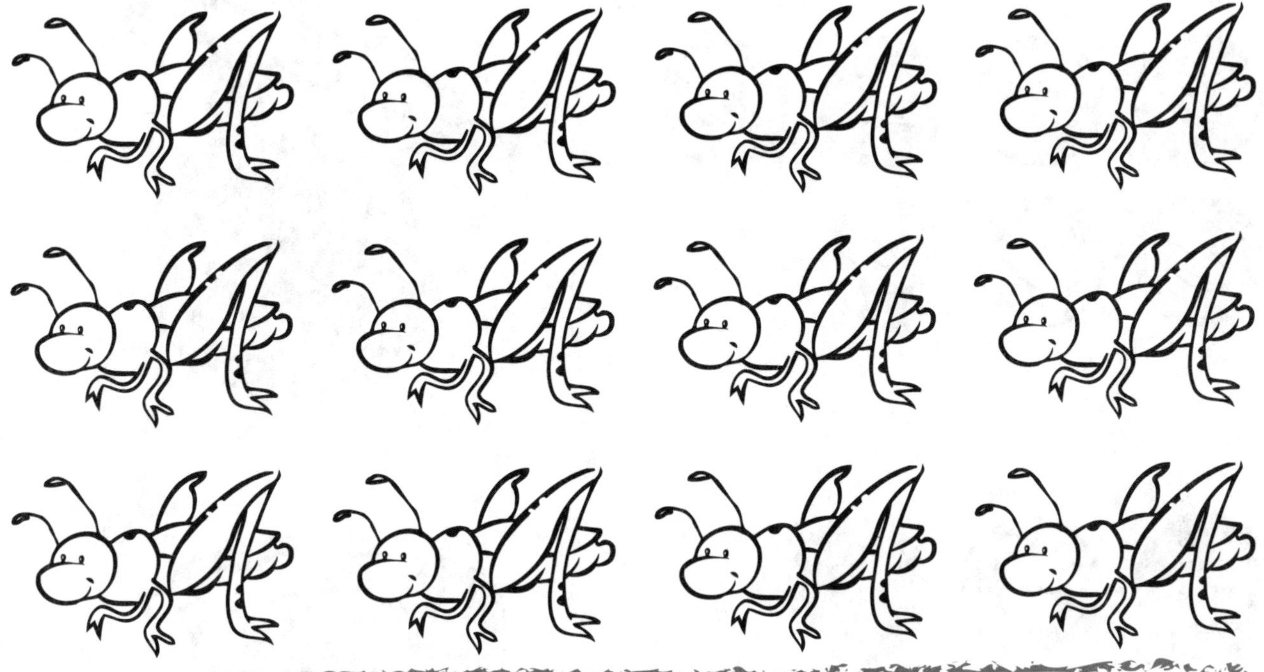

Parents: Ask your child to color eight pictures in each group.

MATH

Let's Play Marbles

Draw a line to the correct number.

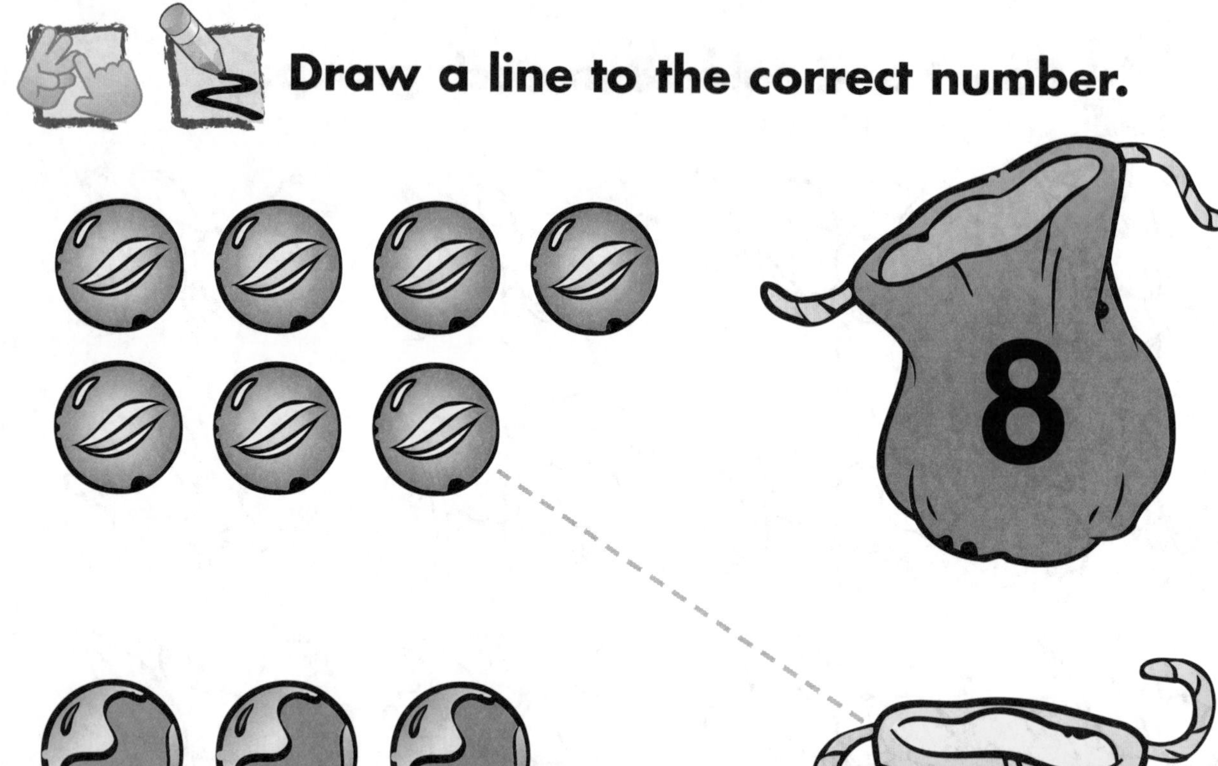

Parents: Point to the first group of marbles and ask, "How many marbles are there?" Point to the numbers and ask, "Which number shows how many?" Have your child trace the line to connect the marbles with the number. Continue with the other groups.

Understanding numbers; matching groups of objects and numerals 6-8

Play Ball!

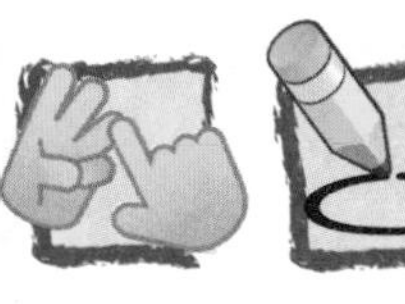

Circle the correct number.

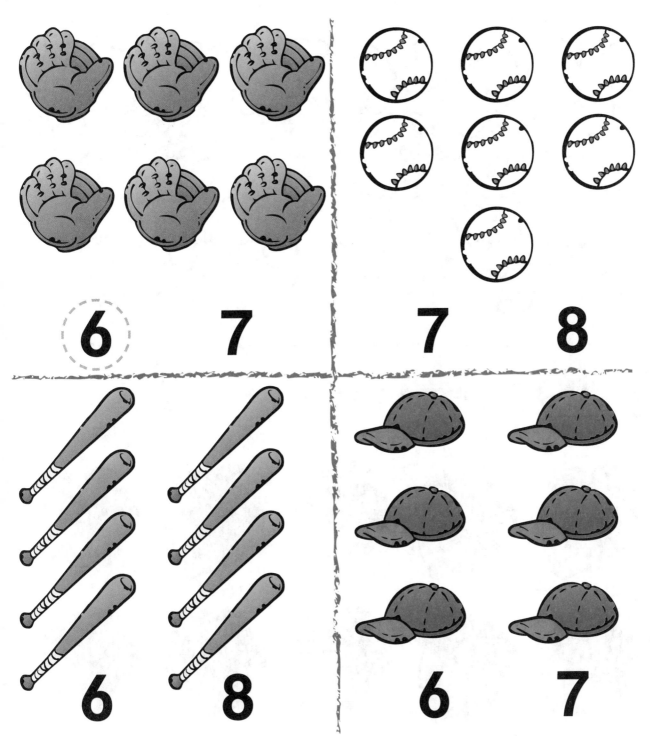

6 7

7 8

6 8

6 7

Parents: **Ask your child to count the number of objects in each group. Have him or her circle the number that shows how many there are.**

Counting to 9

9

Count and color 9.

Count and circle 9.

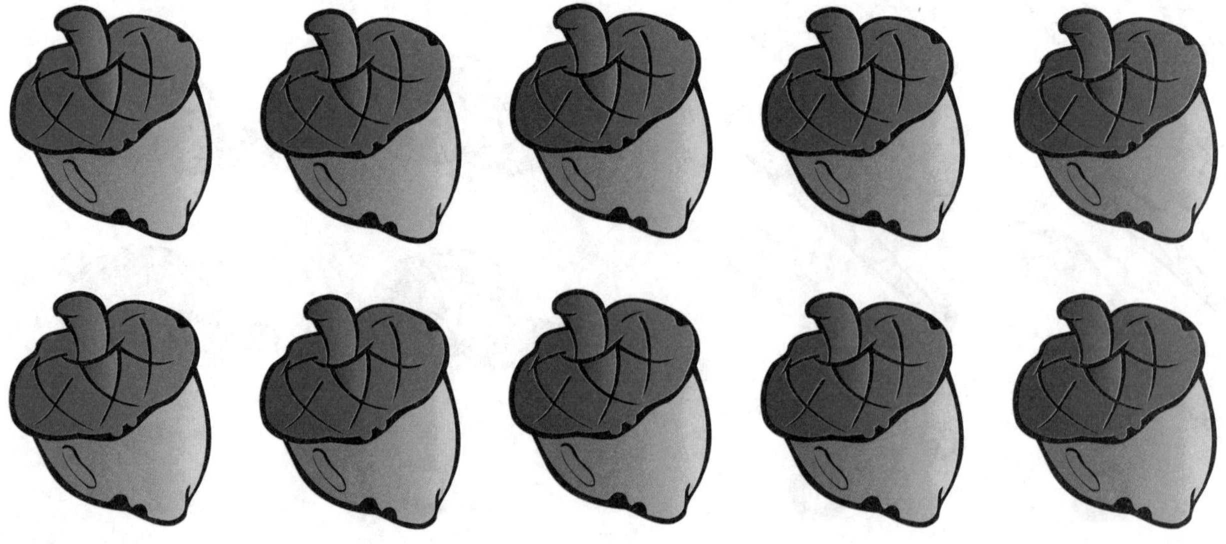

Parents: (Top) Point to the number 9 and say, "This is the number 9." Ask your child to count nine squirrels and color them. (Bottom) Ask your child to count and circle nine acorns.

yard Work

Count and color 9 in each group.

Parents: **Ask your child to count and color nine pictures in each group.**

Counting to 10

10

Count and color 10.

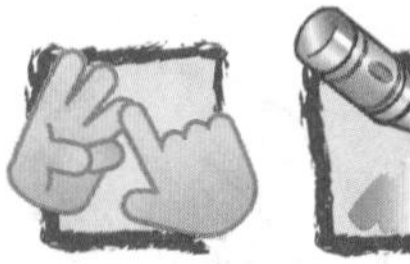

Count and circle 10.

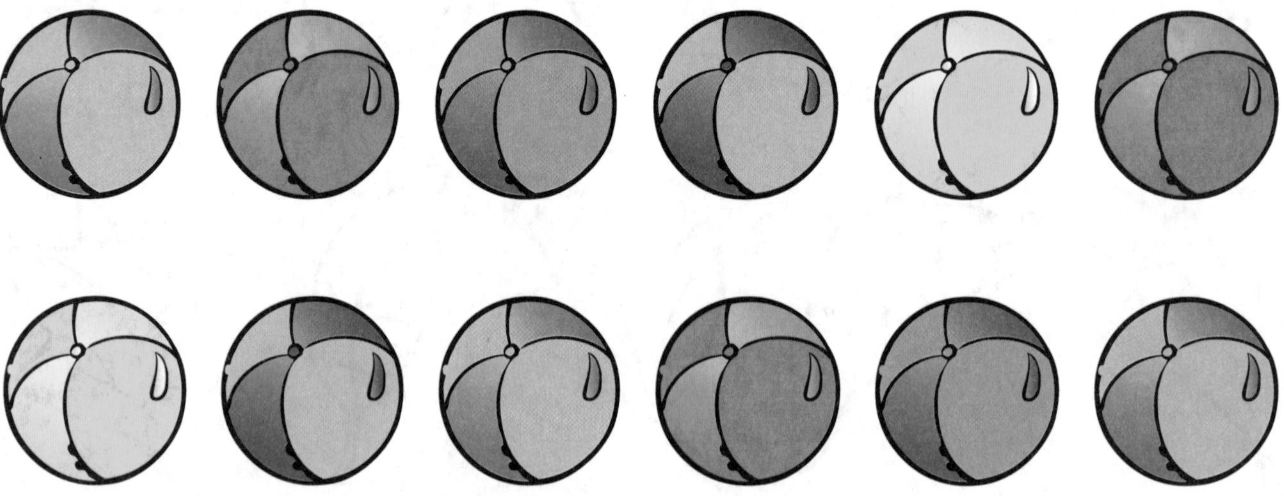

Parents: (Top) Point to the number 10 and say, "This is the number 10." Ask your child to count ten seals and color them. (Bottom) Ask your child to count and circle ten balls.

Kitten Play

  **Count and color 10 in each group.**

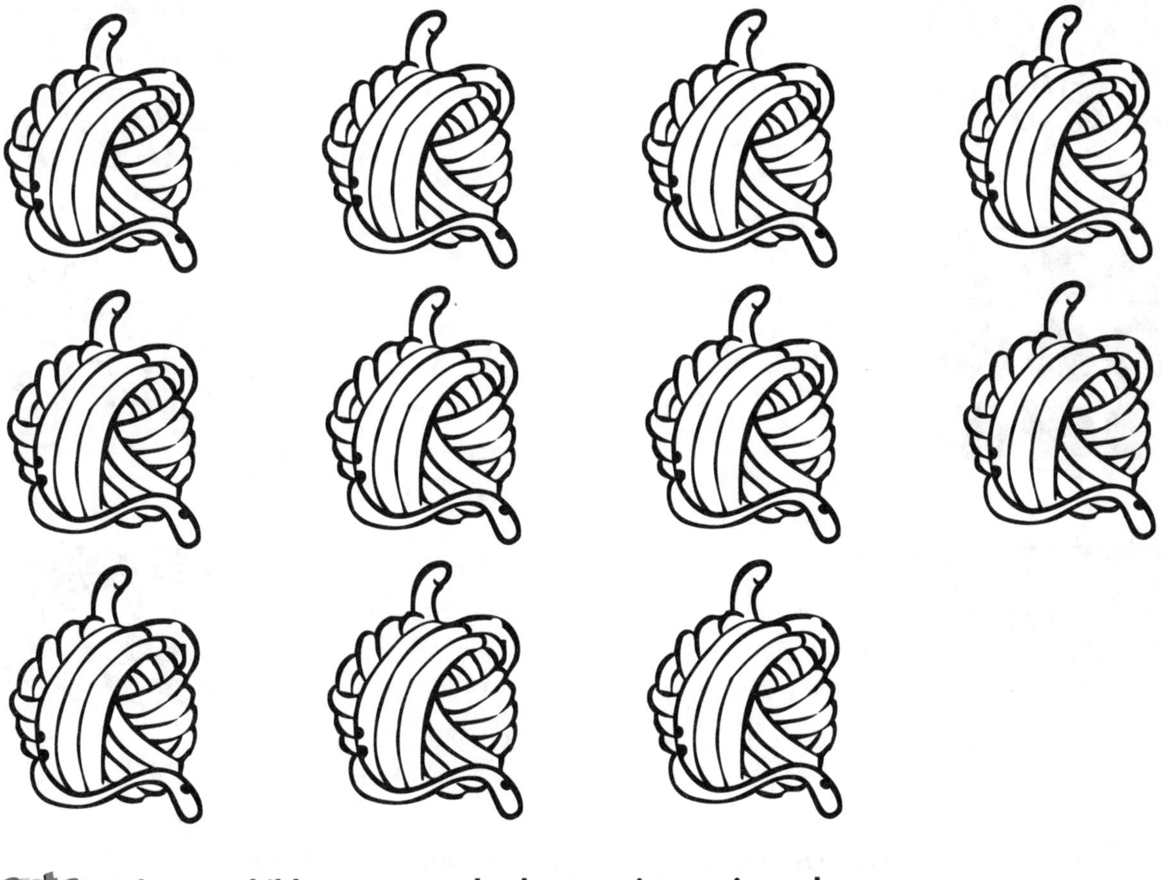

Parents: Ask your child to count and color ten pictures in each group.

Vegetable Patch

Match the ones with the same number.

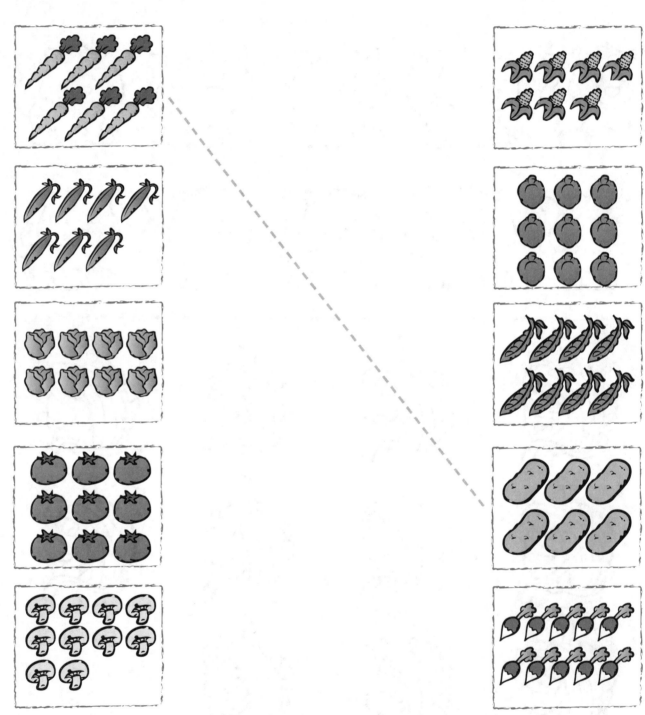

Parents: Help your child count the carrots in the first box and trace the line to the potatoes. Ask, "Why do the carrots and the potatoes go together?" (There are 6 carrots and 6 potatoes.) Have your child draw lines to match the other sets with the same number of vegetables.

Feathered Friends

Count and color to show the correct number.

6

7

8

9

10

Parents: Have your child read the number at the beginning of each row and color that many birds in the row.

Camping Out

Count and circle the correct number.

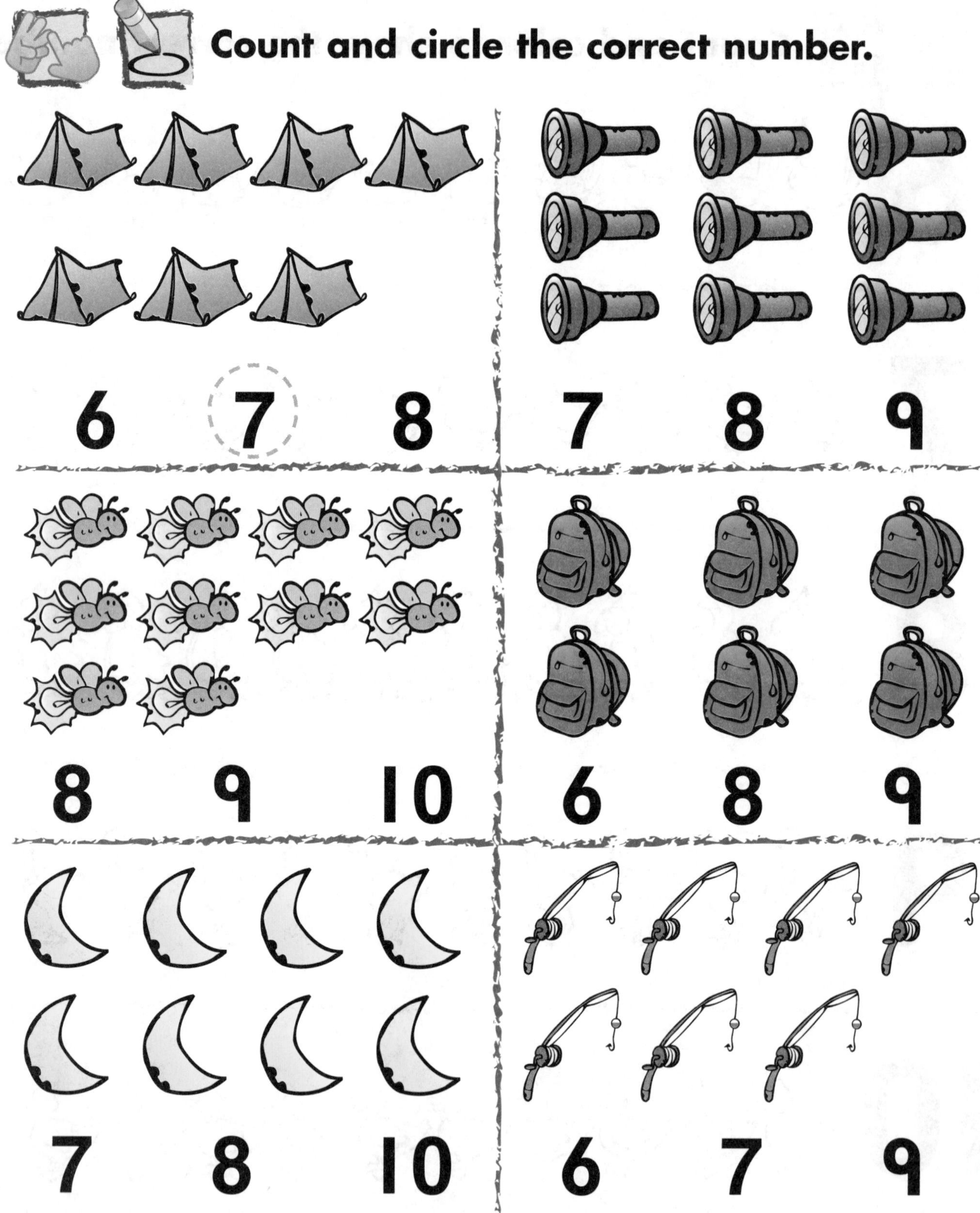

Parents: Have your child count the tents. Then ask him or her, "Which number shows how many tents there are?" Have your child trace the dashed circle to show there are seven tents. Continue with the other groups.

Jelly Bean Jars

Draw a line to the correct number.

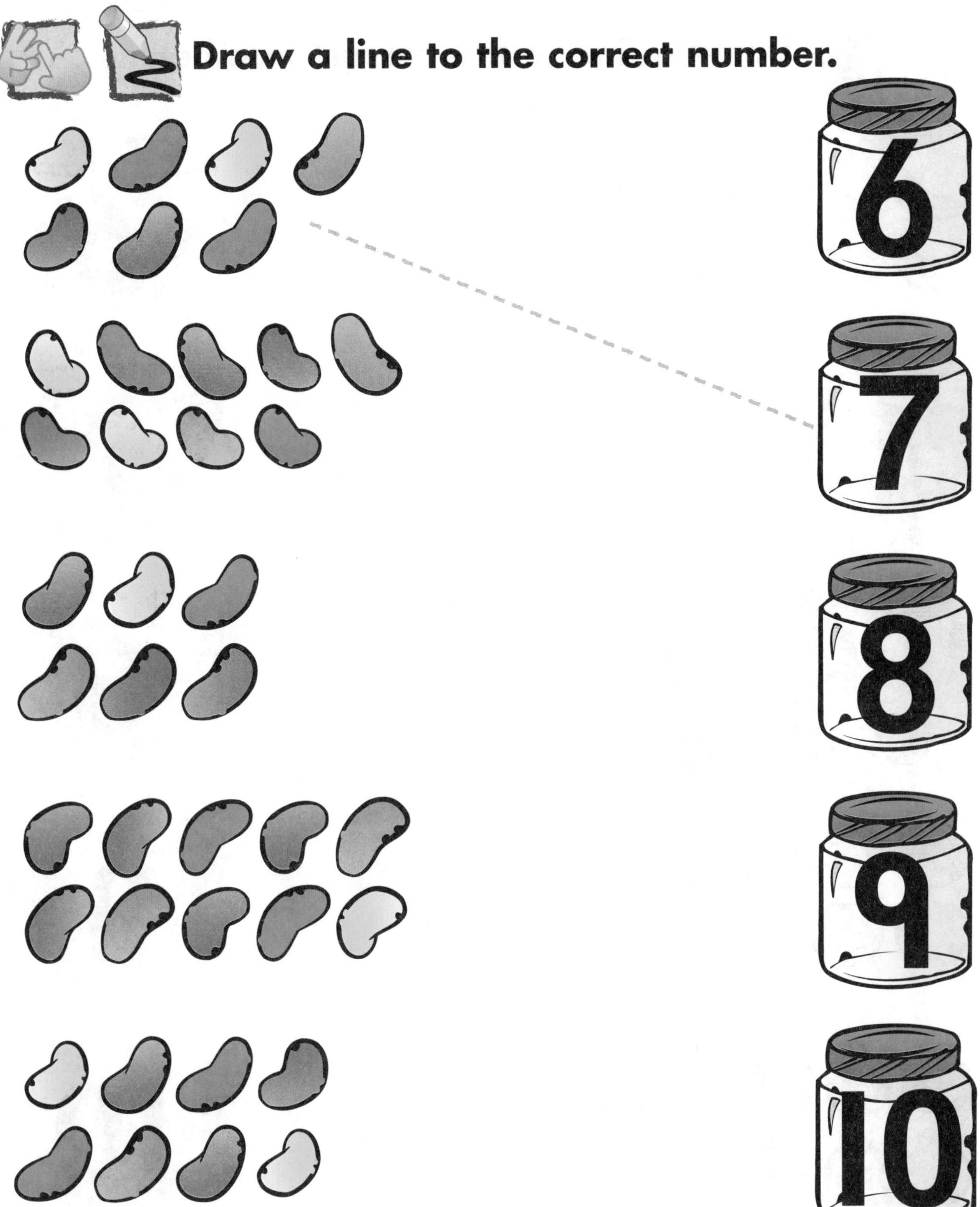

Parents: Have your child count the jelly beans in each set and draw a line to the jar with the correct number.

Fruit Bowls

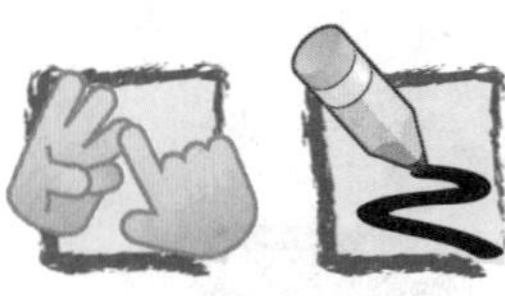

Draw a line to the correct number.

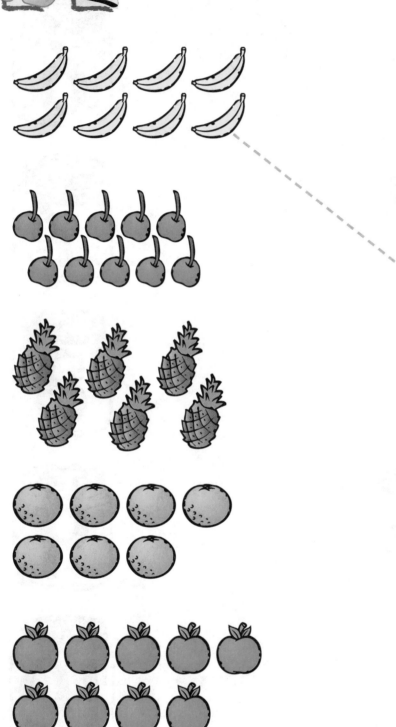

Parents: Have your child count the fruit in each set and draw a line to the bowl with the correct number.

Counting to 10; matching groups of objects and numerals

Go Fly a Kite

Color.

Parents: Have your child read the numeral on each crayon and identify the crayon colors. Then have him or her follow the code to color the picture.

MATH

Playing Dress Up

Color. 6 7 8 9 10

Parents: Have your child read the numeral on each crayon and identify the crayon colors. Then have him or her follow the code to color the picture.

Chocolate Chip Cookies

 **Draw ●s on the** 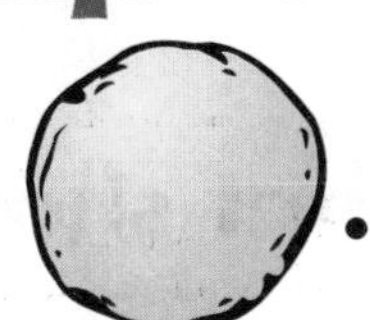**.**

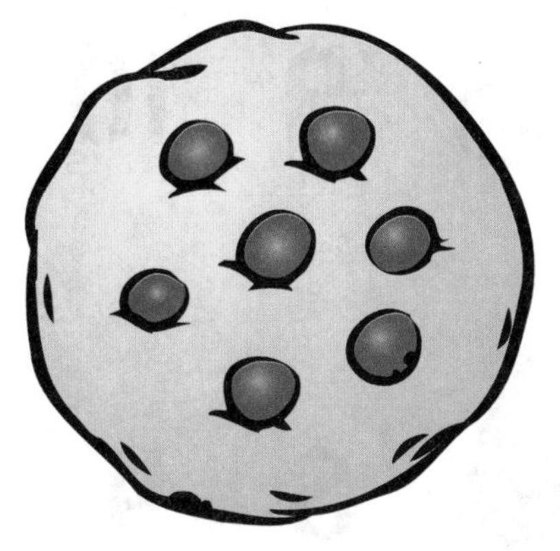 7

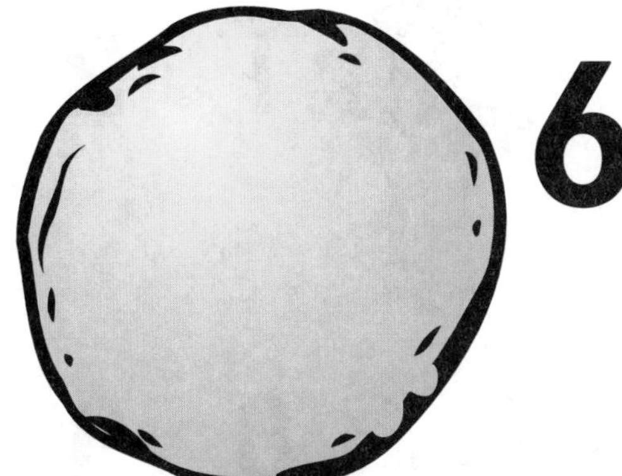 6

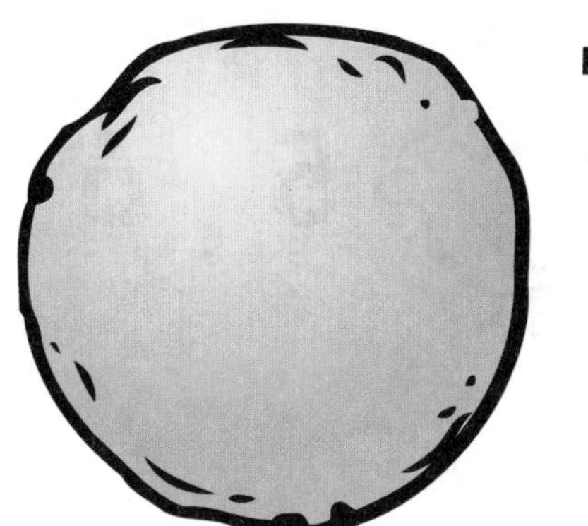 7

 8

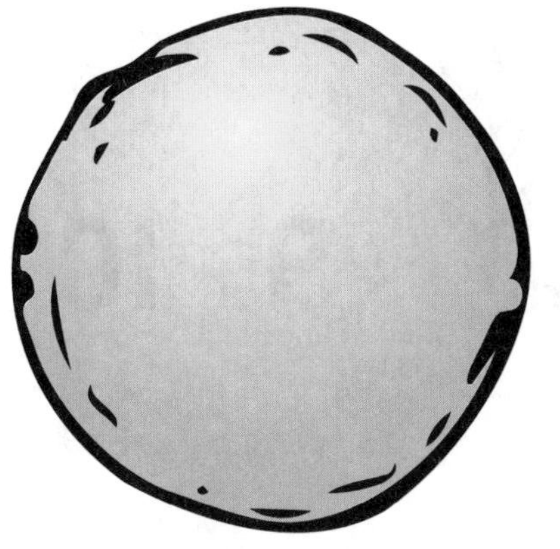 9

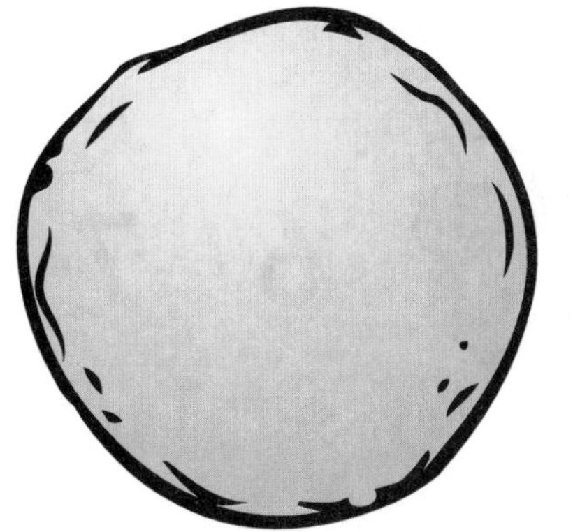 10

Parents: Have your child read the number next to each cookie and draw that many chocolate chips on the cookie.

Understanding numbers; drawing to show numbers 6-10

MATH

On the Farm

Circle the number that shows how many.

1 2

9 10

8 9

3 4

2 3

5 6

4 5

2 3

6 7

9 10

Parents: Have your child count the scarecrow in the picture on pages 249 and then trace the line around the numeral 1 above. Ask, "Why did you circle the number 1?" (There is one scarecrow in the picture.) Continue by having your child count the other objects in the picture and circle the numbers that show how many there are.

MATH

Bubble Dot-to-Dot

Connect the dots. Color the picture.

1 10 9 8 7 2 3 4 5 6

Parents: **Have your child read aloud and point to the numerals in order from 1 to 10. Then have him or her draw a line to connect the numbers in order and color the picture.**

Fishing Dot-to-Dot

Connect the dots. Color the picture.

1 2 3 4 5 6 7 8 9 10

Parents: Have your child read aloud and point to the numerals in order from 1 to 10. Then have him or her draw a line to connect the numbers in order and color the picture.

Bake Shop

Trace the numerals.

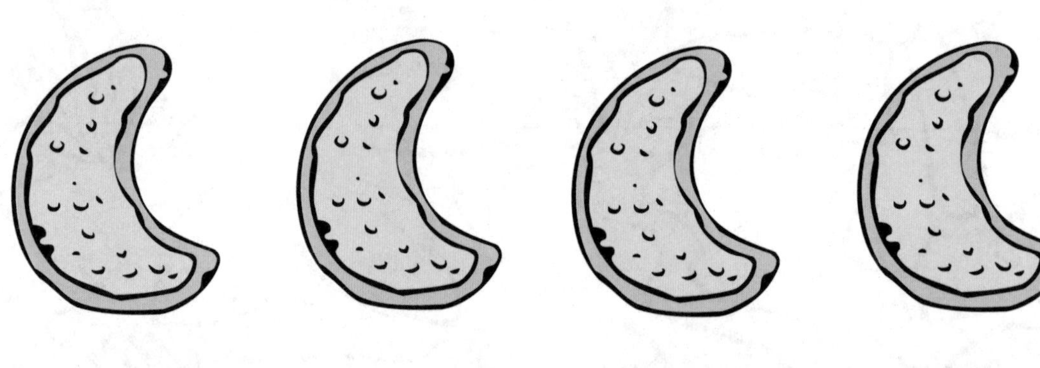

Parents: Have your child count the items on each line. Then ask him or her to trace the numerals.

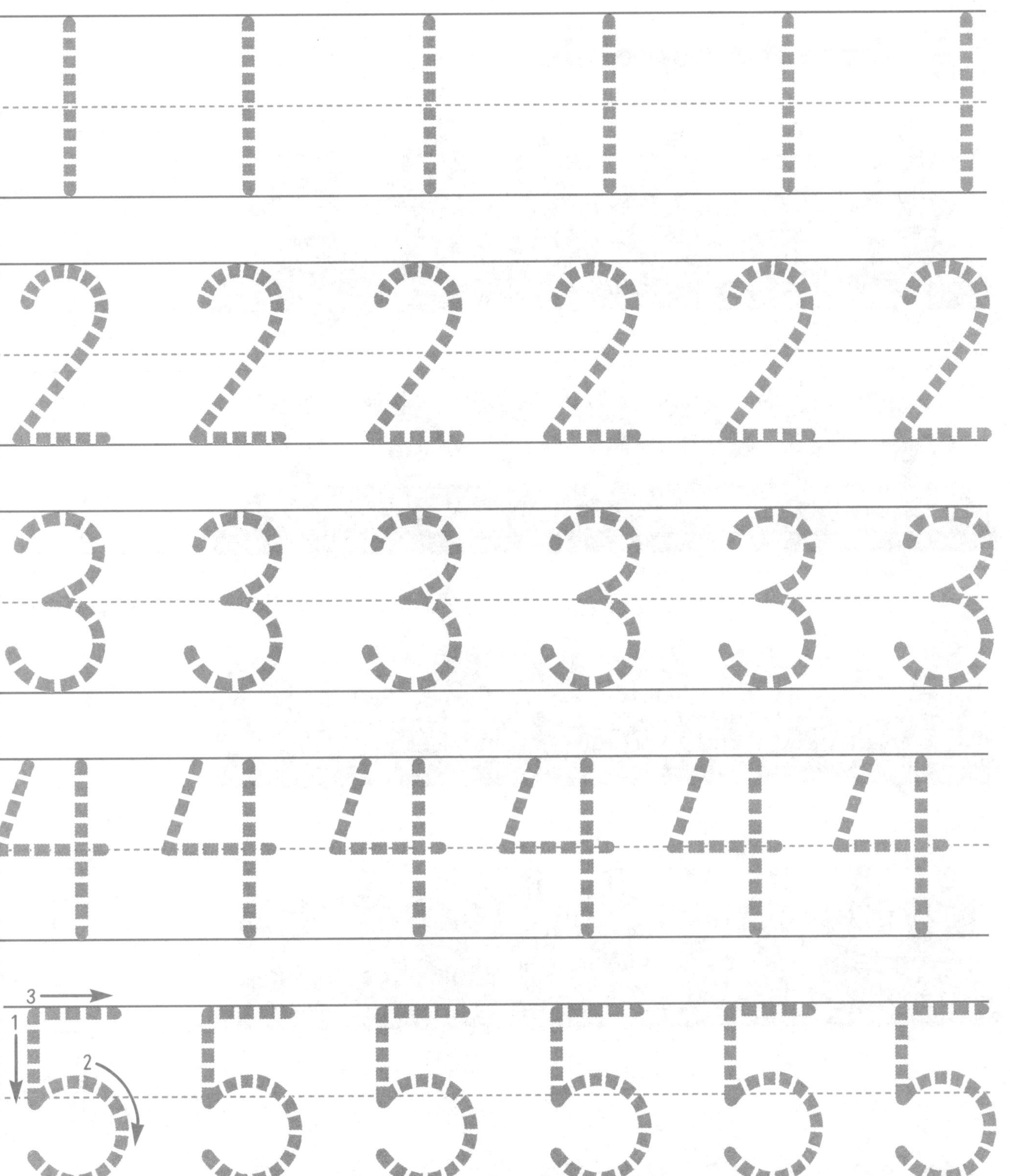

1
2
3

MATH

Toy Count

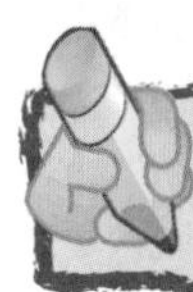

Trace the numerals.

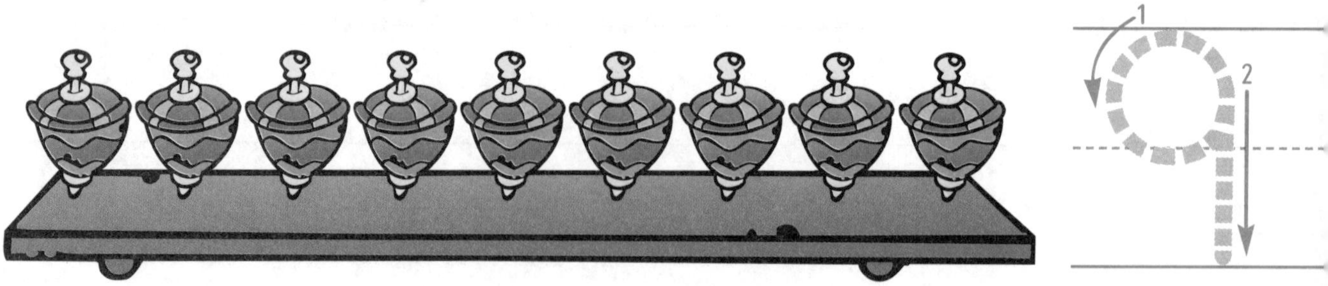

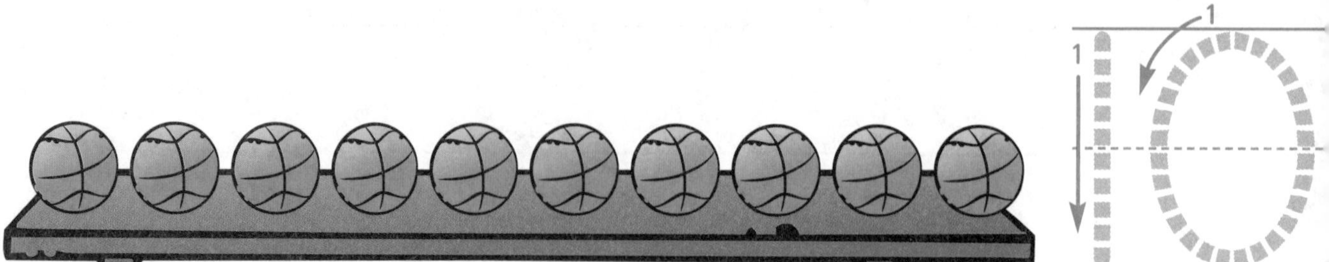

6

7

8

9

10

Parents: **Have your child count the items on each line. Then ask him or her to trace the numerals.**

What's Missing?

Write the missing numbers.

1 3 7 9

6 8 4 6

3 5 8 10

Parents: **Have your child point to the animals at the top of the page and count them in order from 1 to 10. Then have him or her write the missing numbers in the activity below.**

Month 9 Checklist

Hands-on activities to help prepare your child for school!

ALPHABET

Letter Recognition A-P: pages 259-278

One of the first steps in learning the alphabet is learning to recognize and identify each letter. Although your child might be able to recite the alphabet in order, he or she may not be able to identify the letters on a page. You can help your child learn to recognize letters with these activities:

- ❑ Complete the worksheets.
- ❑ Invite your child to have a "breakfast of champions" by exploring the letters on cereal boxes. To stimulate your child's concentration, you might first ask him or her to identify colors and shapes on the boxes. Then point to a letter, say it, and ask your child to repeat it with you.
- ❑ Play "I Spy Letters." Look for letters in a picture book. Encourage your child to find the letter you spied. Take turns switching roles.
- ❑ Many children learn about their world through touch. Make a batch of cookie dough and invite your child to help you shape the dough into letters. Try using letters from A to P to write a cookie message, like "HELLO." (Of course, you can also apply this activity to the letters Q through Z.) Try making both capital and lowercase letters. After the cookie letters are baked and cooled off, ask your child to close his or her eyes and hand him or her a cookie. Have your child try to identify the letter by feeling its shape.
- ❑ Write capital and lowercase letters on self-stick notes and place them on two similar foods or fruits. For example, place a capital *A* on one apple and a lowercase *a* on another. Other examples of food to use are bananas, cookies, donuts, eggs, ham, jelly, ketchup, lemons, milk, nuts, olives, and peaches. Mix up the labeled food and have your child find the matching letters. Ask him or her to pull off the sticky notes and place them side by side on the table. Say each letter together.

Letter Recognition, Q-Z: pages 279-290

The task of learning all 26 letters at once might seem daunting to your child. It's okay to teach and review letters in small groups. Here are activities to help your child recognize the last 10 letters of the alphabet. Feel free to use these activities for the letters A through P as well.

- ❑ Complete the worksheets.
- ❑ Create two sets of capital letter cards for the letters Q through Z. Use index cards. Mix up the cards and place them face down on a table. Have your child turn over one card and say the letter. Repeat with a second card. Ask your child if the two cards are the same letter. If they are, your child keeps the pair. If not, he or she turns the cards over and tries again. Play along with your child, encouraging him or her to help you identify the letters and find matches. Try this with lowercase letters, too.
- ❑ Create yarn prints. Cut out squares pieces of cardboard. As your child watches, pour glue on the cardboard in the shape of a letter. Give your child a string of yarn and have him or her place it on the glue to form the letter. Make both capital and lowercase letters. When the yarn has dried in place, have your child close his or her eyes. Ask him or her to feel the yarn and try to figure out which letter it is.
- ❑ Invite your child to "go fishing" and sort letters. Help your child cut out fish shapes. Write one letter on each fish, but make several fish with the same letter. Encourage your child to identify the letter as you write it. Attach a paper clip to each fish and place all of them in a large plastic container or tub. Attach a piece of string to a pole or stick and tie a magnet to the other end of the string. Then have your child use the fishing pole to catch the letter fish. (The magnet will attract the paper clips.) Ask your child to identify the letter on each fish he or she catches. Continue until all the fish are caught. Encourage your child to sort the fish by grouping the same letters together.

The Letters A and a

Circle the letters A and a.

A B a

O A a s

A a K I A

C E a A d

Parents: Point to the letter next to the ant at the top of the page and say, "This is the capital letter *A*." Point to the letter next to the apple and say, "This is the lowercase letter *a*." Have your child find and circle all the letters *A* and *a* on the anthill.

The Letters B and b

Draw the path to the baby birds.

B b b b
O K
B T R
n p P
r o b
y b B b B r p
p
b
U H T n K
u
B L h
S D
b B b

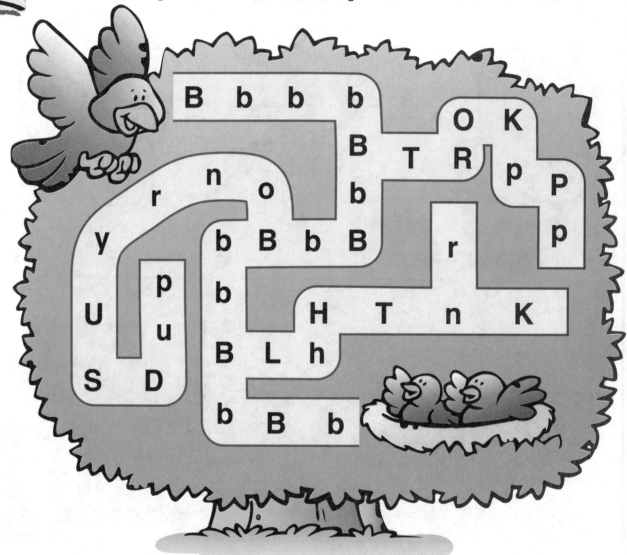

Parents: Point to the letter next to the bird at the top of the page and say, "This is the capital letter *B*." Point to the letter next to the basket and say, "This is the lowercase letter *b*." Have your child draw a line from the mother bird to her babies by following the letters *B* and *b*.

The Letters C and c

Color the 🍪s with C or c.

c S C V

C c o C

L C B c

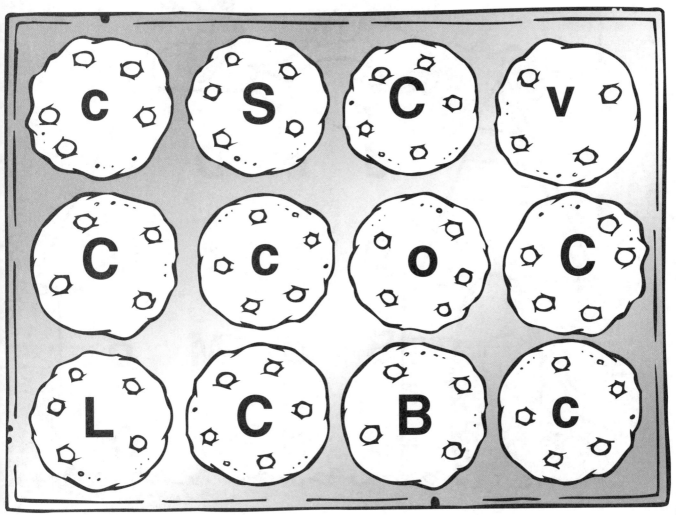

Parents: Point to the letter next to the cat at the top of the page and say, "This is the capital letter *C*." Point to the letter next to the cookie and say, "This is the lowercase letter *c*." Have your child color the cookies with the letters *C* or *c*.

The Letters D and d

Circle the letters D and d.

d	e	D	L
D	F	b	D
B	d	M	d
D	d	h	D

Parents: Point to the letter next to the dog at the top of the page and say, "This is the capital letter *D*." Point to the letter next to the duck and say, "This is the lowercase letter *d*." Have your child find and circle all the letters *D* and *d* on the doghouse.

It's a Party!

Match the ones with the same letter.

Aa

Bb

Cc

Dd

Cc

Dd

Aa

Bb

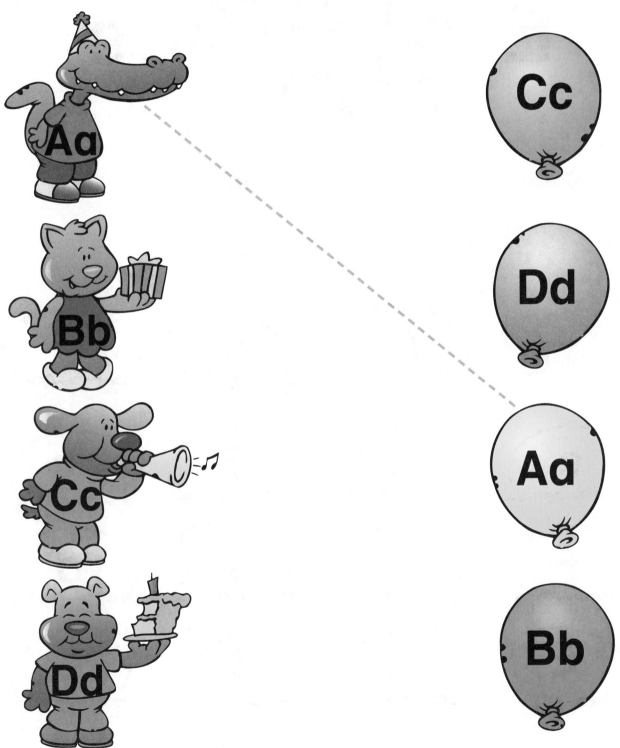

Parents: **Ask your child to say the letters on the animals' shirts. Have him or her draw a line from each animal to the balloon with the matching letters.**

The Letters E and e

Parents: Point to the letter next to the elephant at the top of the page and say, "This is the capital letter *E*." Point to the letter next to the basket of eggs and say, "This is the lowercase letter *e*." Have your child find and color all the eggs with the letters *E* or *e*.

The Letters F and f

Draw the path to the football.

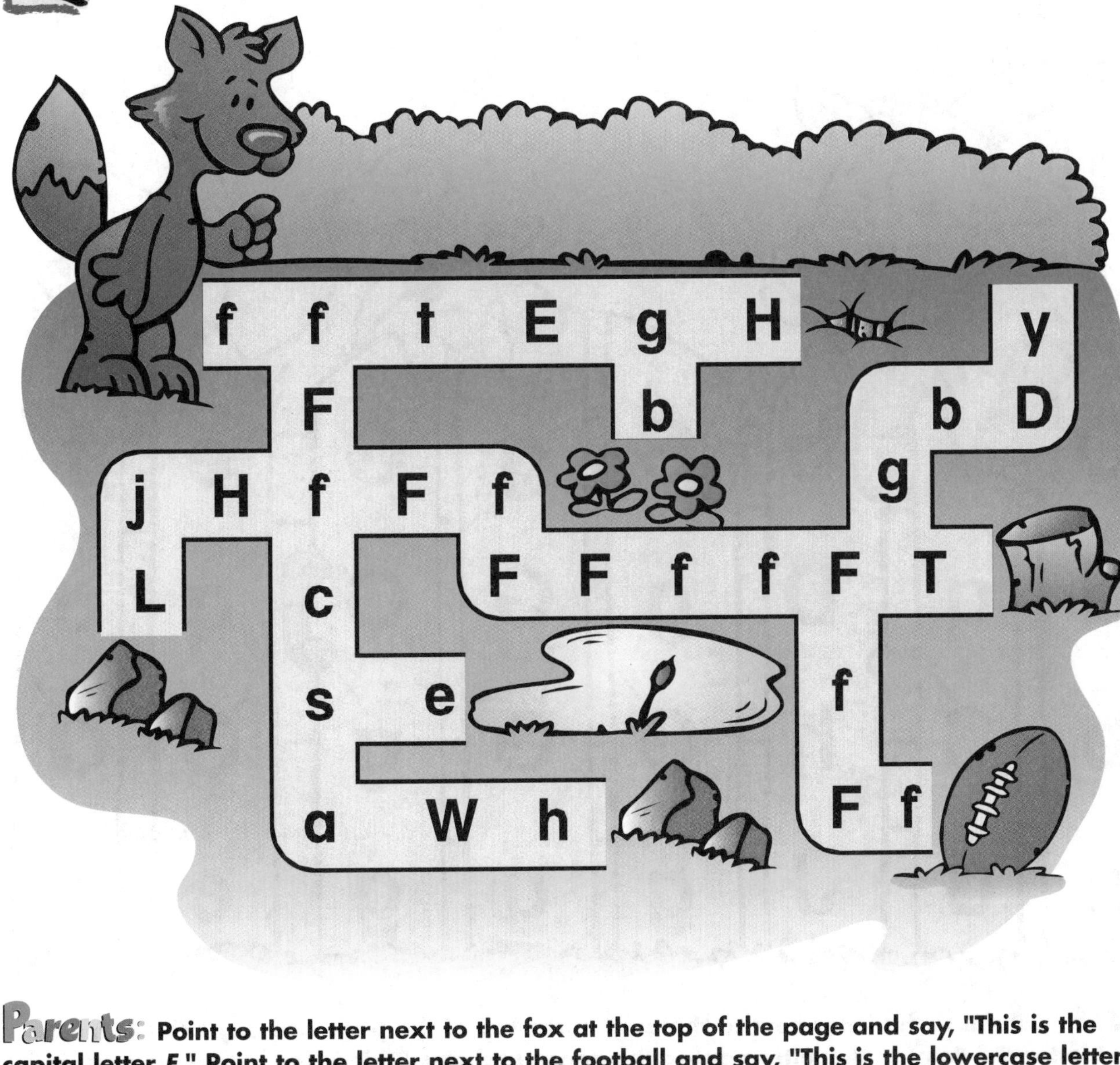

f f t E g H y
F b b D
j H f F f g
L c F F f f F T
s e f
a W h F f

Parents: Point to the letter next to the fox at the top of the page and say, "This is the capital letter *F*." Point to the letter next to the football and say, "This is the lowercase letter *f*." Have your child draw a line from the fox to the football by following the letters *F* and *f*.

The Letters G and g

Color the [fence post]s with G and g.

O V b G g G e t

d q D g G G q a

b C h G G g O Q

c a J g g g c o

Parents: Point to the letter next to the goat at the top of the page and say, "This is the capital letter *G*." Point to the letter next to the goose and say, "This is the lowercase letter *g*." Have your child find and color the fence posts with the letters *G* and *g*.

The Letters H and h

Circle the letters H and h.

H	b	h	A
h	H	t	D
R	h	H	h
h	S	h	H

Parents: Point to the letter next to the horse at the top of the page and say, "This is the capital letter *H*." Point to the letter next to the hippo and say, "This is the lowercase letter *h*." Have your child find and circle all the letters *H* and *h* on the harp.

Heading Home

Match the ones with the same letters.

Ee

Ff

Gg

Hh

Gg

Ee

Hh

Ff

Parents: Ask your child to say the letters on the animals' bags. Have him or her draw a line from each animal to the house with the matching letters.

The Letters I and i

Color the letters I and i green.

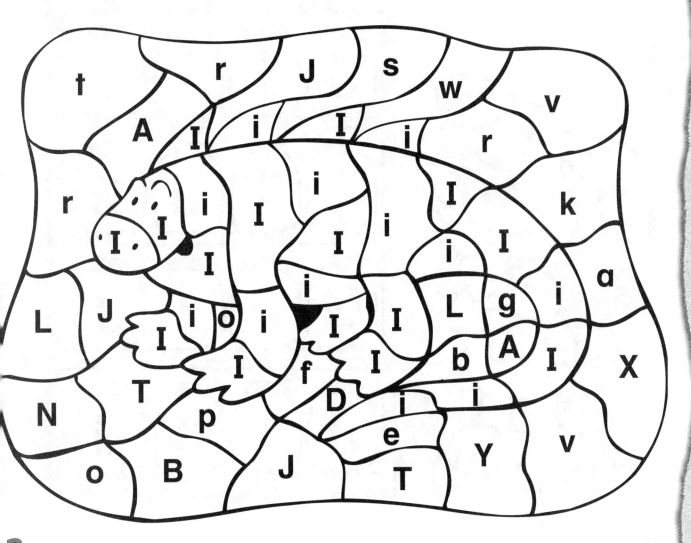

Parents: Point to the letter next to the iguana at the top of the page and say, "This is the capital letter *I*." Point to the letter next to the igloo and say, "This is the lowercase letter *i*." Have your child color all the letters *I* and *i* green to reveal the hidden picture.

The Letters J and j

Color the [jar]s with J or j.

J	j	I	l
j	T	J	g
G	J	j	J
J	i	c	d

Parents: **Point to the letter next to the dog juggler and say, "This is the capital letter *J.*" Point to the letter next to the puppy jumping rope and say, "This is the lowercase letter *j.*" Have your child find and color all the jars with letters *J* or *j.***

The Letters K and k

Draw the path to the key.

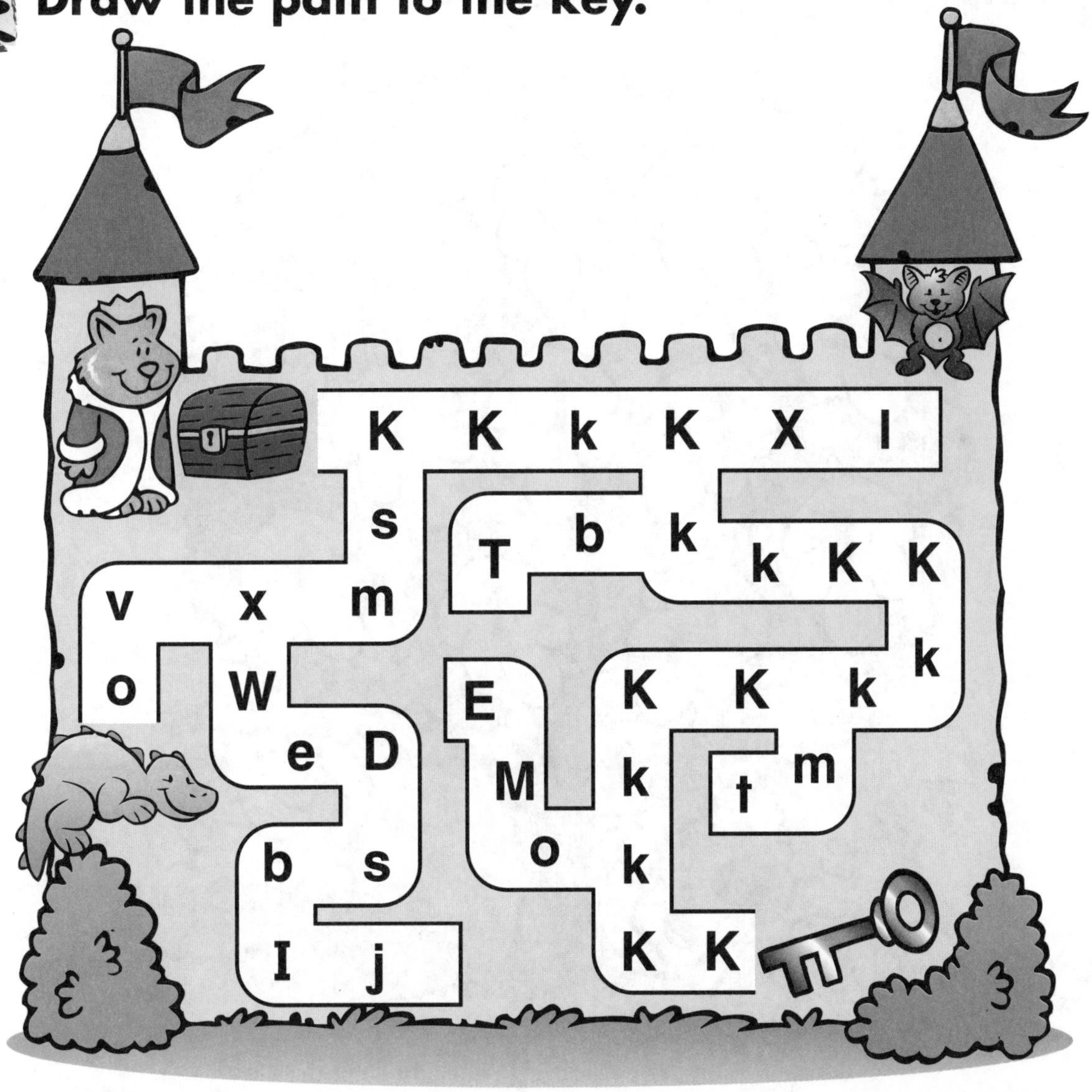

K K k K X I
s
T b k
k K K
v x m
k
o W E K K k
e D
M k t m
o
b s k
I j K K

Parents: Point to the letter next to the king at the top of the page and say, "This is the capital letter *K*." Point to the letter next to the kite and say, "This is the lowercase letter *k*." Have your child draw a line from the king to the key by following the letters *K* and *k*.

ALPHABET

The Letters L and l

Color the [leaf] s with L or l

l J L

E h

F L i

l L t l

Parents: **Point to the letter next to the lion at the top of the page and say, "This is the capital letter *L*." Point to the letter next to the leaves and say, "This is the lowercase letter *l*." Have your child find and color all the leaves with the letters *L* or *l*.**

Puzzle Pieces

Match the ones with the same letters.

Ii

Jj

Kk

Ll

Kk

Ll

Ii

Jj

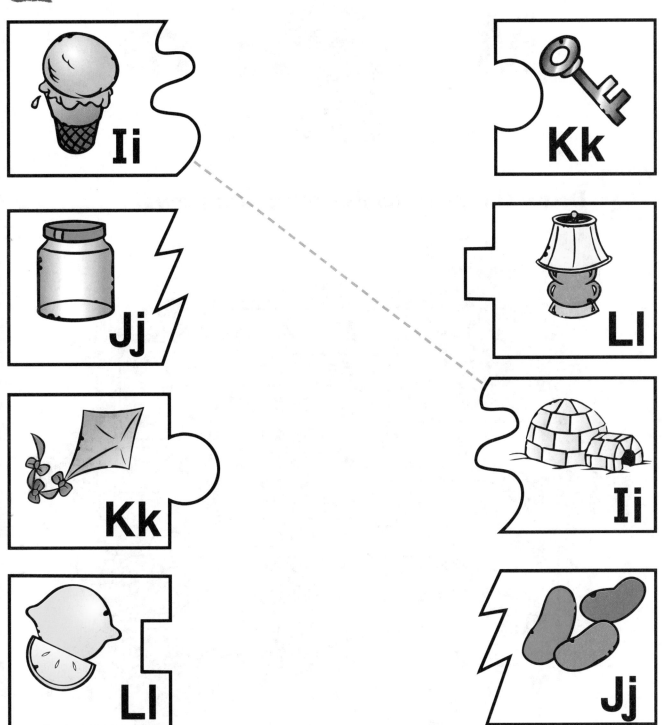

Parents: Ask your child to say the letters on the puzzle pieces. Have him or her draw a line from each puzzle piece on the left to the puzzle piece on the right with the matching letters.

The Letters M and m

Draw the path to the marshmallows.

m M M m
n U
M
m m
b s
r d N M B
D k
m M m
G h
M
l
w
m
MARSHMALLOWS
M m

Parents: Point to the letter next to the mouse at the top of the page and say, "This is the capital letter *M*." Point to the letter next to the mittens and say, "This is the lowercase letter *m*." Have your child draw a line from the mouse to the other mice by following the letters *M* and *m*.

The Letters N and n

Circle the letters N and n.

N n

n m N

M s n N

R N n N t

N b n g n N

Parents: Point to the letter next to the nightingale at the top of the page and say, "This is the capital letter *N*." Point to the letter next to the noodles and say, "This is the lowercase letter *n*." Have your child find and circle all the letters *N* and *n* in the noodles.

The Letters O and o

Color the letters O and o purple.

q e a h c N f
P O Y
o g o b
s Q
x a t
w
c o O O o v
o o e
W S o O O o g
O O M
x O o o s
V o l O r o
O s E
m U o C
B b Z
h D

Parents: Point to the letter next to the ostrich at the top of the page and say, "This is the capital letter *O*." Point to the letter next to the otter and say, "This is the lowercase letter *o*." Have your child color all the letters *O* and *o* purple to reveal the hidden picture.

The Letters P and p

Circle the letters P and p on each  **.**

P p Q

p r H

a P d

p P o

c e p

P K F

p q P

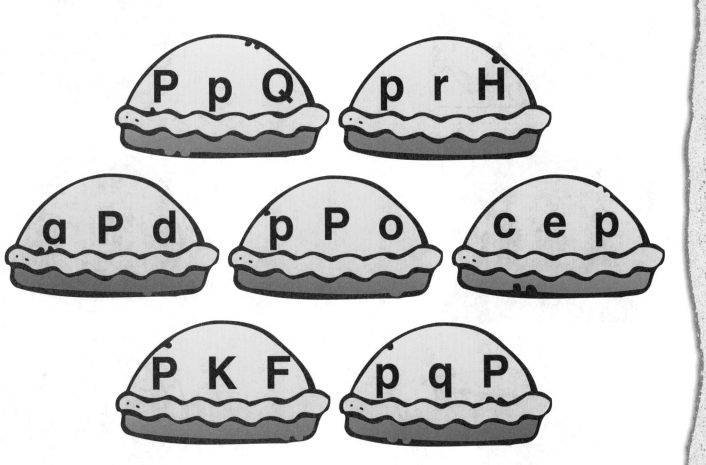

Parents: Point to the letter next to the penguin at the top of the page and say, "This is the capital letter *P*." Point to the letter next to the pig and say, "This is the lowercase letter *p*." Have your child circle all the letters *P* and *p* on the pies.

Pizza Time

Match the ones with the same letters.

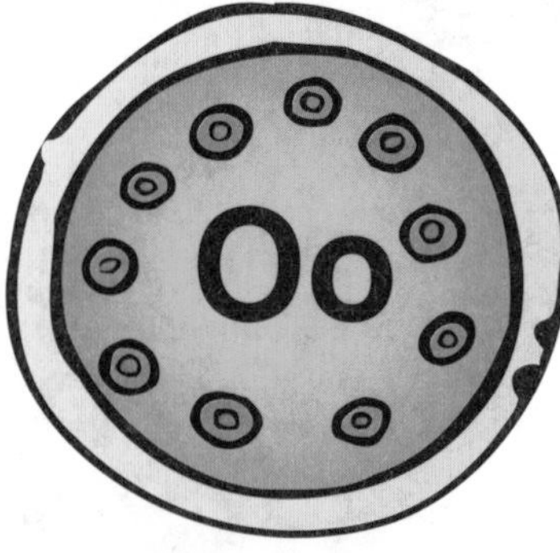

Parents: Ask your child to say the letters on the characters. Have him or her draw a line from each character to the pizza with the matching letters.

The Letters Q and q

Color the letters Q and q.

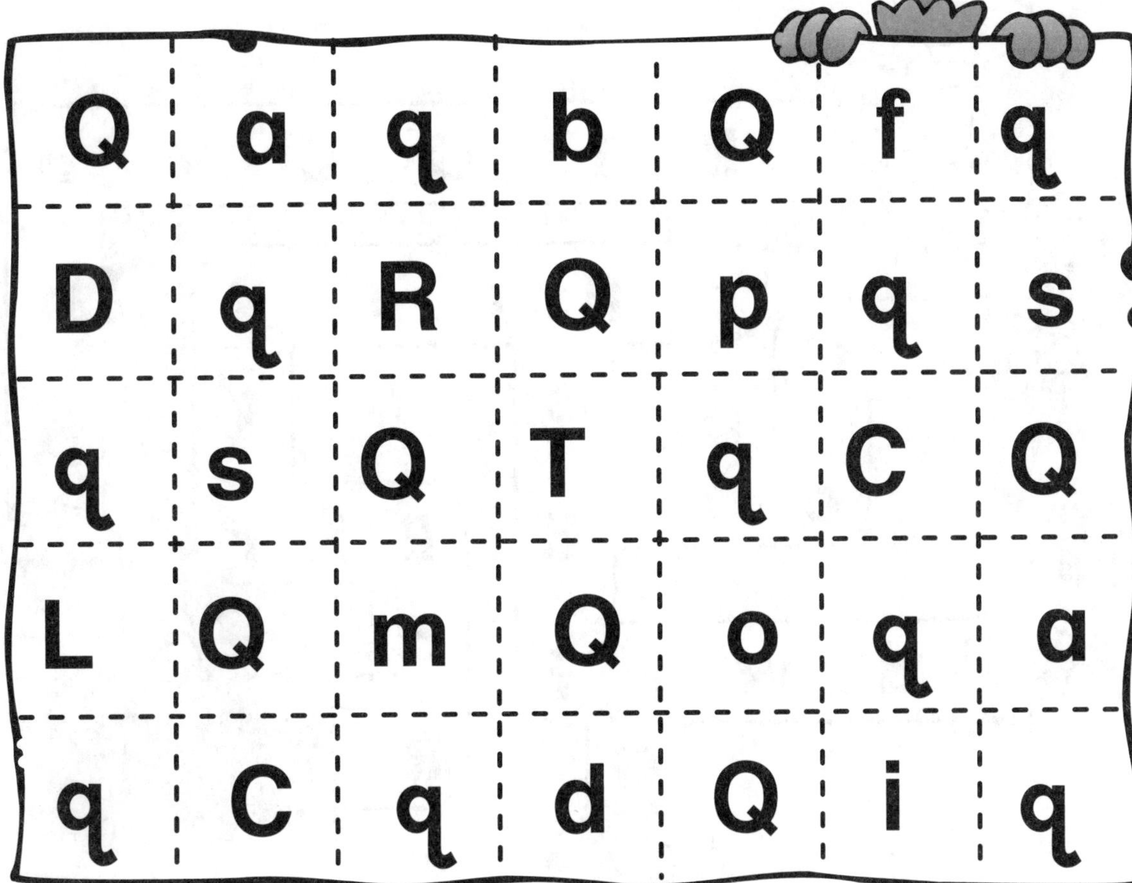

Q a q b Q f q
D q R Q p q s
q s Q T q C Q
L Q m Q o q a
q C q d Q i q

Parents: Point to the letter next to the queen at the top of the page and say, "This is the capital letter *Q*." Point to the letter next to the quilt and say, "This is the lowercase letter *q*." Have your child find and color all the sections on the quilt with the letters *Q* and *q*.

The Letters R and r

Draw the path to the pot of radishes.

R f Q C v b
r R r r R n
L U s R A
e k K R R r
d w c f r
G R

Parents: **Point to the letter next to the rainbow at the top of the page and say, "This is the capital letter *R*." Point to the letter next to the rabbit and say, "This is the lowercase letter *r*." Have your child draw a line from the rabbit to the radishes by following the letters *R* and *r*.**

The Letters S and s

S  s

Circle the letters S and s.

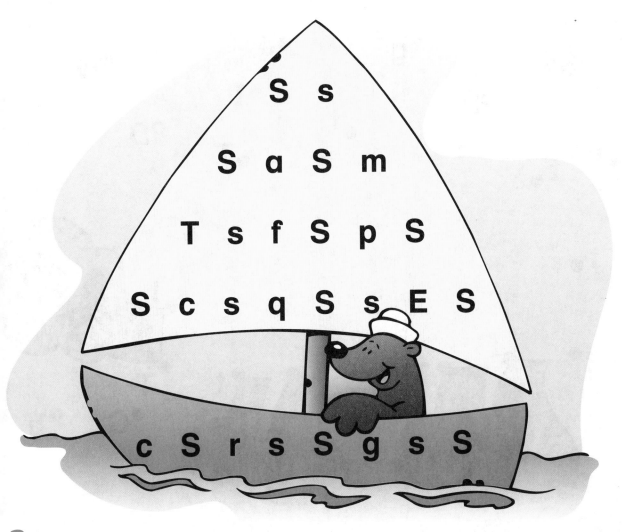

S s

S a S m

T s f S p S

S c s q S s E S

c S r s S g s S

Parents: Point to the letter next to the sun at the top of the page and say, "This is the capital letter *S*." Point to the letter next to the seal and say, "This is the lowercase letter *s*." Have your child find and circle all the letters *S* and *s* on the sailboat.

ALPHABET

The Letters T and t

T  t

Connect the letters T and t.

S g J w p I t D T T l t T t f t T T T t T C b

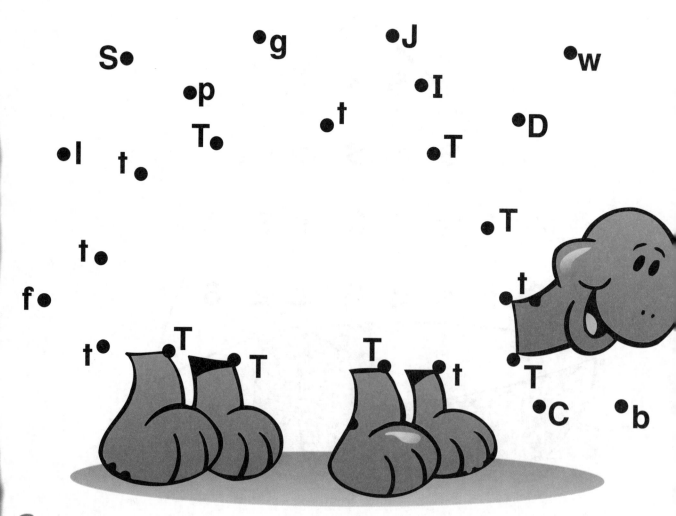

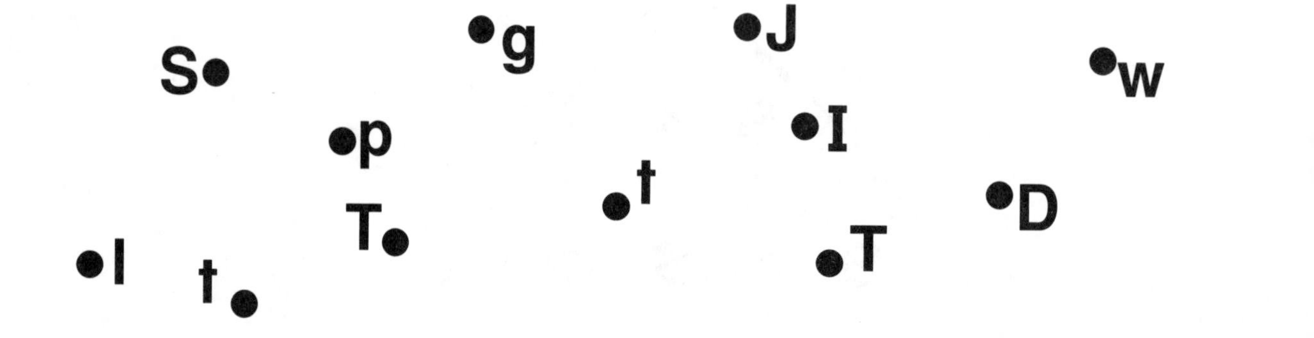

Parents: Point to the letter next to the tiger at the top of the page and say, "This is the capital letter *T*." Point to the letter next to the turtle and say, "This is the lowercase letter *t*." Have your child finish the picture by drawing a line to connect the letters *T* and *t*.

The Letters U and u

Color the letters U and u.

C e o B z P D L h k W v
U u U U u u U u U U u u U

Parents: Point to the letter next to the umpire at the top of the page and say, "This is the capital letter *U*." Point to the letter next to the umbrella and say, "This is the lowercase letter *u*." Have your child find and color all the spaces with the letters *U* and *u*.

Fine Art

Match the ones with the same letters.

Qq

Rr

Ss

Tt

Uu

Parents: Ask your child to say the letters on the animals' easels. Have him or her draw a line from each animal to the painting with the matching letters.

The Letters V and v

ALPHABET

Color the letters V and v red.

p i
Y k C
w K i I
g v z
V V V
d i v D
v V v v v
V v s x
Y v V P
f
V v j
u L i n
i N k
c

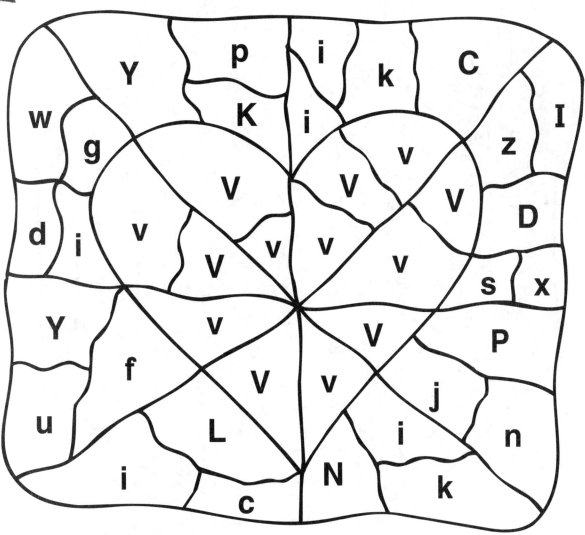

Parents: Point to the letter next to the boy vulture at the top of the page and say, "This is the capital letter *V*." Point to the letter next to the girl vulture and say, "This is the lowercase letter *v*." Have your child color all the sections with the letters *V* and *v* red to reveal the hidden picture.

The Letters W and w

Draw the path to the baby spider.

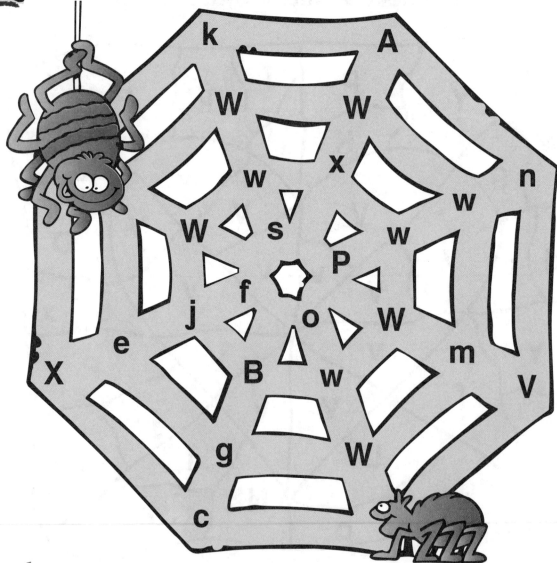

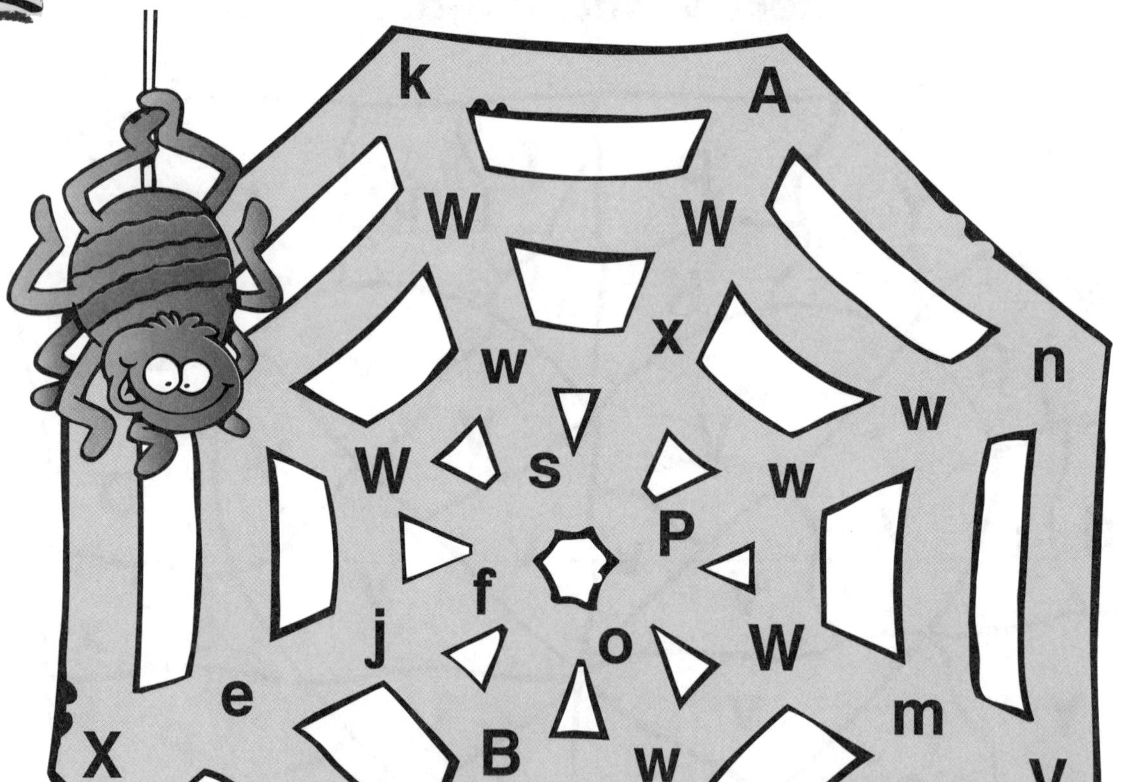

Parents: **Point to the letter next to the worm at the top of the page and say, "This is the capital letter *W*." Point to the letter next to the web and say, "This is the lowercase letter *w*." Have your child draw a line from the mother spider to her baby by following the letters *W* and *w*.**

The Letters X and x

Circle the letters X and x.

X-RAY

K w I X x X B m X X x w x N Z X y M K n L Y

Parents: **Point to the letter next to the dog x-ray at the top of the page and say, "This is the capital letter X." Point to the letter next to the cat x-ray and say, "This is the lowercase letter x." Have your child finish the picture by circling the letters *X* and *x*.**

The Letters Y and y

Circle the letters Y and y.

Y

V Y

S

y

Z y

W

V

y u

A Y Y B

Parents: Point to the letter next to the yak at the top of the page and say, "This is the capital letter *Y*." Point to the letter next to the yo-yo and say, "This is the lowercase letter *y*." Have your child find and circle all the letters *Y* and *y* on the yak.

The Letters Z and z

Color the areas with Z and z black.

Parents: Point to the letter to the left of the zebra at the top of the page and say, "This is the capital letter *Z*." Point to the letter to the right of the zebra and say, "This is the lowercase letter *z*." Have your child color the spaces with the letters *Z* and *z* black to show the zebra's stripes.

Good Job!

Match the ones with the same letters.

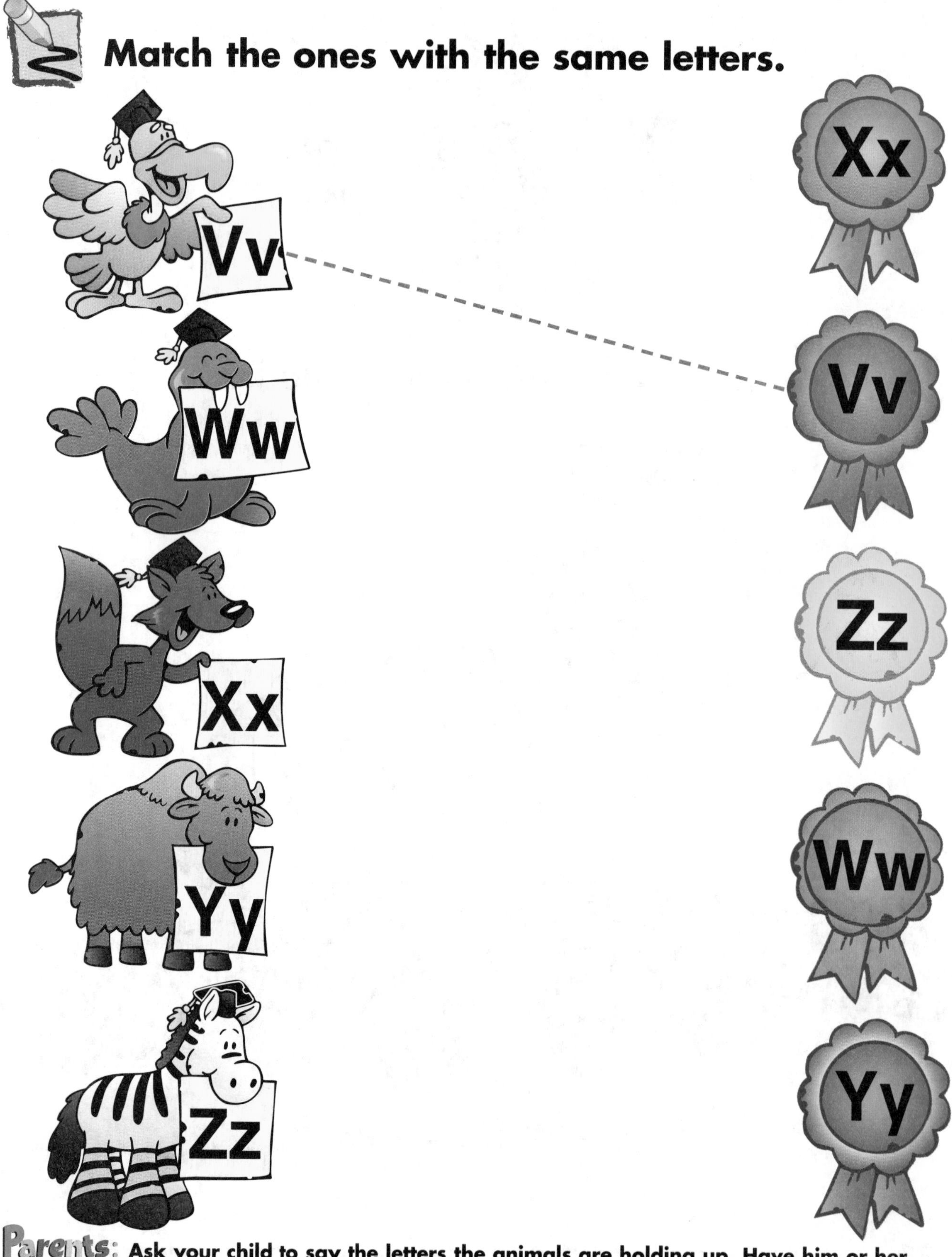

Parents: Ask your child to say the letters the animals are holding up. Have him or her draw a line from each animal to the ribbon with the matching letters.

Month 10 Checklist

Hands-on activities to help prepare your child for school!

LANGUAGE

Rhyming Words: pages 293-297

Some of the worksheets for this month focus on rhyming words. Learning rhyming words helps your child listen for specific sounds at the end of a word—a necessary skill for beginning readers.

- ❑ Complete the worksheets.
- ❑ Play a rhyming game around the house. Pick up an object and ask your child to find an object that rhymes with it. For example, if you pick up a *sock*, your child might find a *block* or *clock*.
- ❑ Let your child choose his or her favorite nursery rhymes to "read" to you. Point out all the rhyming words.
- ❑ Play "I'm Going on a Trip" at the dinner table or in the car. Begin by saying, "I'm going on a trip to (pick a favorite location) and I'm taking a *pan*." Go around the table or car and have each person repeat the sentence, replacing the word *pan* with an object that rhymes with it. See how far you can go before you run out of things that rhyme. Try it with other rhyming words, too.
- ❑ Also, try the rhyming activities suggested on page 97.

Names for Places, Things, and Actions: pages 298-304

As your child grows and develops, his or her speaking vocabulary will increase. Provide opportunities for your child to learn new words and to use them in conversations.

- ❑ Complete the worksheets.
- ❑ Play "I Spy" using words for places or things. You may begin by saying, "I spy with my little eye something red, white, and blue. It has 50 stars. What is it?" When your child guesses the object correctly, change roles.
- ❑ Play animal charades. Imitate a duck by waddling, quacking, and flapping your arms as wings. Ask your child to guess what animal you are imitating. Then have him or her choose an animal to act out.
- ❑ Let your child make a collage by cutting out pictures of his or her favorite places or things. Help your child glue the pictures on a large sheet of construction paper. Talk about the pictures in the collage.
- ❑ Sing action songs like "The Hokey Pokey," "I'm a Little Teapot," and "London Bridge." Name and demonstrate each action word in the song.
- ❑ Use index cards to write down the names of objects in your home, such as door, sink, computer, bed, and toys. Place the cards beside the corresponding objects and read them often.

LANGUAGE

Position Words: pages 305-311

Understanding positions and position words is a prerequisite for many academic tasks, such as following directions, thinking, math, and handwriting. The activities here will help you make positions more tangible for your child.

- ❑ Complete the worksheets.
- ❑ Play "Hide and Seek." Let your child hide a small object. Encourage him or her to give directions to help you find the object. For example, "It is in the living room. It is on top of the bookcase. It is to the left of the vase."
- ❑ Listen for words that tell the positions of people, animals, and objects as you say nursery rhymes together. Start off with "Little Miss Muffet," who has a spider beside her, "Little Boy Blue," who is asleep under a haystack, and "Jack Be Nimble," who jumps over a candlestick.
- ❑ Draw a large circle on paper. Give your child a cup with four different colored buttons. Have him or her turn the cup upside down, spilling the button onto the paper. Ask your child to describe where each button landed in relation to the circle.
- ❑ Play "Simon Says" using left and right. For example, ask your child to touch his or her left foot, left knee, right ear, left shoulder, etc. Face the same direction as your child to avoid confusing him or her with mirror images as you demonstrate the actions.

Following Directions: pages 312-320

Your child can begin learning how to follow directions by listening to and repeating one verbal direction at a time. When your child is successful with one direction, increase the steps required to perform a task. Continue until your child is comfortable following three or four directions in a row.

- ❑ Complete the worksheets.
- ❑ Give your child verbal directions for folding a piece of paper in half and then in half again to make a card. Let him or her decorate the card and give it to someone.
- ❑ Demonstrate how to brush teeth with up and down strokes. Then have your child follow the directions for brushing his or her teeth: (1) Put toothpaste on the brush, (2) brush up and down, and (3) rinse mouth with water.
- ❑ Play games where players are asked to follow simple directions. Two games that your child may already know how to play are "Mother May I?" and "Simon Says."
- ❑ Bake cookies using prepared dough. Have your child listen as you say the directions aloud: slice the dough, put the cookies on a baking sheet, and sprinkle the cookies with sugar crystals.
- ❑ Enlist your child's help in setting the table. You may ask him or her to fold the napkins a certain way or to set the forks, spoons, and napkins in a particular place for each place setting.
- ❑ Experiment with soap bubbles and a wand to see who can blow the most bubbles. Have your child follow these directions: (1) Dip the wand into the soap, (2) take a deep breath, (3) blow the soap out of the wand, and (4) count the bubbles.

Food Rhymes

Color the pictures with names that rhyme.

Parents: Point to each picture on the first plate and say its name. Have your child do the same. Explain that *jam* and *ham* rhyme because they have the same sound at the end. Help your child complete the rest of the page.

On-the-Go Rhymes

Match the ones that rhyme.

truck

train

boat

van

plane

man

duck

goat

Parents: Point to the truck and say its name. Have your child draw a line from the truck to the duck. Explain that *truck* and *duck* rhyme because they have the same sound at the end. Help your child complete the rest of the page.

Dress-Up Rhymes

Match the ones that rhyme.

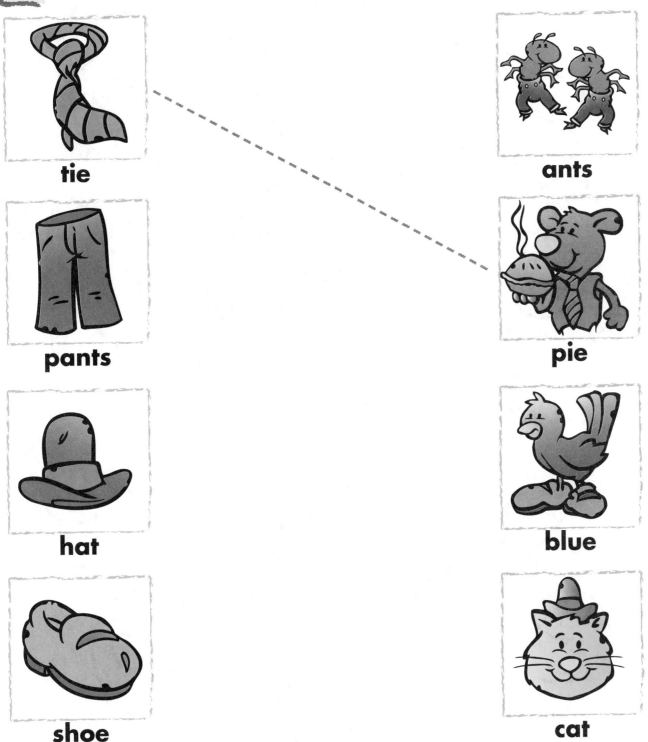

tie — **ants**

pants — **pie**

hat — **blue**

shoe — **cat**

Parents: Point to the tie and say its name. Have your child draw a line from the tie to the pie. Explain that *tie* and *pie* rhyme because they have the same sound at the end. Help your child complete the rest of the page.

Number Rhymes

Color the pictures with names that rhyme.

Parents: Point to each picture on the first balloon and say its name. Have your child do the same. Explain that *four* and *door* rhyme because they have the same sound at the end. Help your child complete the rest of the page.

Art Rhymes

Match the ones that rhyme.

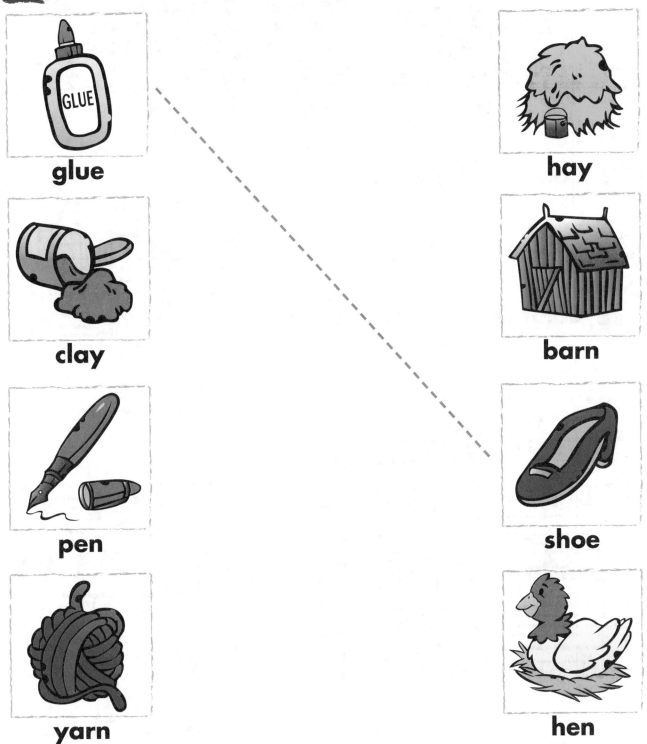

glue

hay

clay

barn

pen

shoe

yarn

hen

Parents: Point to the glue and say its name. Have your child draw a line from the glue to the shoe. Explain that *glue* and *shoe* rhyme because they have the same sound at the end. Help your child complete the rest of the page.

Names for Places

house store fire station

Color the house blue.

Color the store green.

Color the fire station red.

Parents: Read the words *house, store,* and *fire station* at the top of the page and explain that they are names for places. Ask your child to tell a story about each place. Then have your child color the page using the color code.

More Names for Places

park **zoo** **beach**

Color the park green.

Color the zoo brown.

Color the beach yellow.

Parents: **Read the words *park, zoo,* and *beach* at the top of the page and explain that they are names for places. Ask your child to describe things he or she might see or do when visiting each place. Then have your child color the page using the color code.**

Names for Things

carrot lettuce tomato

Color the carrot orange.

Color the lettuce green.

Color the tomato red.

Parents: Read the words *carrot, lettuce,* and *tomato* at the top of the page and explain that they are names for things in a garden. Ask your child to tell about his or her favorite vegetables. Then have him or her color the page using the color code.

More Names for Things

shell crab castle

Color the shell brown.

Color the castle yellow.

Color the crab red.

Parents: Read the words *shell, crab,* and *castle* at the top of the page and explain that they are names for things at the beach. Ask your child to tell a story about the beach. Then have him or her color the page using the color code.

LANGUAGE

You Can Do It!

Match the ones that are the same.

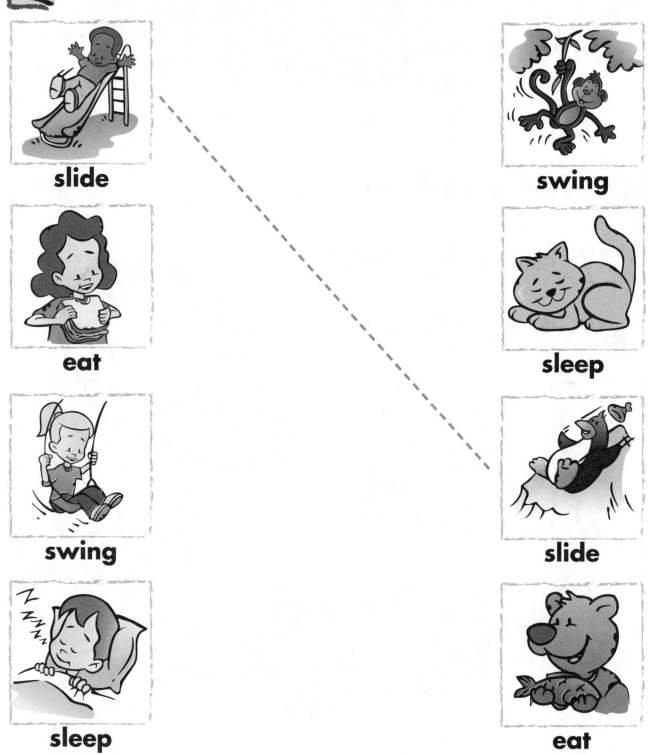

slide	swing
eat	sleep
swing	slide
sleep	eat

Parents: Ask your child to tell a story about each picture on the page. Look together at the picture of the boy going down the slide. Point to the word slide as you read it. Have your child draw a line from the boy who is sliding to the animal that is sliding. Then help your child complete the rest of the page.

Identifying names for actions

Action Words

Cut out the cards.

run	fly	dig
dig	fly	run

Parents: Have your child say what each animal is doing on this page and the next one. Point to the word for each action and read it aloud. Then help your child cut along the lines to make six cards. Ask him or her to match the cards that show the same words and actions.

More Action Words

Cut out the cards.

lick	hop	climb
climb	hop	lick

Parents: Have your child say what each animal is doing on this page and the previous one. Point to the word for each action and read it aloud. Then help your child cut along the lines to make six cards. Ask him or her to match the cards that show the same words and actions.

Top and Bottom

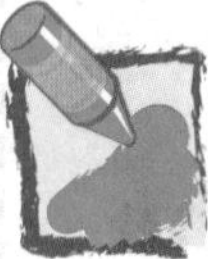

Color the bricks at the top red.

Color the bricks at the bottom green.

Parents: Retell the story "The Three Little Pigs." Ask your child to point to the pig that is on top of a ladder and then to the one that is on the bottom of a ladder. Point to and say the words *top* and *bottom*. Then say, "Find the bricks on top of the third little pig's house and color them red. Color the bricks at the bottom of the house green."

In and Out

in

out

Color the dogs that are in the tub brown.

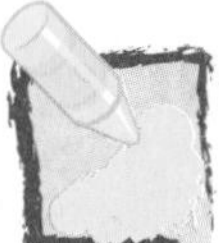

Color the dogs that are out of the tub yellow.

Parents: Ask your child to point to the dog that is in the mud and then to the dog that is out of the mud. Point to and say the words *in* and *out*. Then say, "Find the dogs that are in the tub and color them brown. Color the dogs that are out of the tub yellow."

Position Review

Match the ones that are the same.

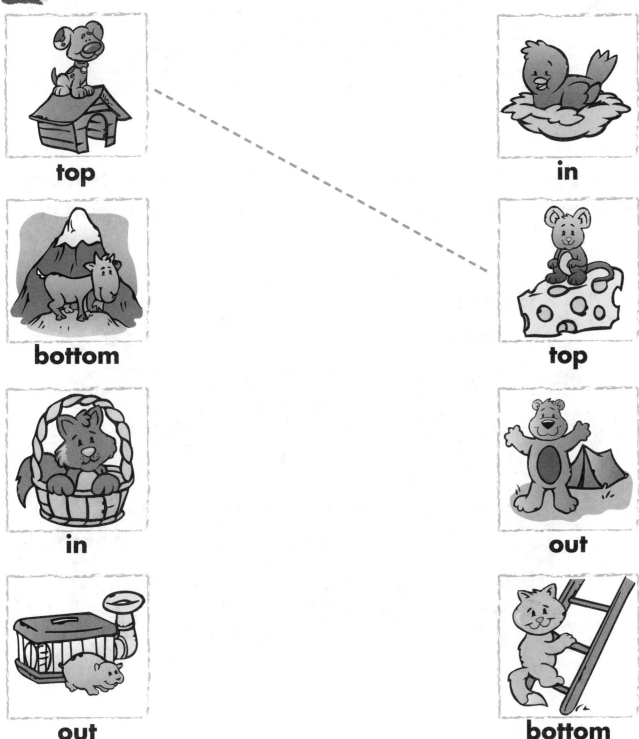

top

in

bottom

top

in

out

out

bottom

Parents: Look together at the picture of the dog sitting on top of the doghouse. Point to and say the word *top*. Have your child draw a line from the dog to the other animal that is on top of something. Then help him or her complete the rest of the page.

On and Off

Color the fish that are on the pan purple.

Color the fish that are off the pan red.

Parents: Ask your child to point to the polar bear that is on the ice and then to the one that is jumping off. Point to and say the words *on* and *off.* Then say, "Find the fish that are on the pan and color them purple. Color the fish that are off the pan red."

Left and Right

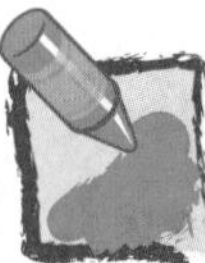

Color the object on the left red.

Color the object on the right green.

Parents: Ask your child to point to the car that is turning left and then to the truck that is turning right. Point to and say the words *left* and *right*. Then say, "Use a red crayon to color the object in the police officer's left hand. Color the object in his right hand green."

Next to and Between

next to

between

Color the building next to the firefighter yellow.

Color the building between the other buildings green.

Parents: Ask your child to point to the firefighter that is next to a dog and then to the firefighter that is between two dogs. Point to and say the words *next to* and *between*. Then say, "Use a yellow crayon to color the building that is next to the firefighter. Color the building that is between the other buildings green."

Position Review

Circle the pictures that show the same position.

left

next to

right

Parents: Have your child tell about the first picture in each row. Point to and read the word(s) under the picture. Then have your child circle the picture that shows the same position.

The Three Bears

Color Baby Bear's bowl red.

Color Papa Bear's shirt green.

Parents: Retell the story of "The Three Bears" with your child. Ask him or her to listen carefully to the directions for the activity. Read the directions and have your child repeat each step in his or her own words before completing it.

Bumper Cars

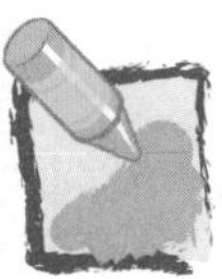

Color the raccoon's car orange.

Circle the duck.

Parents: Have your child tell about his or her favorite rides at the fair or amusement park. Ask him or her to listen carefully to the directions for the activity. Read the directions and have your child repeat each step in his or her own words before completing it.

Robot Twins

Circle the apple.

Color the little robot.

Parents: Have your child make up a story about the robots. Ask him or her to listen carefully to the directions for the activity. Read the directions and have your child repeat each step in his or her own words before completing it.

Jack and Jill

Draw a pail in Jack's hand.
Draw a line from the top of the hill to the bottom.

Circle the well.

Parents: Say the nursery rhyme "Jack and Jill" with your child. Ask him or her to listen carefully to the directions for the activity. Read the directions and have your child repeat each step in his or her own words before completing it.

On Top of Spaghetti

Color the plate blue.

Draw 3 more meatballs.

Circle the fork.

Parents: Sing the song "On Top of Spaghetti" with your child. Ask him or her to listen carefully to the directions for the activity. Read the directions and have your child repeat each step in his or her own words before completing it.

Bingo

Draw a collar on the dog.

Color black spots on the dog.

Circle the dog's dish.

Parents: Sing the song "Bingo" with your child. Ask him or her to listen carefully to the directions for the activity. Read the directions and have your child repeat each step in his or her own words before completing it.

Gumball Machine

Draw 10 gumballs inside the gumball machine.

Color the gumballs.

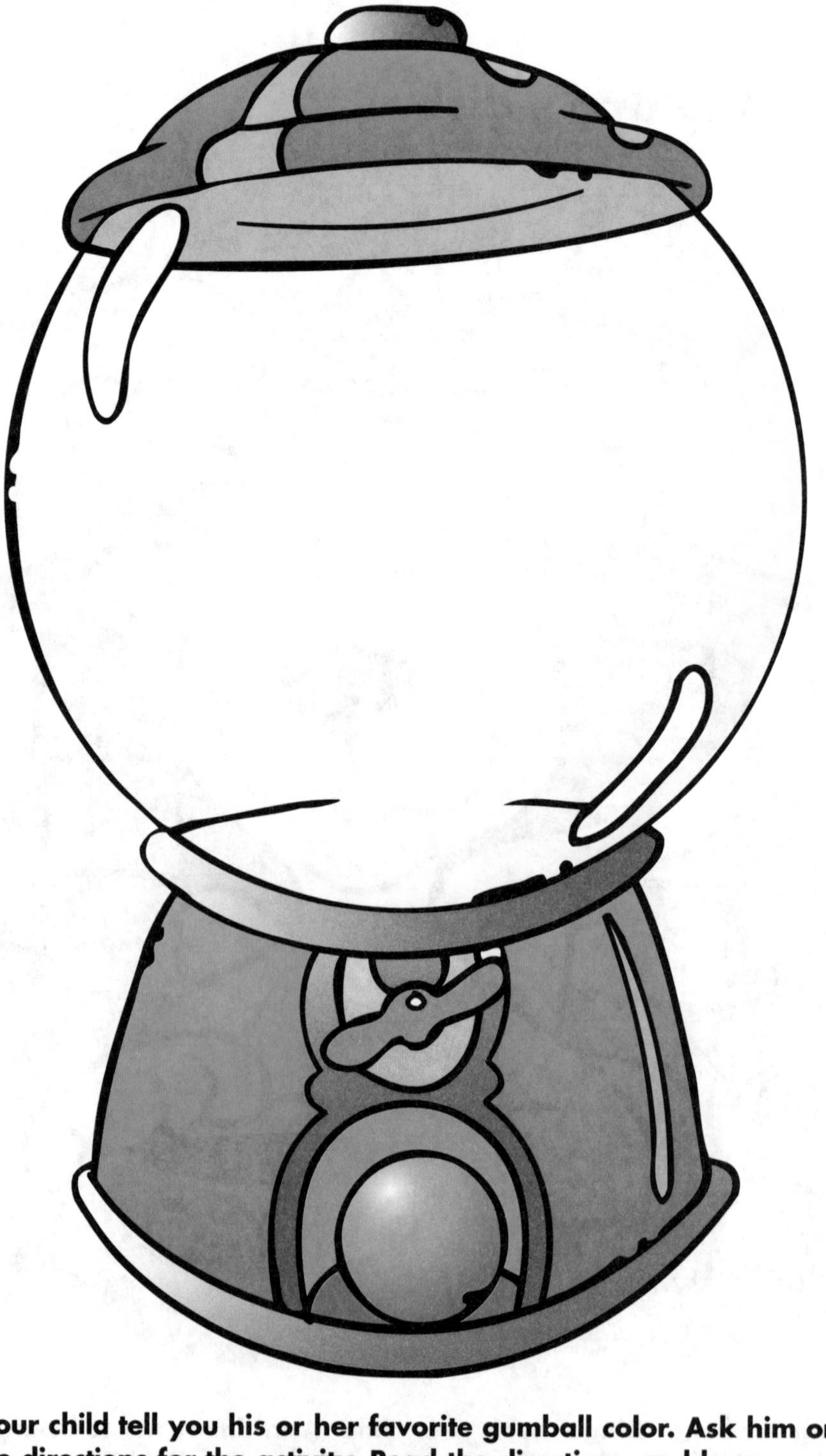

Parents: Have your child tell you his or her favorite gumball color. Ask him or her to listen carefully to the directions for the activity. Read the directions and have your child repeat each step in his or her own words before completing it.

Apple Tree

Cut out the pictures of the birds and apples.

Paste the birds in the nest.
Paste the apples in the basket.

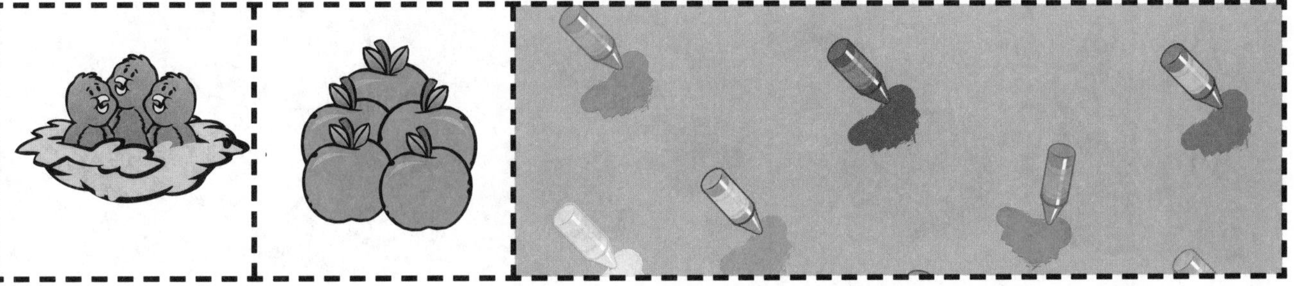

Parents: Have your child tell what goes in the nest and what goes in the basket. Ask him or her to listen carefully to the directions for the activity. Read the directions and have your child repeat each step in his or her own words before completing it.

Reviewing multi-step directions

Delicious Desserts

Cut out the pictures of the candles, cherry, and chocolate chips.

Paste the candles on the cake.
Paste the cherry on the cupcake.
Paste the chocolate chips on the cookie.

Parents: Have your child tell what his or her favorite dessert is. Ask him or her to listen carefully to the directions for the activity. Read the directions and have your child repeat each step in his or her own words before completing it.

Month 11 Checklist

Hands-on activities to help prepare your child for school!

ALPHABET

Writing Letters, Aa through Mm: pages 323-335, 349, 351

Once your child has learned to identify and recognize letters, as well as the sounds they make, the next step is to begin writing the letters. First, young children must learn how to hold writing instruments with comfort and ease. Next, they must refine their eye-hand coordination in order to copy what they see. In time, your child will be able to form letters without copying from a model. You can help him or her learn to write letters by trying some of these activities.

- ❑ Complete the worksheets.
- ❑ Set up a table with paints, brushes, and art paper. Draw a large capital letter on a sheet of art paper and help your child identify it. Then have your child use a paintbrush and paint to trace over the letter. Invite your child to continue tracing over letters that you draw, each on a separate piece of paper. Each time your child makes a letter, point out the movements he or she makes with the paintbrush. For example, for the capital letter L, you might say, "Down, across."
- ❑ After your child is finished painting letters, mix up the paintings and pick letters at random. Help your child identify each letter and encourage him or her to write its lowercase equivalent. Say, "I think I know this letter! I think it's a capital L. Do you know how to write a small l?"
- ❑ On another day, invite your child to paint letters again. This time let him or her fingerpaint the letters in both capital and lowercase form. The movements used in fingerpainting will be slightly smaller than the movements used in painting with a paintbrush. This will prepare your child for writing with a traditional instrument, such as a pencil or crayon.
- ❑ Try fingerpainting along with your child using a separate sheet of paper. Invite your child to watch as you form the letters Aa through Mm. Point out the movements you use to make each letter and encourage your child to copy them.
- ❑ Have your child fingerpaint a picture that represents a letter sound. For example, for the letter F, he or she could fingerpaint a fish swimming underwater. Encourage your child to have fun as he or she makes the connection between the letter being painted, the sound the letter makes, and the word that begins with that letter's sound.
- ❑ Make instant pudding and spread some on a cookie sheet. Invite your child to use his or her finger to write letters in the pudding mix.
- ❑ Have your child create letters of the alphabet using play dough. Begin with capital letters and advance to lowercase letters when your child is ready.

Writing Letters, Nn through Zz: pages 336-348, 350, 352

The task of writing all 26 letters at once might be a lot for your child. Therefore, it is fine to teach and review the letters in small groups. The following activities will help your child write the second half of the alphabet. Feel free to use these activities for the letters Aa through Mm as well.

- ❑ Complete the worksheets.
- ❑ Invite your child to make sparkle letters. You will need sheets of construction paper or other sturdy paper, glue, and glitter. First, write a letter yourself on the paper. You can write the letter using a pencil, crayon, or marker. Then ask your child to trace over the letter with glue. Make sure your child uses the correct movements for forming the letter. While the glue is still wet, let him or her have fun sprinkling glitter over it. (Be sure to cover your tabletop with newspaper first!) Set the sparkle letter aside so the glue can dry. In the meantime, work with your child to make other letters. After all the letters have dried, help your child shake away the excess glitter onto newspaper to reveal the letters you made. As the letters are revealed, encourage your child to name them.
- ❑ Ask your child to look at children's magazines or posters he or she currently has. Point out letters in titles or headings and ask your child if the letters are capital or lowercase. After identifying a letter, have your child trace it with a finger. Once again, make sure your child uses the correct movements for forming each letter, as shown by the directional arrows on the activity worksheets.
- ❑ Let your child try tracing letters onto paper. Help him or her place tracing paper on top of the letters he or she finds in a magazine or on a poster. Guide your child in tracing the letter, using the correct movements for writing.

Writing Aa

Color the letters.

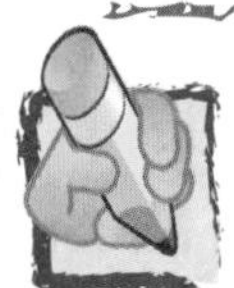

Trace and write the letters.

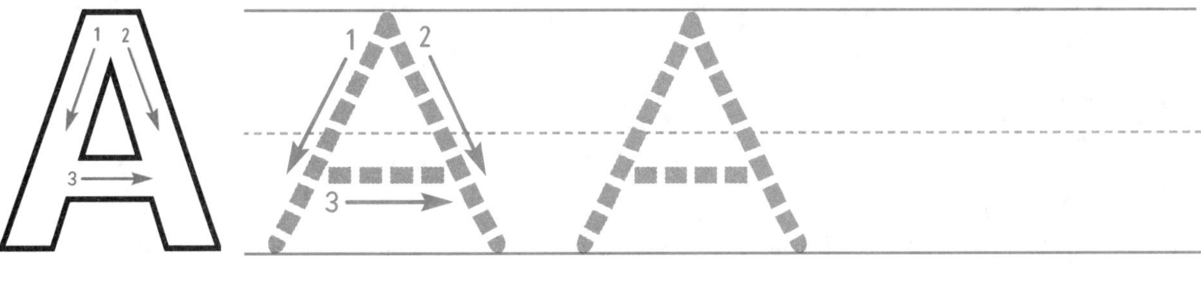

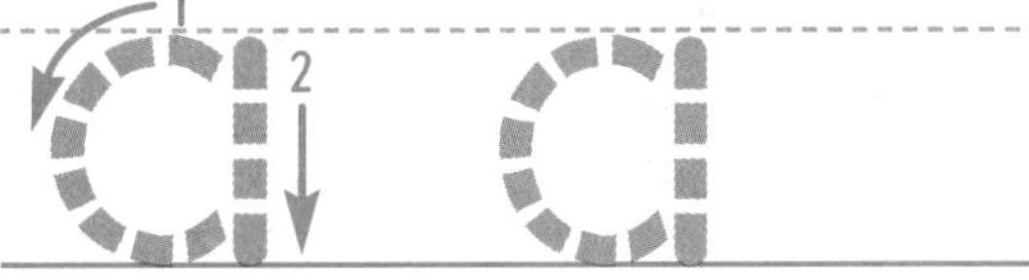

Parents: (Top) Ask your child to identify the capital and lowercase letters *A* and *a*. Help him or her name the pictures that begin with the letter *A*. Encourage your child to trace the hollow letters with a finger, following the arrows. Then have him or her color the letters. (Bottom) Have your child use a pencil or crayon to trace and write the letters.

Writing Bb

Color the letters.

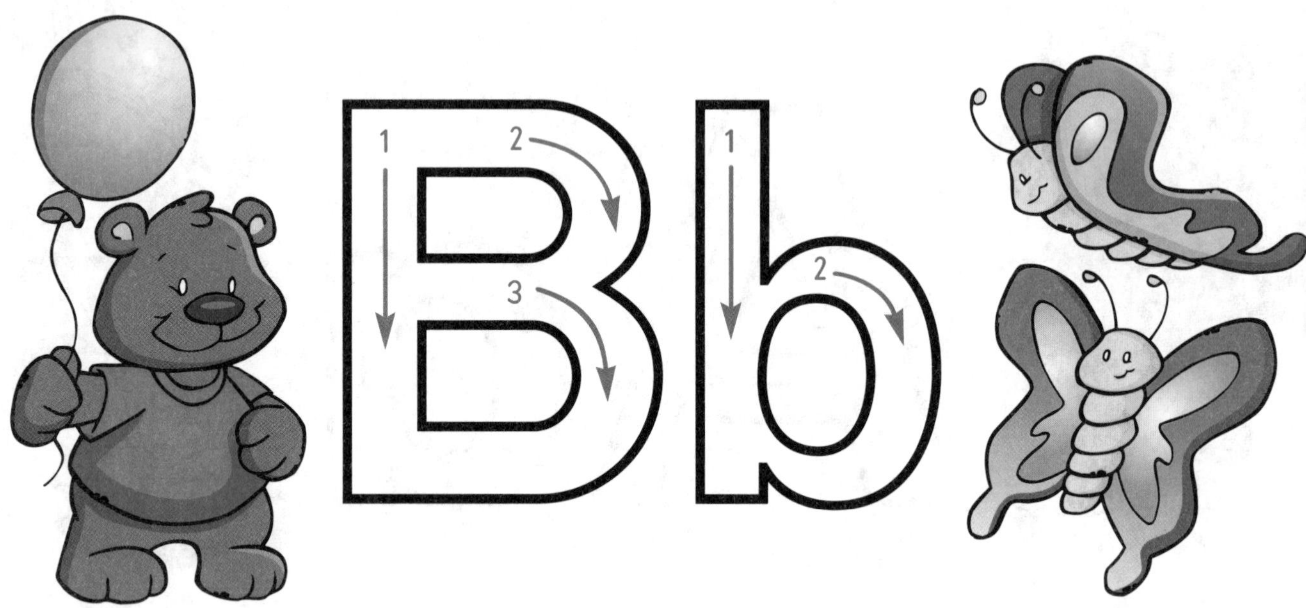

Trace and write the letters.

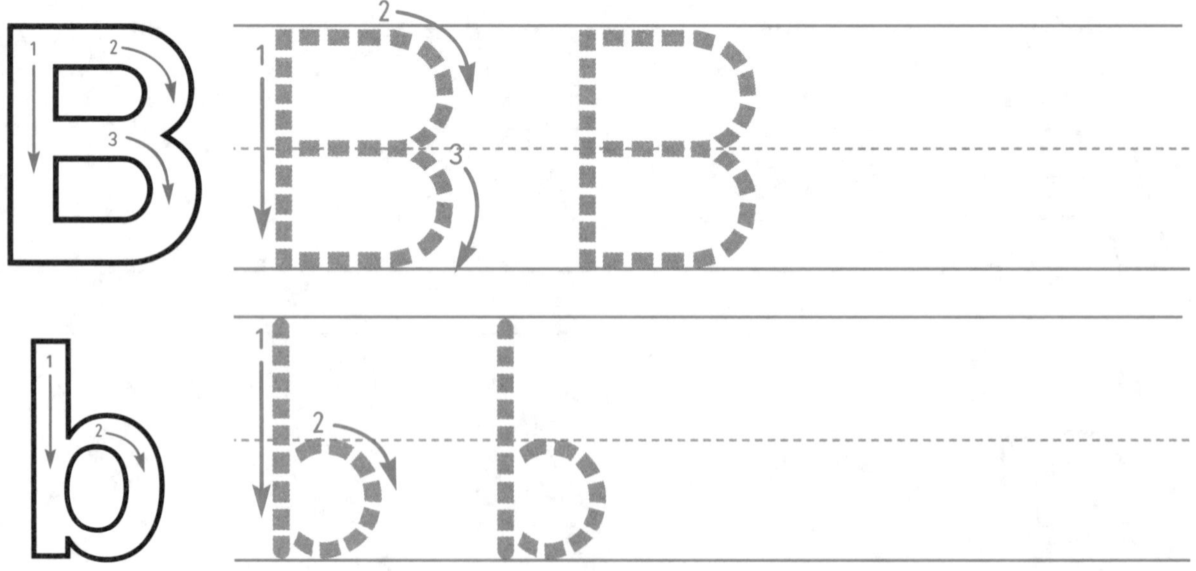

Parents: (Top) Ask your child to identify the capital and lowercase letters *B* and *b*. Help him or her name the pictures that begin with the letter *B*. Encourage your child to trace the hollow letters with a finger, following the arrows. Then have him or her color the letters. (Bottom) Have your child use a pencil or crayon to trace and write the letters.

Writing Cc

Color the letters.

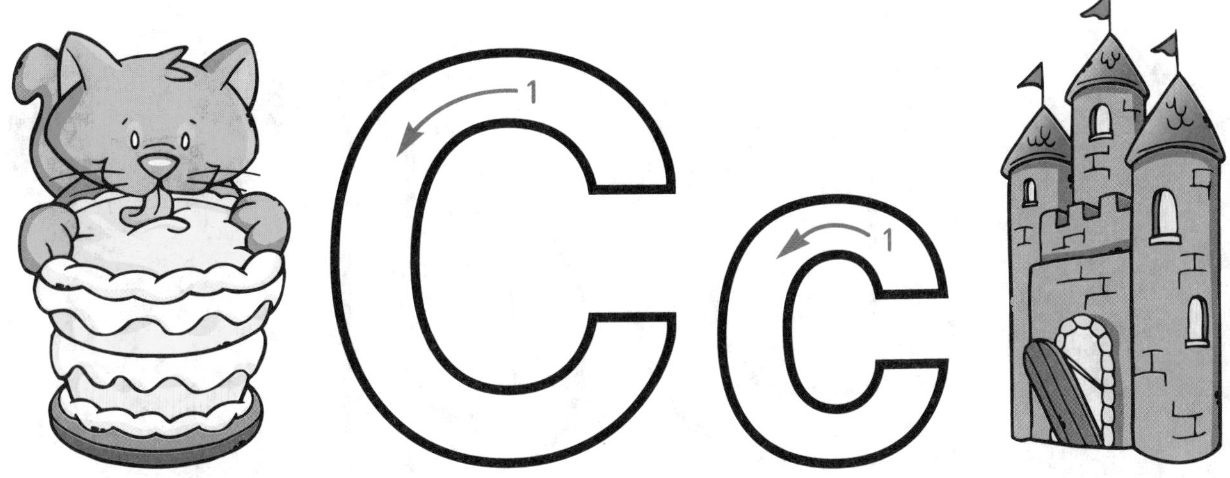

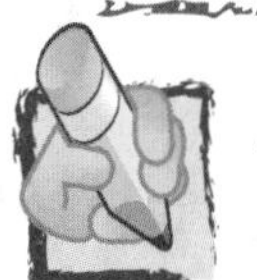

Trace and write the letters.

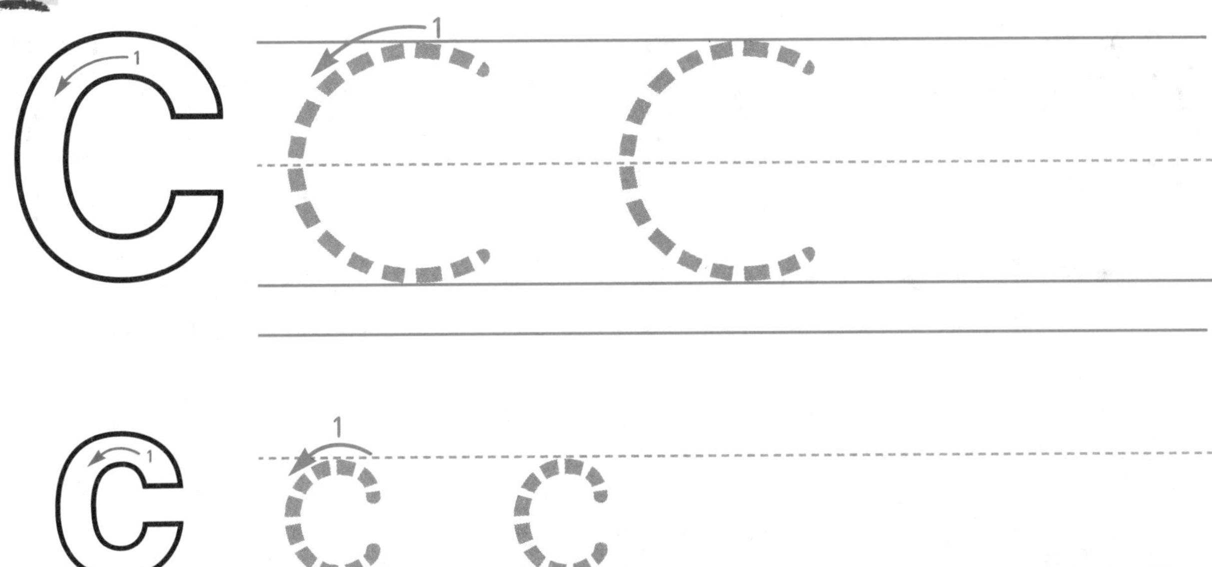

Parents: (Top) Ask your child to identify the capital and lowercase letters *C* and *c*. Help him or her name the pictures that begin with the letter *C*. Encourage your child to trace the hollow letters with a finger, following the arrows. Then have him or her color the letters. (Bottom) Have your child use a pencil or crayon to trace and write the letters.

Writing Dd

Color the letters.

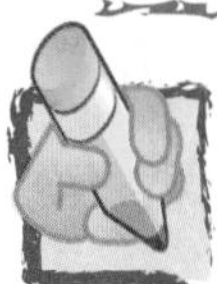

Trace and write the letters.

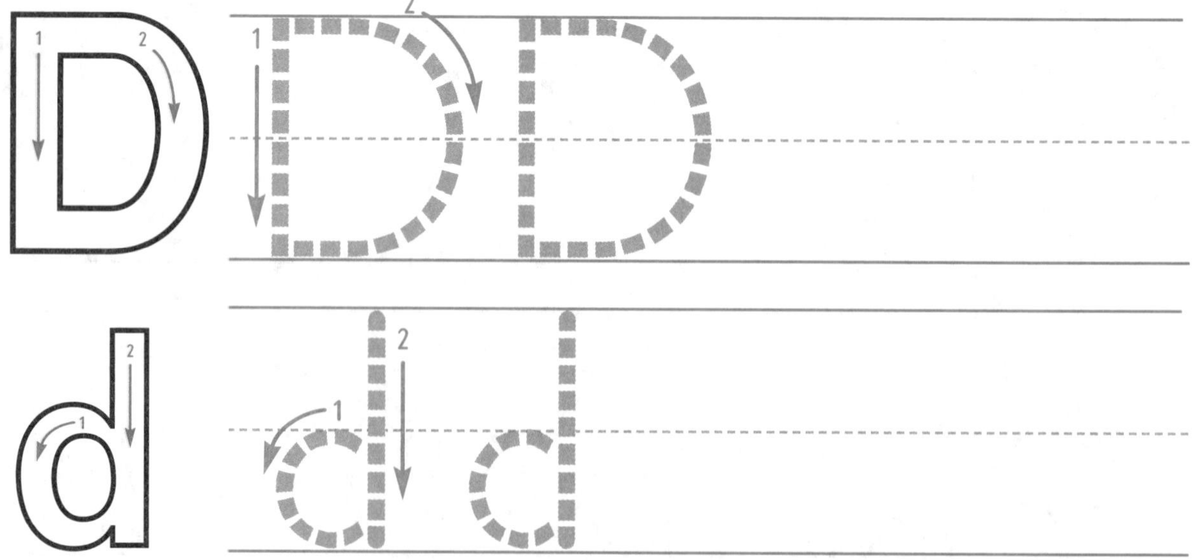

Parents: (Top) Ask your child to identify the capital and lowercase letters *D* and *d.* Help him or her name the pictures that begin with the letter *D.* Encourage your child to trace the hollow letters with a finger, following the arrows. Then have him or her color the letters. (Bottom) Have your child use a pencil or crayon to trace and write the letters.

Writing Ee

Color the letters.

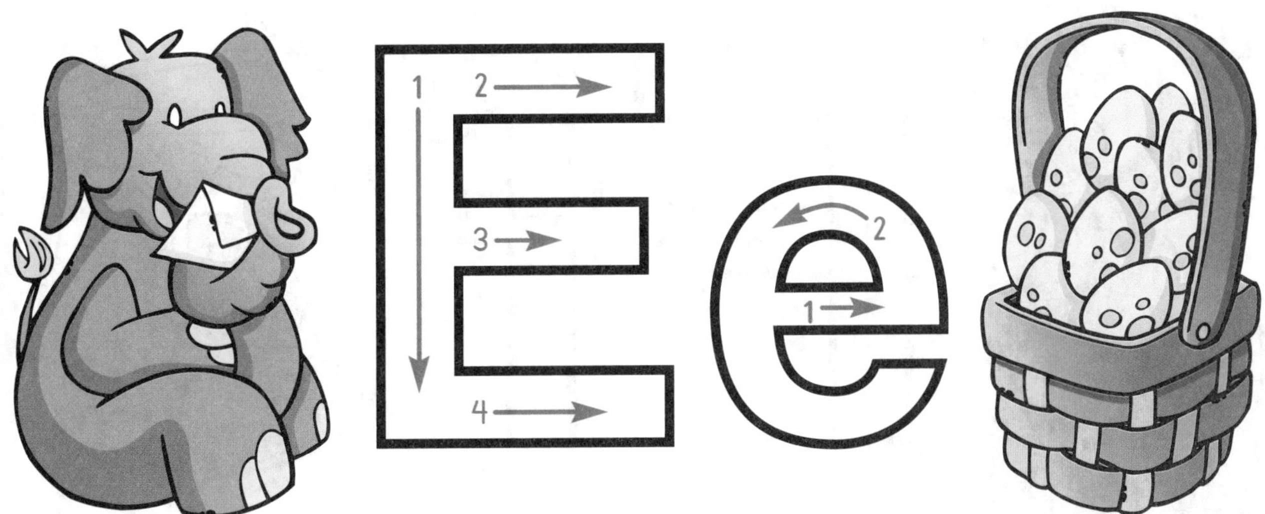

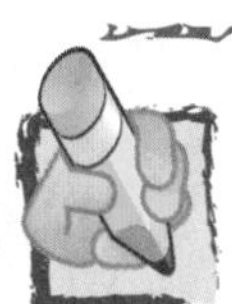

Trace and write the letters.

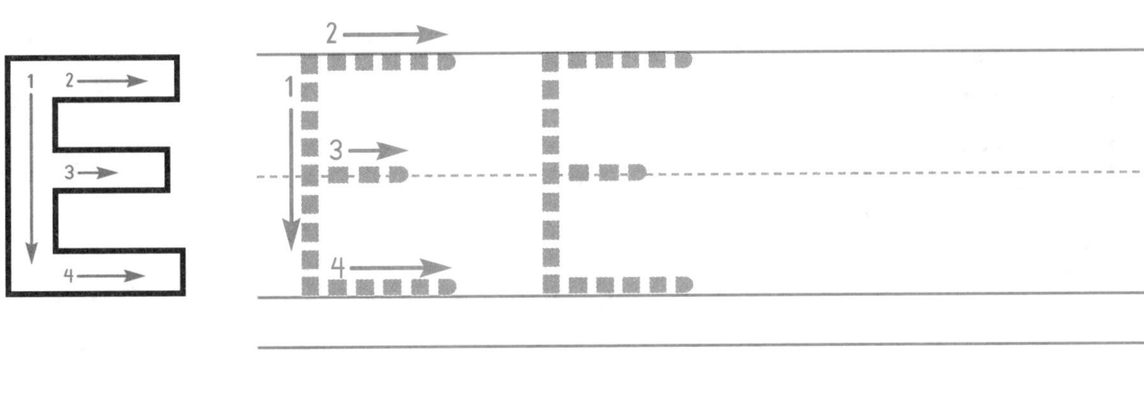

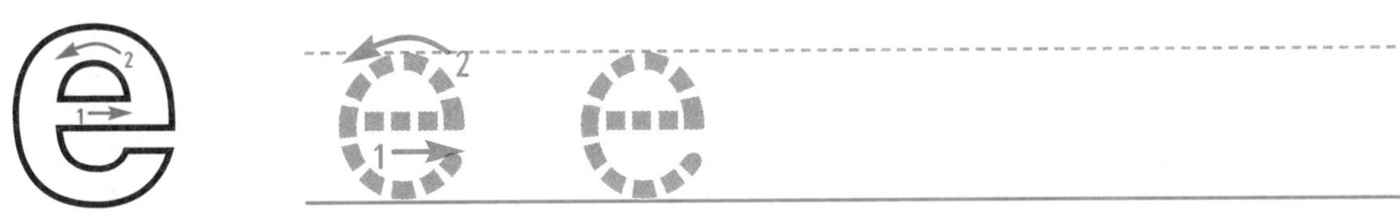

Parents: **(Top) Ask your child to identify the capital and lowercase letters *E* and *e*. Help him or her name the pictures that begin with the letter *E*. Encourage your child to trace the hollow letters with a finger, following the arrows. Then have him or her color the letters. (Bottom) Have your child use a pencil or crayon to trace and write the letters.**

Writing Ff

Color the letters.

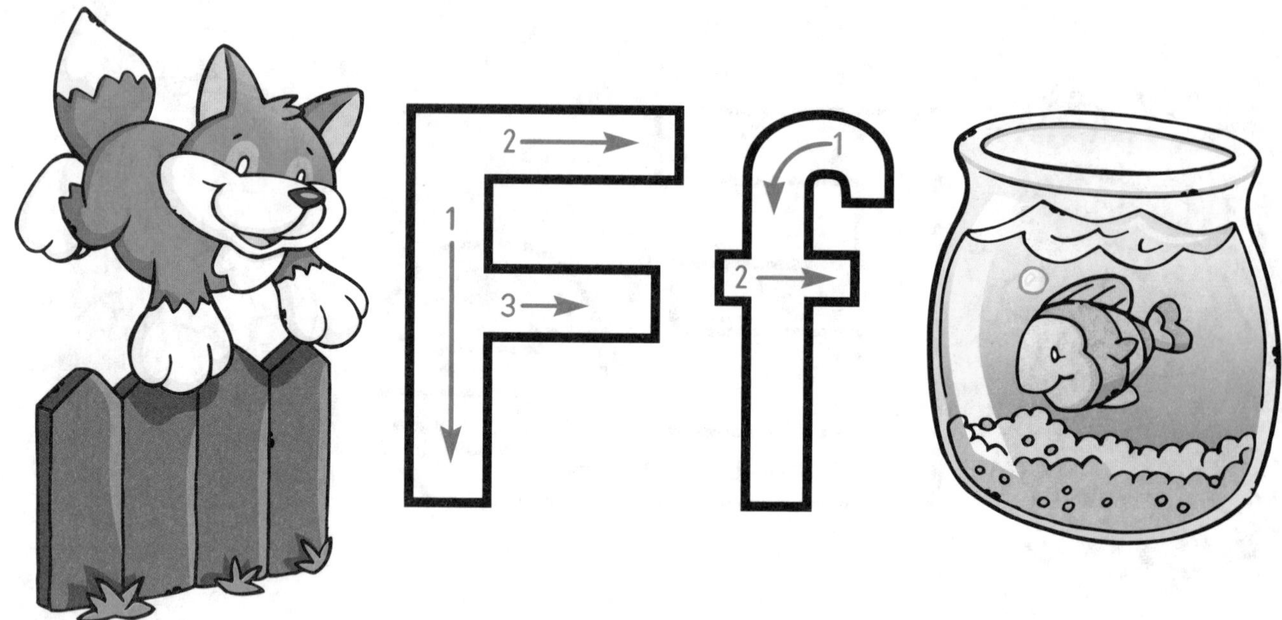

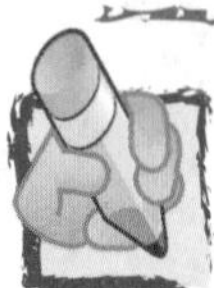

Trace and write the letters.

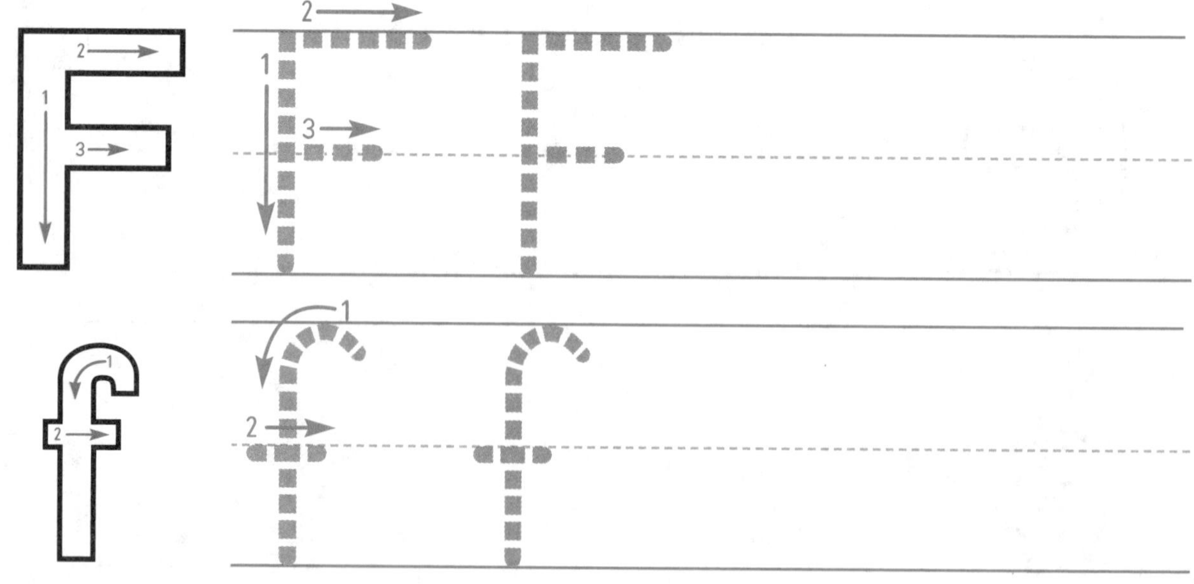

Parents: **(Top) Ask your child to identify the capital and lowercase letters *F* and *f*. Help him or her name the pictures that begin with the letter *F*. Encourage your child to trace the hollow letters with a finger, following the arrows. Then have him or her color the letters. (Bottom) Have your child use a pencil or crayon to trace and write the letters.**

Writing Gg

Color the letters.

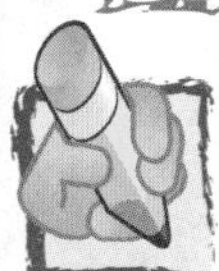

Trace and write the letters.

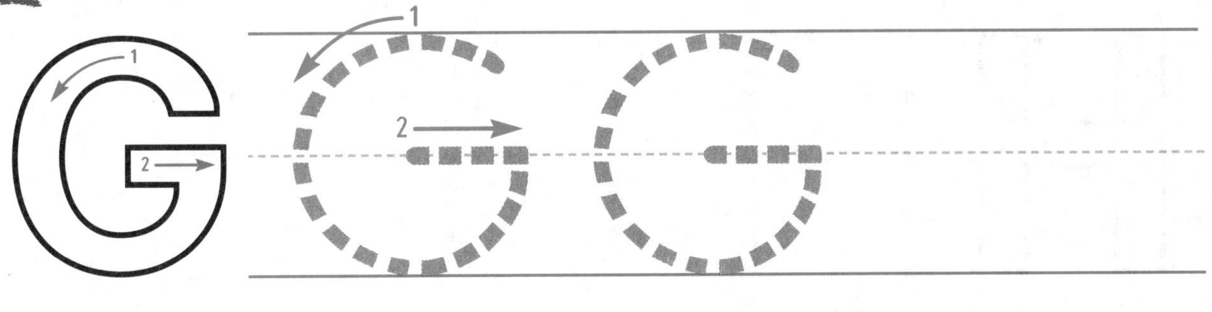

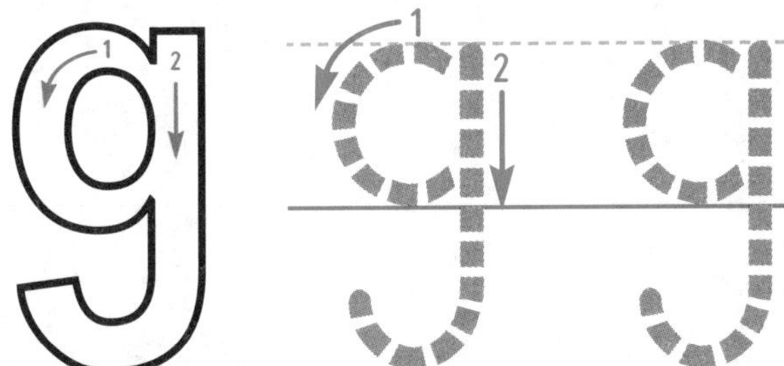

Parents: (Top) Ask your child to identify the capital and lowercase letters *G* and *g*. Help him or her name the pictures that begin with the letter *G*. Encourage your child to trace the hollow letters with a finger, following the arrows. Then have him or her color the letters. (Bottom) Have your child use a pencil or crayon to trace and write the letters.

Writing Hh

Color the letters.

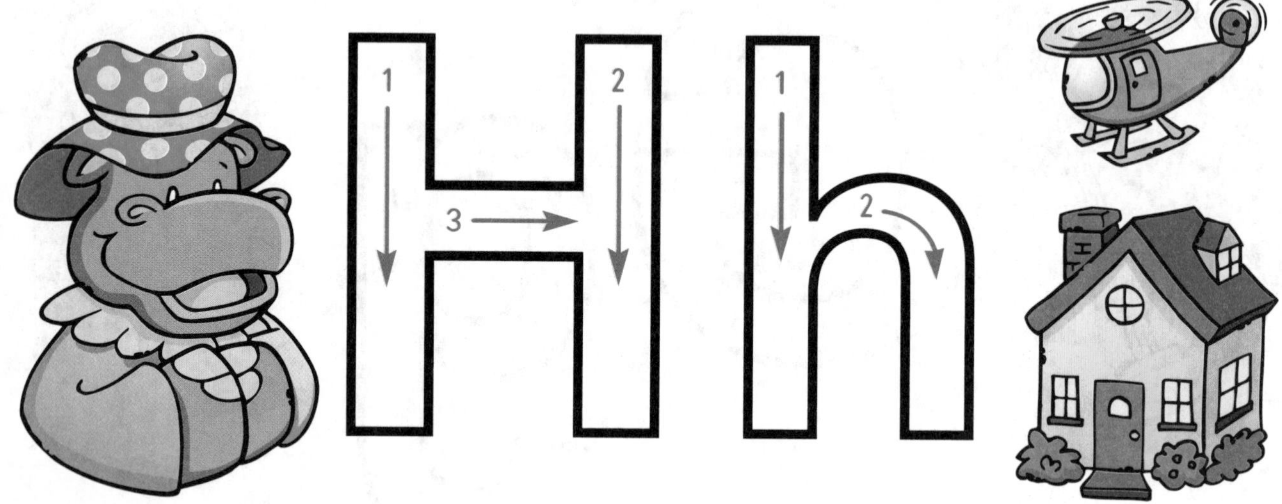

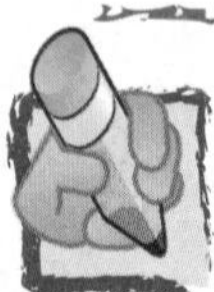

Trace and write the letters.

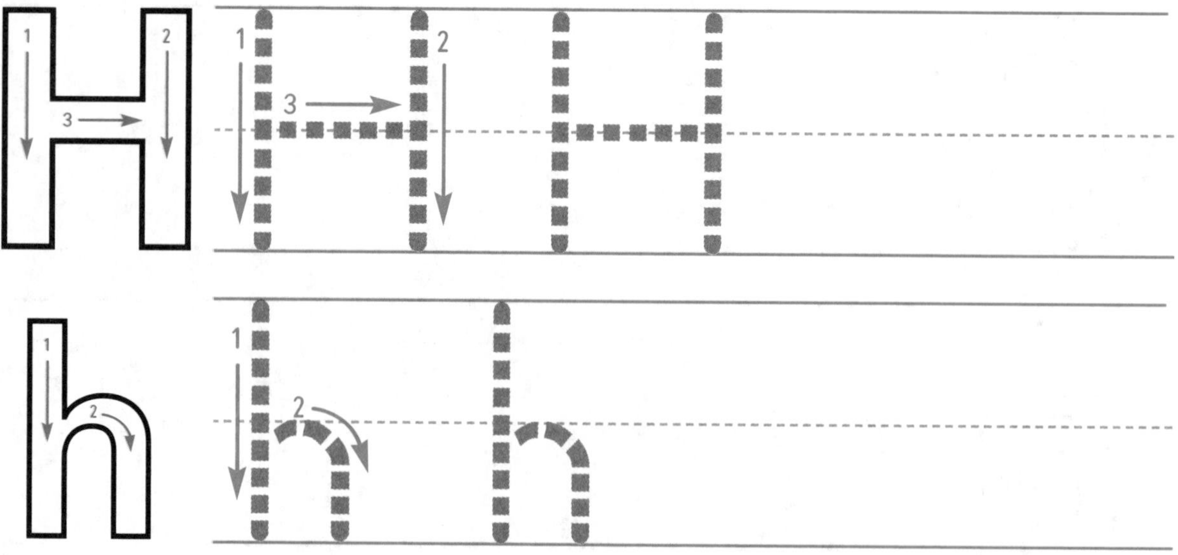

Parents: **(Top) Ask your child to identify the capital and lowercase letters *H* and *h*. Help him or her name the pictures that begin with the letter *H*. Encourage your child to trace the hollow letters with a finger, following the arrows. Then have him or her color the letters. (Bottom) Have your child use a pencil or crayon to trace and write the letters.**

Writing Ii

Color the letters.

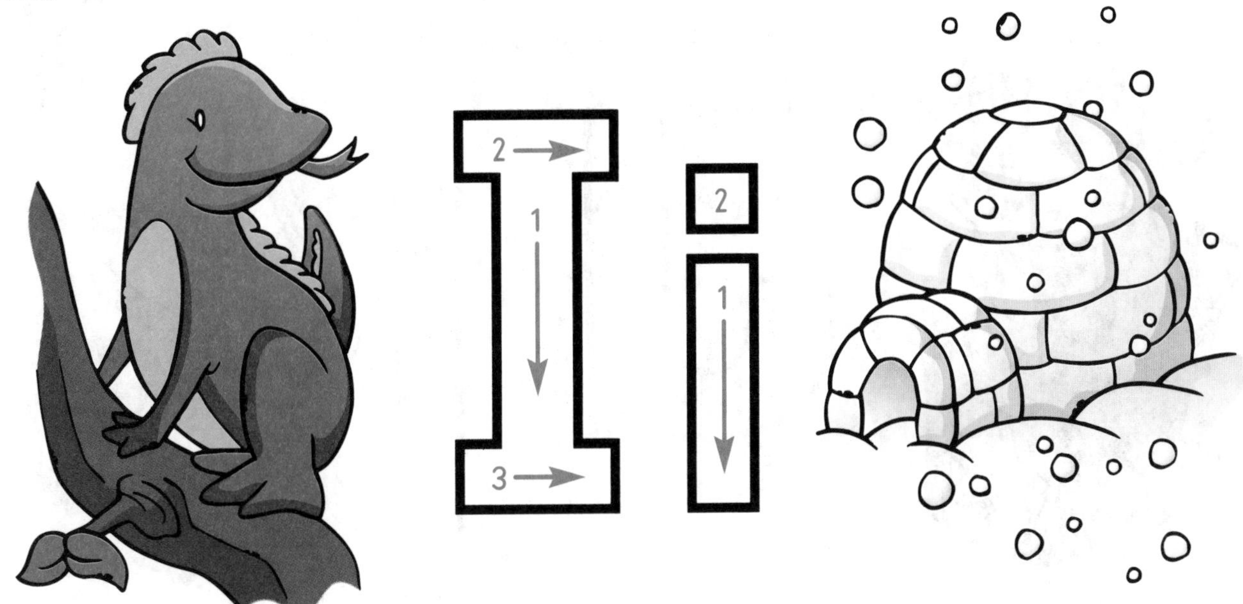

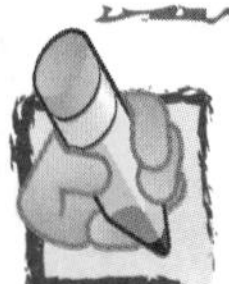

Trace and write the letters.

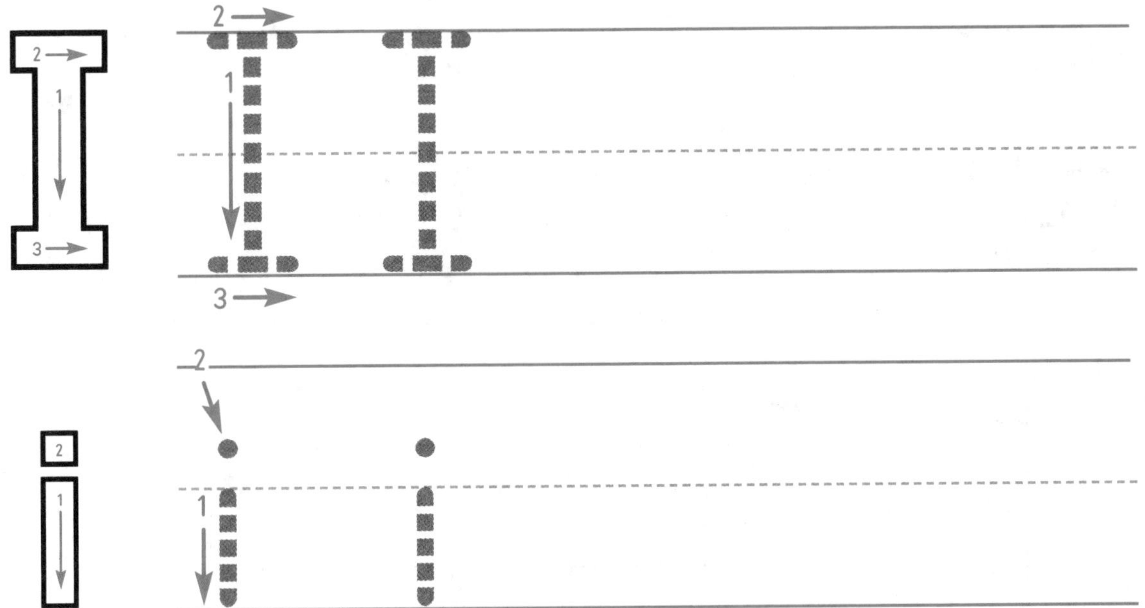

Parents: **(Top) Ask your child to identify the capital and lowercase letters *I* and *i.* Help him or her name the pictures that begin with the letter *I.* Encourage your child to trace the hollow letters with a finger, following the arrows. Then have him or her color the letters. (Bottom) Have your child use a pencil or crayon to trace and write the letters.**

Writing Jj

Color the letters.

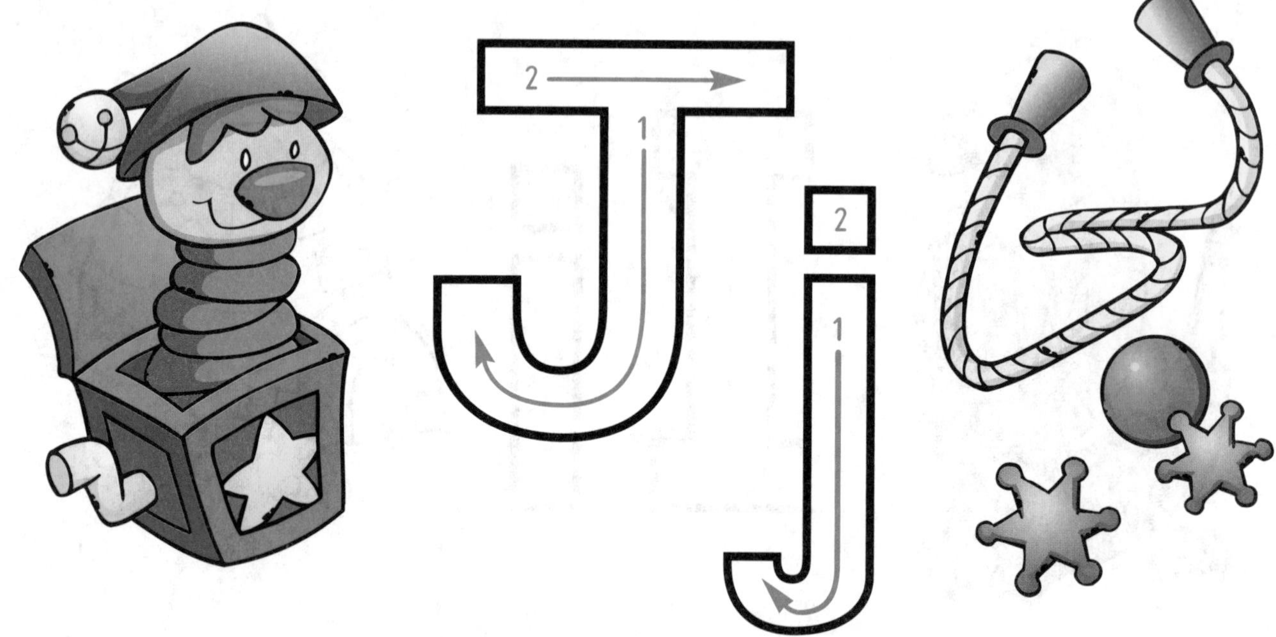

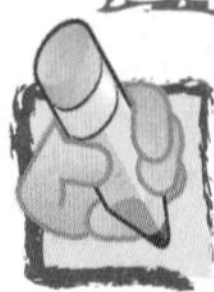

Trace and write the letters.

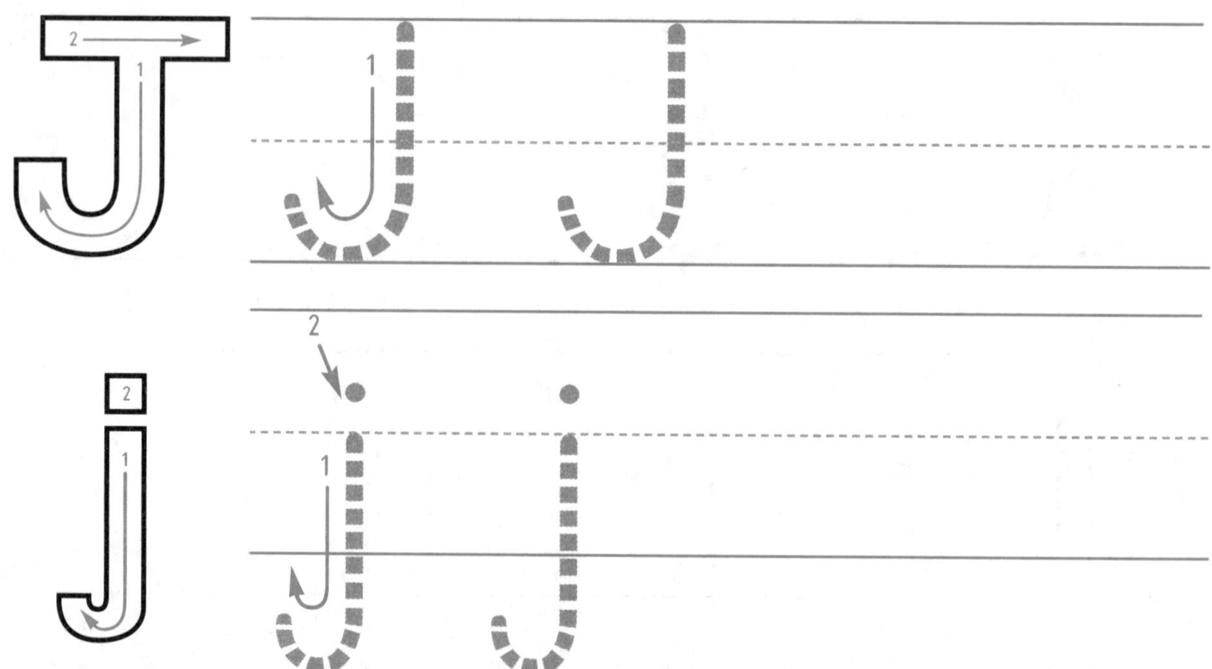

Parents: (Top) Ask your child to identify the capital and lowercase letters *J* and *j*. Help him or her name the pictures that begin with the letter *J*. Encourage your child to trace the hollow letters with a finger, following the arrows. Then have him or her color the letters. (Bottom) Have your child use a pencil or crayon to trace and write the letters.

Writing Kk

Color the letters.

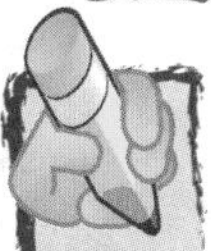

Trace and write the letters.

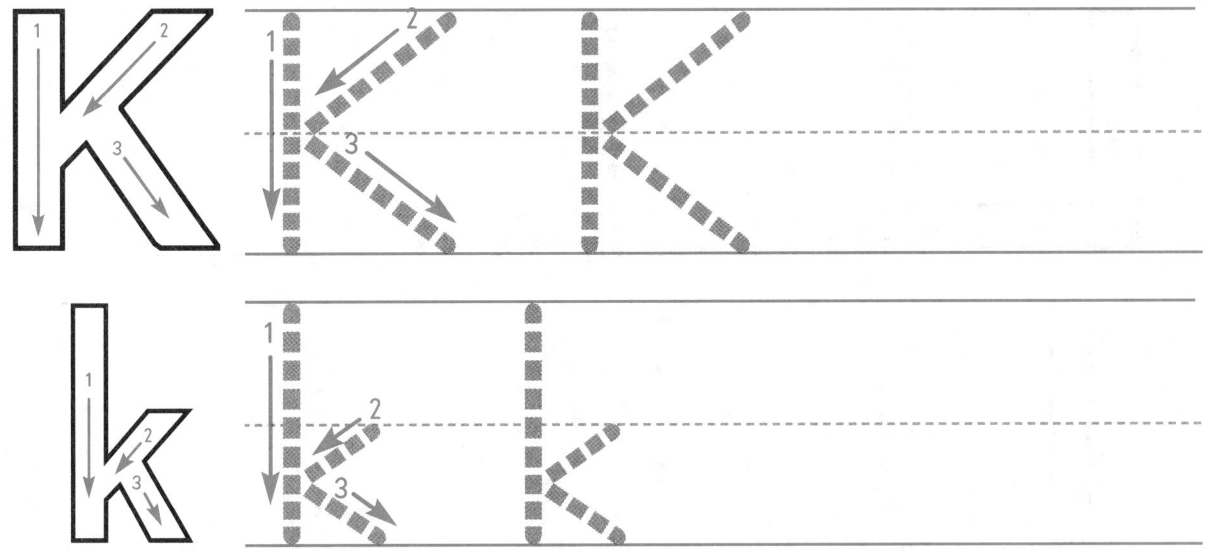

Parents: (Top) Ask your child to identify the capital and lowercase letters *K* and *k*. Help him or her name the pictures that begin with the letter *K*. Encourage your child to trace the hollow letters with a finger, following the arrows. Then have him or her color the letters. (Bottom) Have your child use a pencil or crayon to trace and write the letters.

Writing Ll

Color the letters.

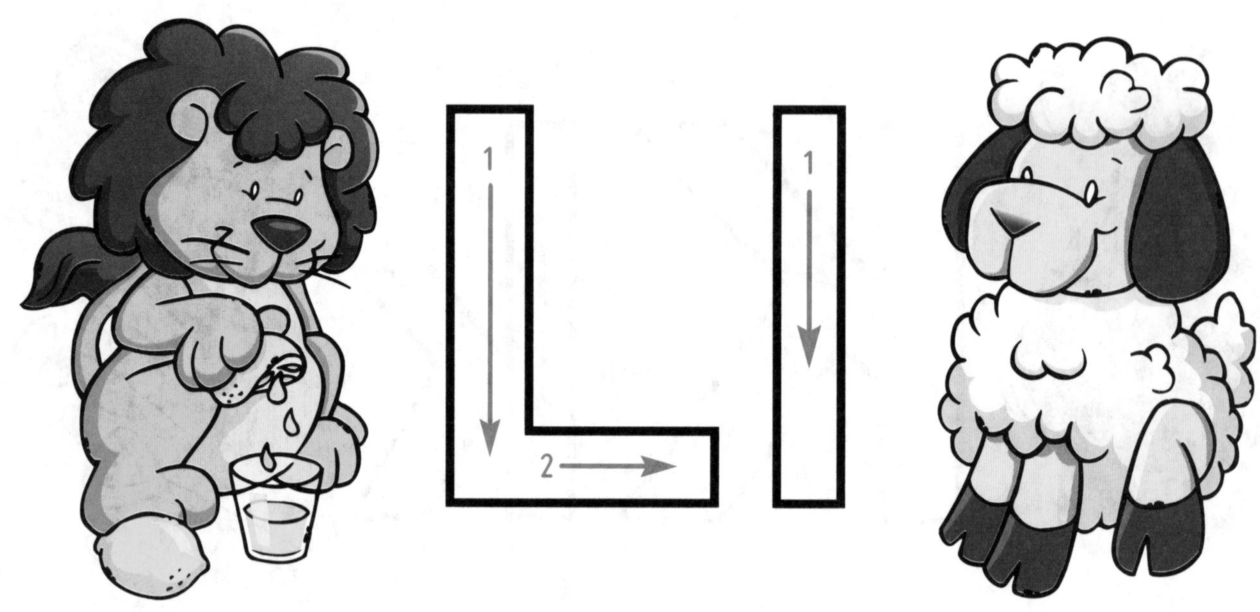

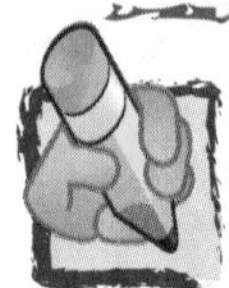

Trace and write the letters.

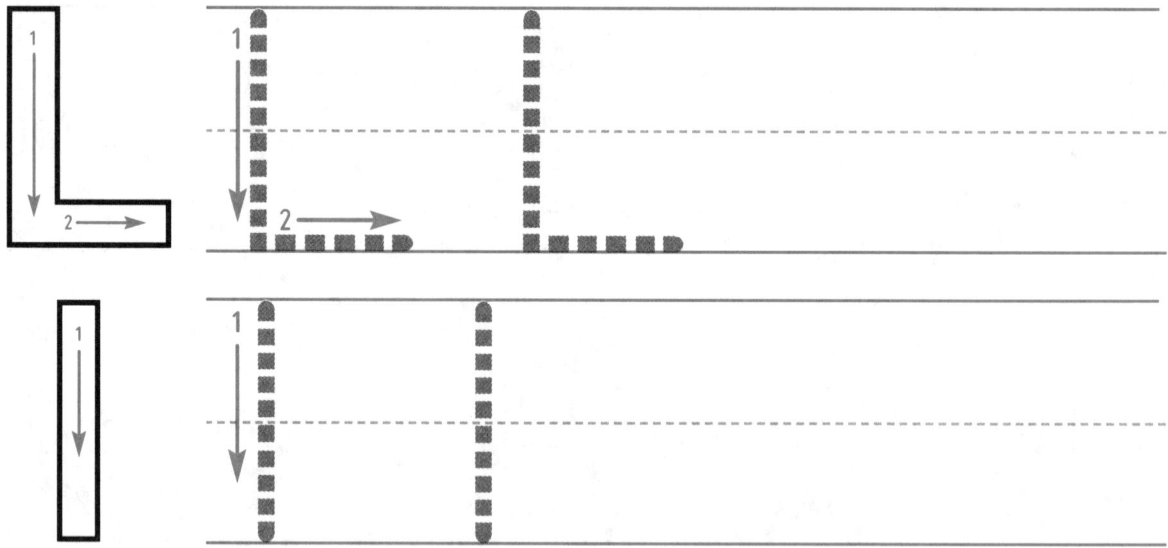

Parents: **(Top) Ask your child to identify the capital and lowercase letters *L* and *l*. Help him or her name the pictures that begin with the letter *L*. Encourage your child to trace the hollow letters with a finger, following the arrows. Then have him or her color the letters. (Bottom) Have your child use a pencil or crayon to trace and write the letters.**

Writing Mm

Color the letters.

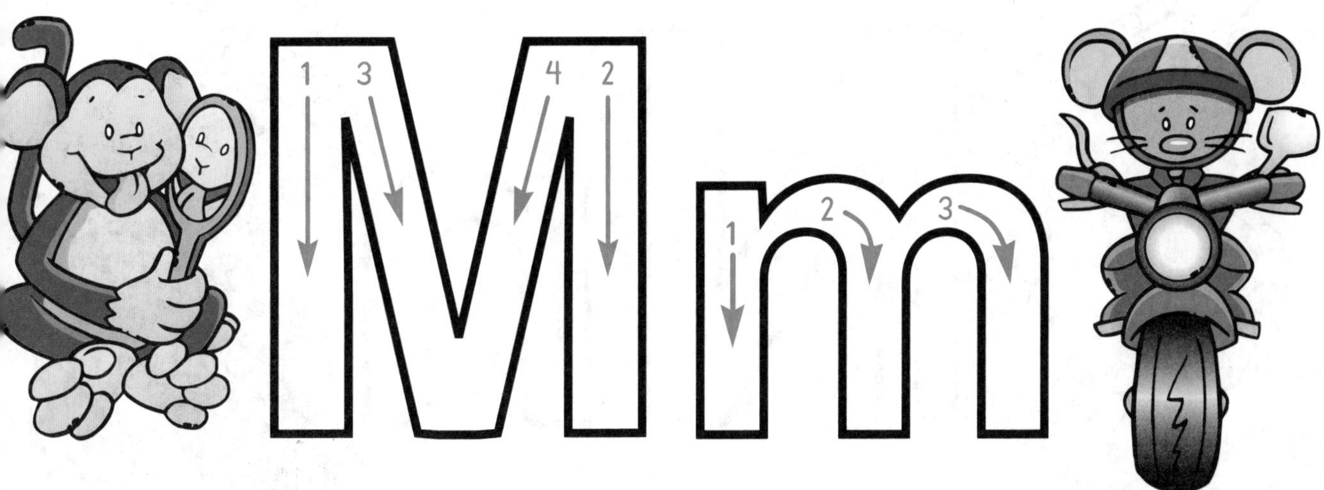

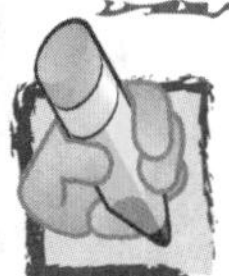

Trace and write the letters.

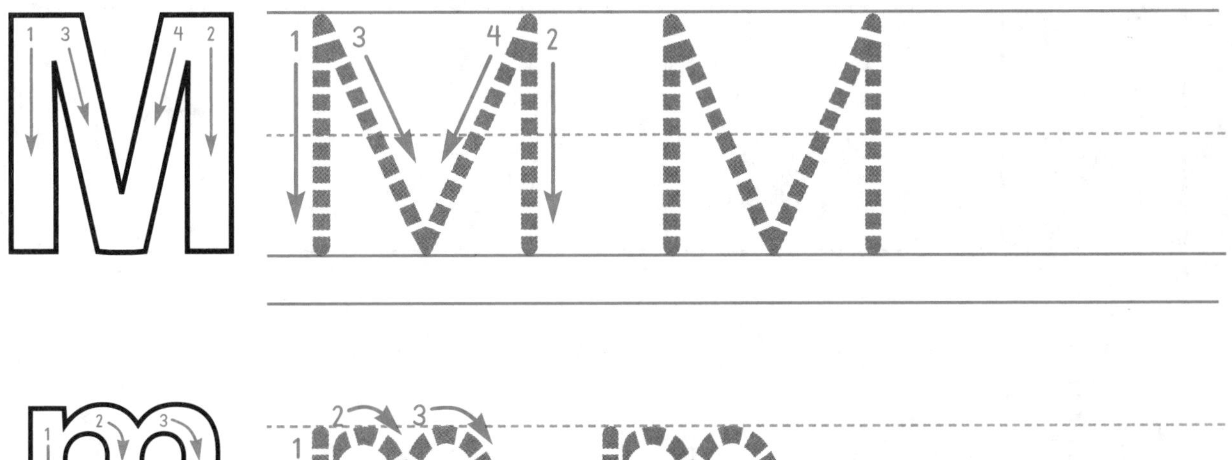

Parents: (Top) Ask your child to identify the capital and lowercase letters *M* and *m*. Help him or her name the pictures that begin with the letter *M*. Encourage your child to trace the hollow letters with a finger, following the arrows. Then have him or her color the letters. (Bottom) Have your child use a pencil or crayon to trace and write the letters.

ALPHABET

Writing Nn

Color the letters.

Trace and write the letters.

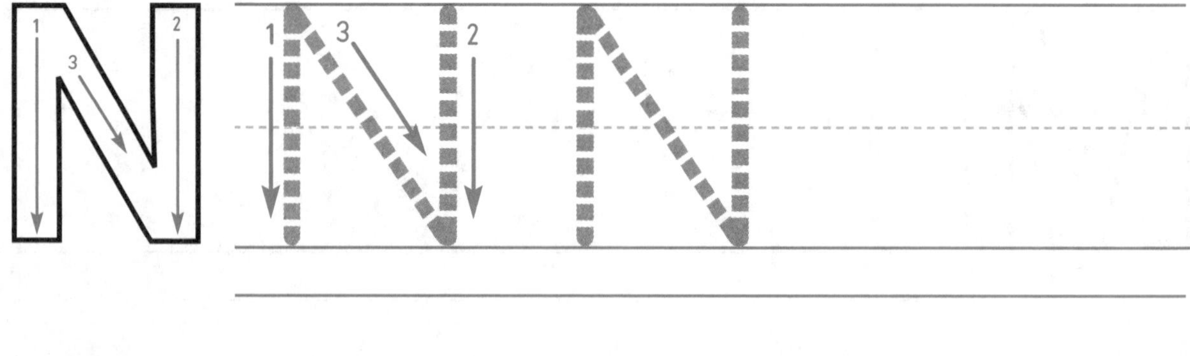

Parents: **(Top) Ask your child to identify the capital and lowercase letters *N* and *n*. Help him or her name the pictures that begin with the letter *N*. Encourage your child to trace the hollow letters with a finger, following the arrows. Then have him or her color the letters. (Bottom) Have your child use a pencil or crayon to trace and write the letters.**

Writing Oo

Color the letters.

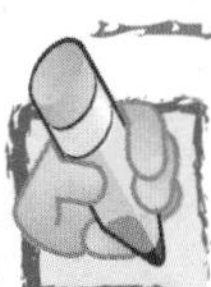

Trace and write the letters.

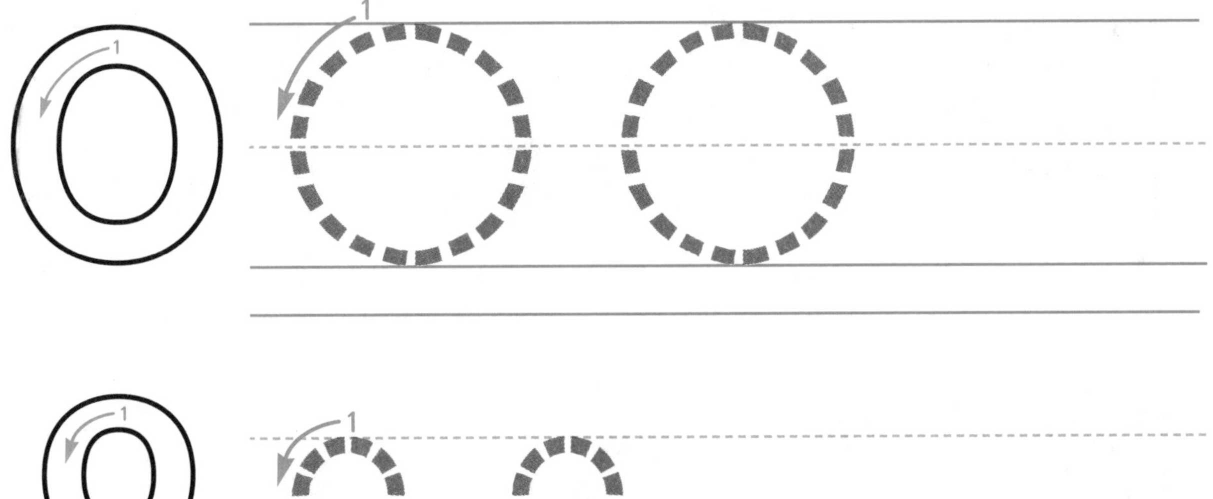

Parents: (Top) Ask your child to identify the capital and lowercase letters *O* and *o*. Help him or her name the pictures that begin with the letter *O*. Encourage your child to trace the hollow letters with a finger, following the arrows. Then have him or her color the letters. (Bottom) Have your child use a pencil or crayon to trace and write the letters.

Writing Pp

Color the letters.

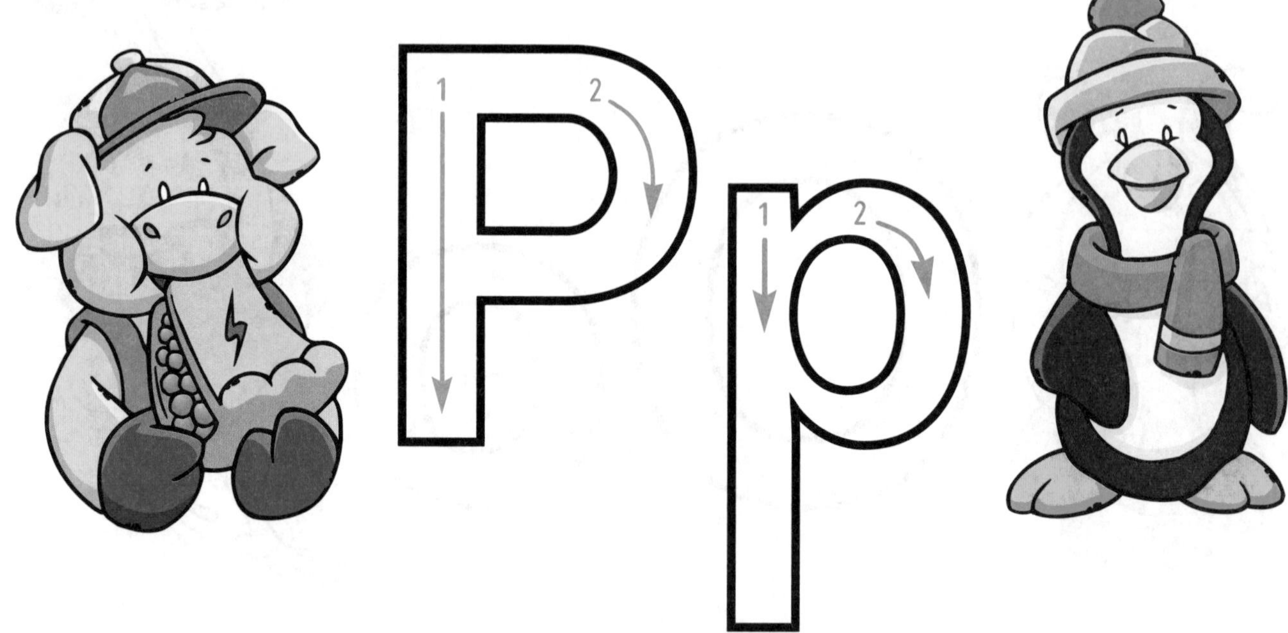

Trace and write the letters.

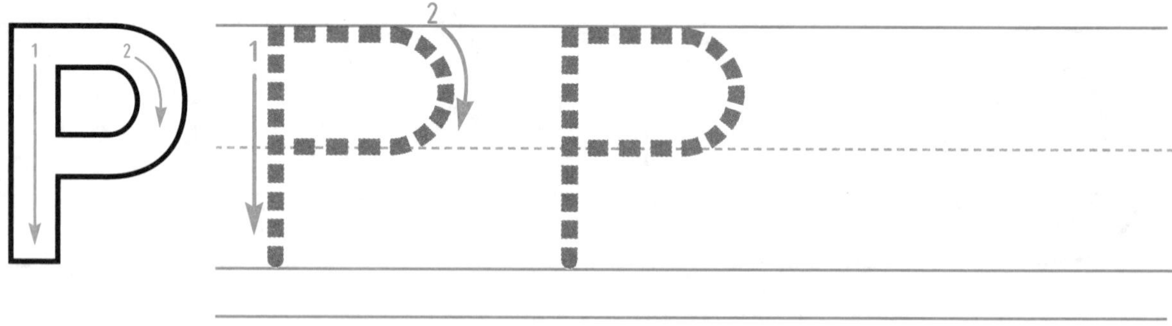

Parents: (Top) Ask your child to identify the capital and lowercase letters *P* and *p*. Help him or her name the pictures that begin with the letter *P*. Encourage your child to trace the hollow letters with a finger, following the arrows. Then have him or her color the letters. (Bottom) Have your child use a pencil or crayon to trace and write the letters.

Writing Qq

Color the letters.

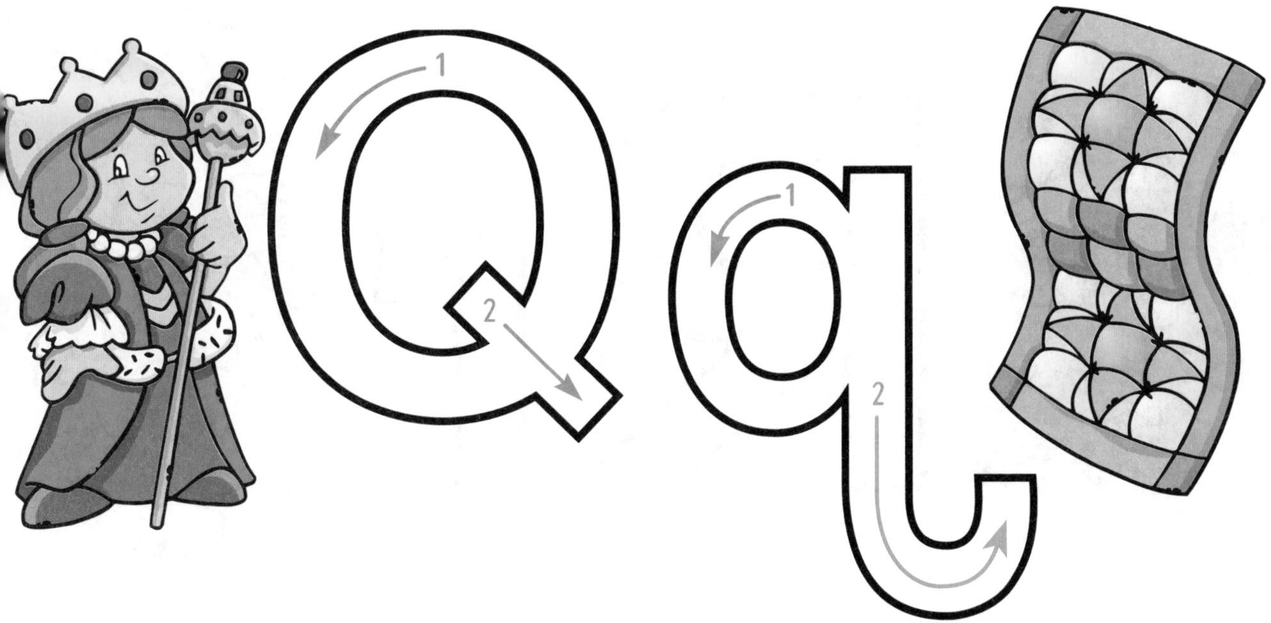

Trace and write the letters.

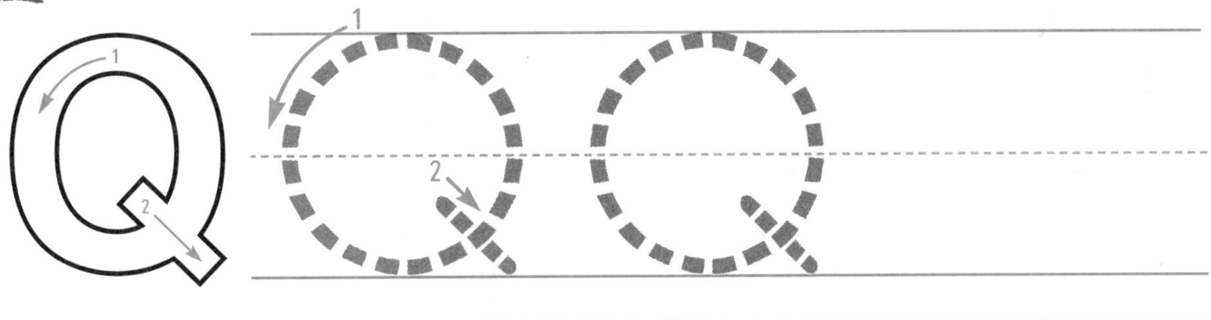

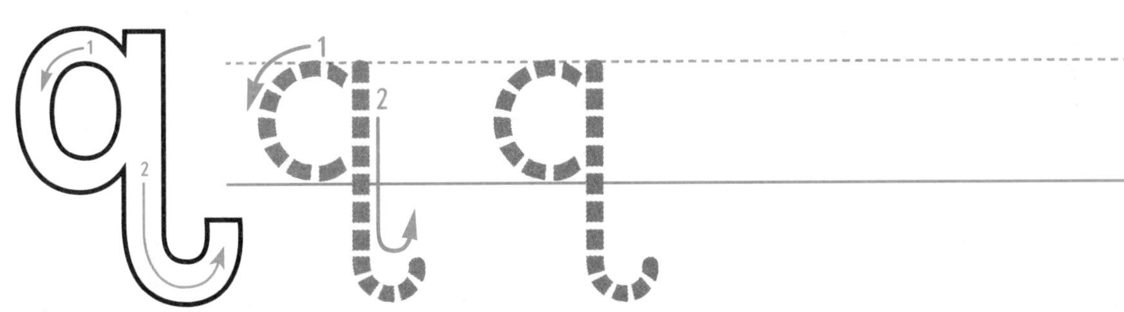

Parents: (Top) Ask your child to identify the capital and lowercase letters Q and *q*. Help him or her name the pictures that begin with the letter Q. Encourage your child to trace the hollow letters with a finger, following the arrows. Then have him or her color the letters. (Bottom) Have your child use a pencil or crayon to trace and write the letters.

Writing Rr

Color the letters.

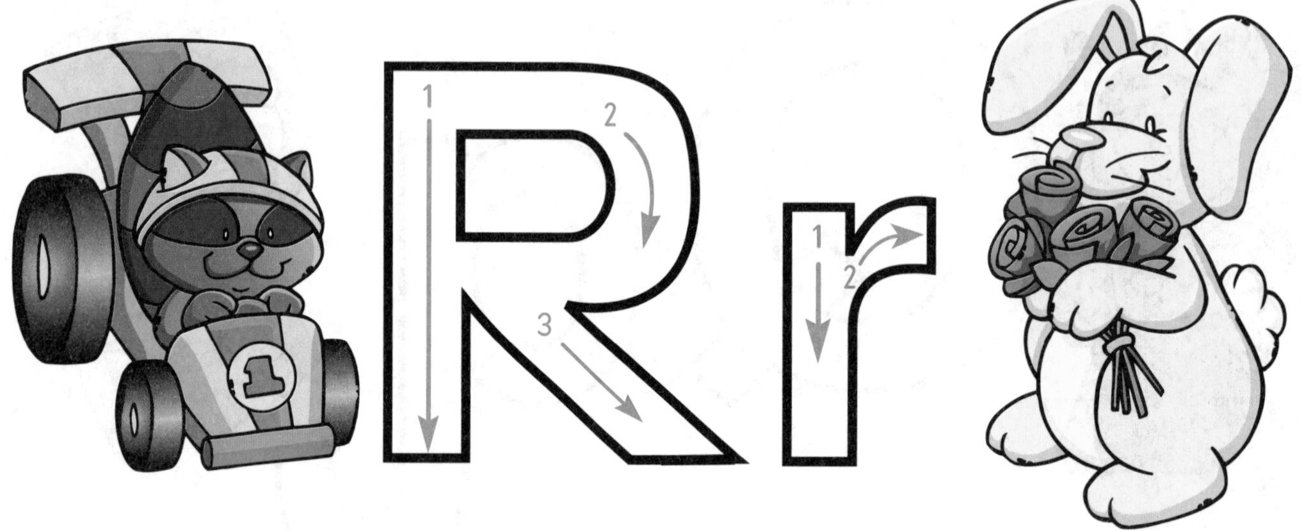

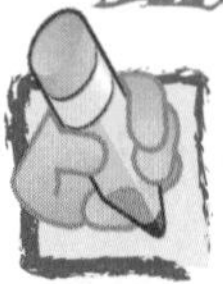

Trace and write the letters.

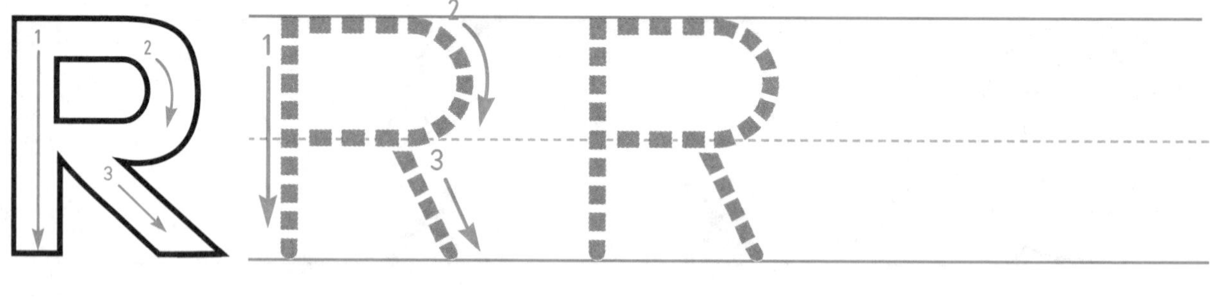

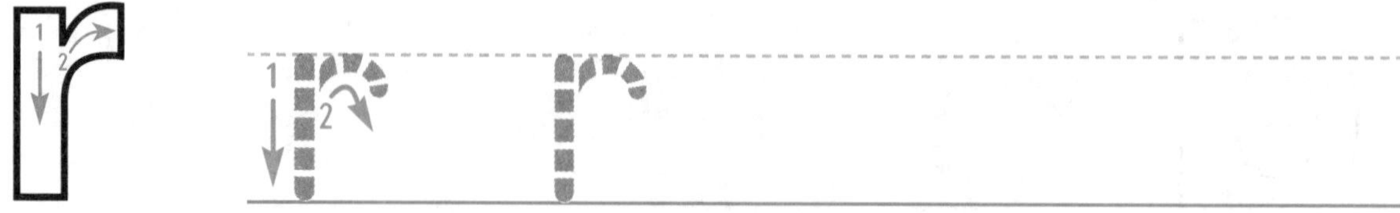

Parents: (Top) Ask your child to identify the capital and lowercase letters *R* and *r*. Help him or her name the pictures that begin with the letter *R*. Encourage your child to trace the hollow letters with a finger, following the arrows. Then have him or her color the letters. (Bottom) Have your child use a pencil or crayon to trace and write the letters.

Writing Ss

Color the letters.

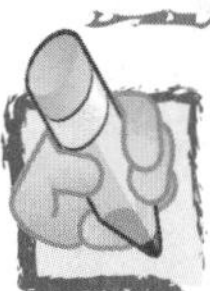

Trace and write the letters.

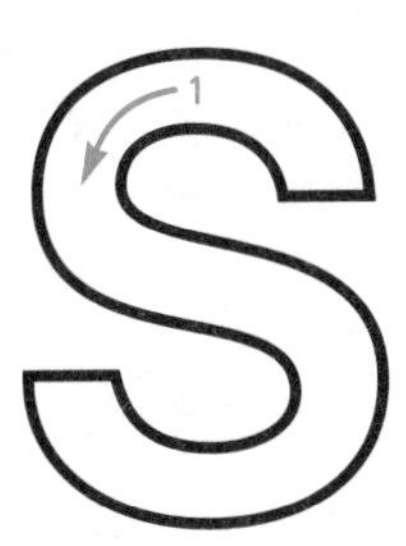

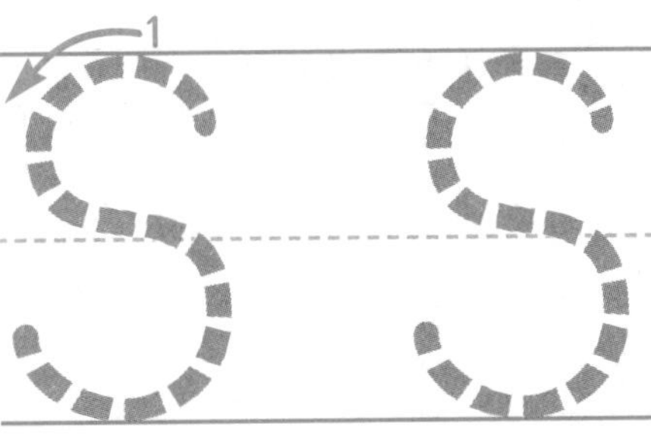

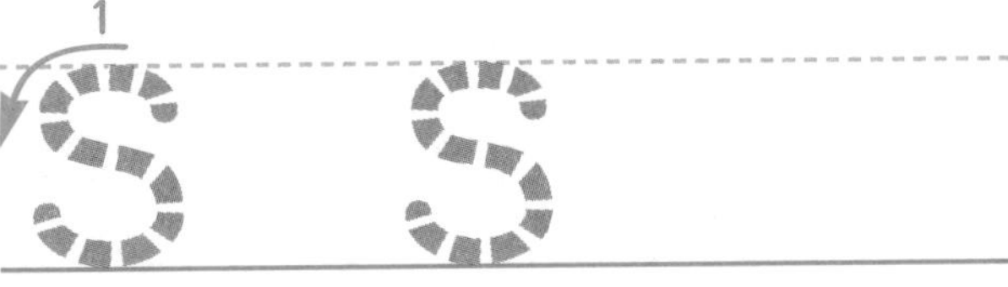

Parents: (Top) Ask your child to identify the capital and lowercase letters *S* and *s*. Help him or her name the pictures that begin with the letter *S*. Encourage your child to trace the hollow letters with a finger, following the arrows. Then have him or her color the letters. (Bottom) Have your child use a pencil or crayon to trace and write the letters.

ALPHABET

Writing Tt

Color the letters.

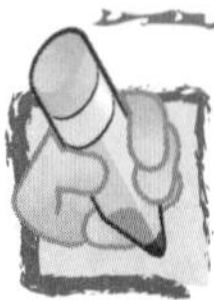

Trace and write the letters.

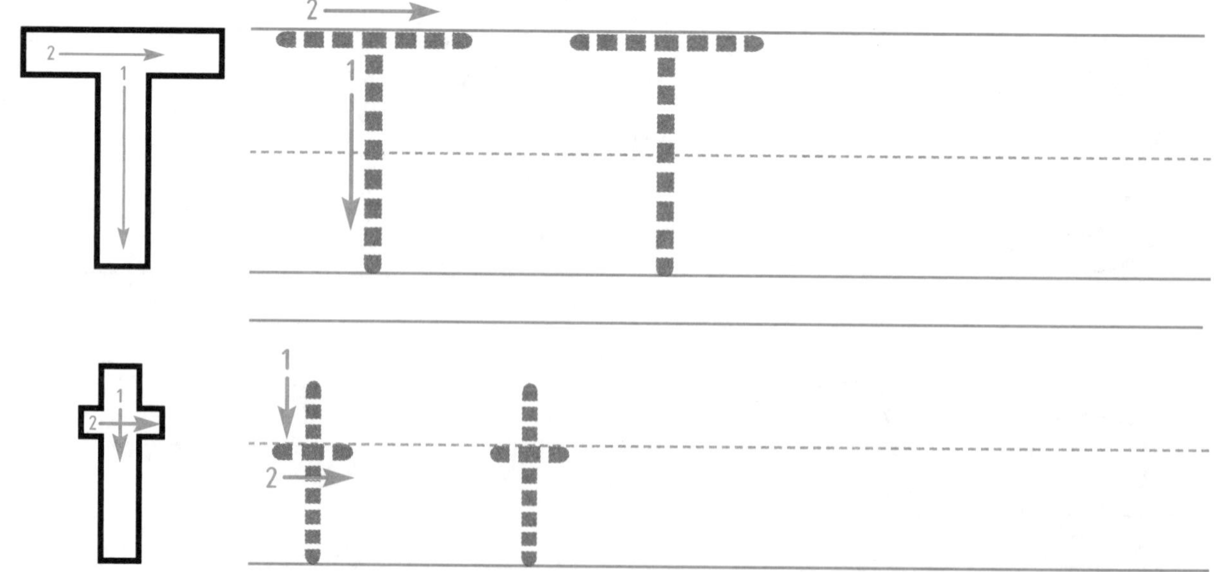

Parents: **(Top) Ask your child to identify the capital and lowercase letters *T* and *t*. Help him or her name the pictures that begin with the letter *T*. Encourage your child to trace the hollow letters with a finger, following the arrows. Then have him or her color the letters. (Bottom) Have your child use a pencil or crayon to trace and write the letters.**

Writing Uu

Color the letters.

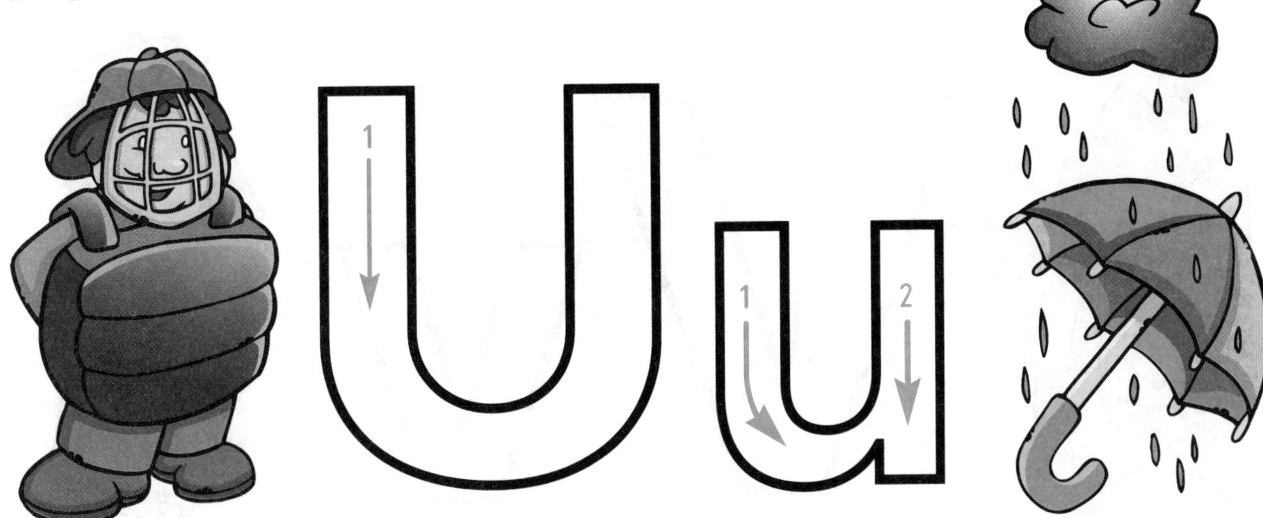

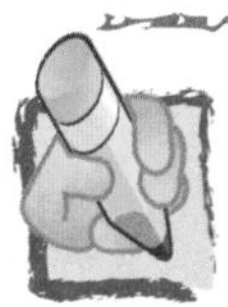

Trace and write the letters.

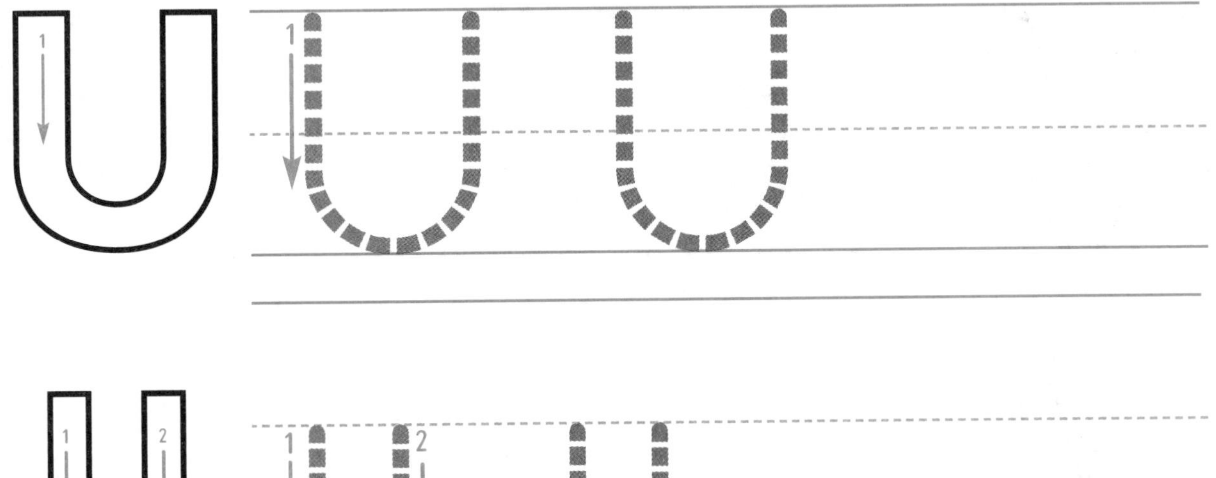

Parents: **(Top) Ask your child to identify the capital and lowercase letters *U* and *u*. Help him or her name the pictures that begin with the letter *U*. Encourage your child to trace the hollow letters with a finger, following the arrows. Then have him or her color the letters. (Bottom) Have your child use a pencil or crayon to trace and write the letters.**

Writing Vv

Color the letters.

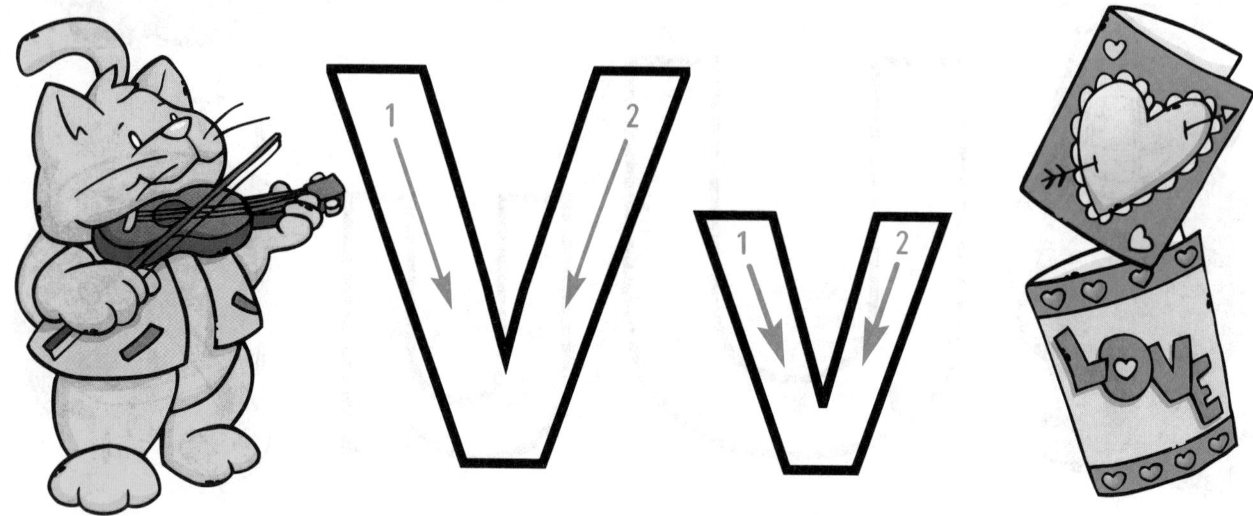

Trace and write the letters.

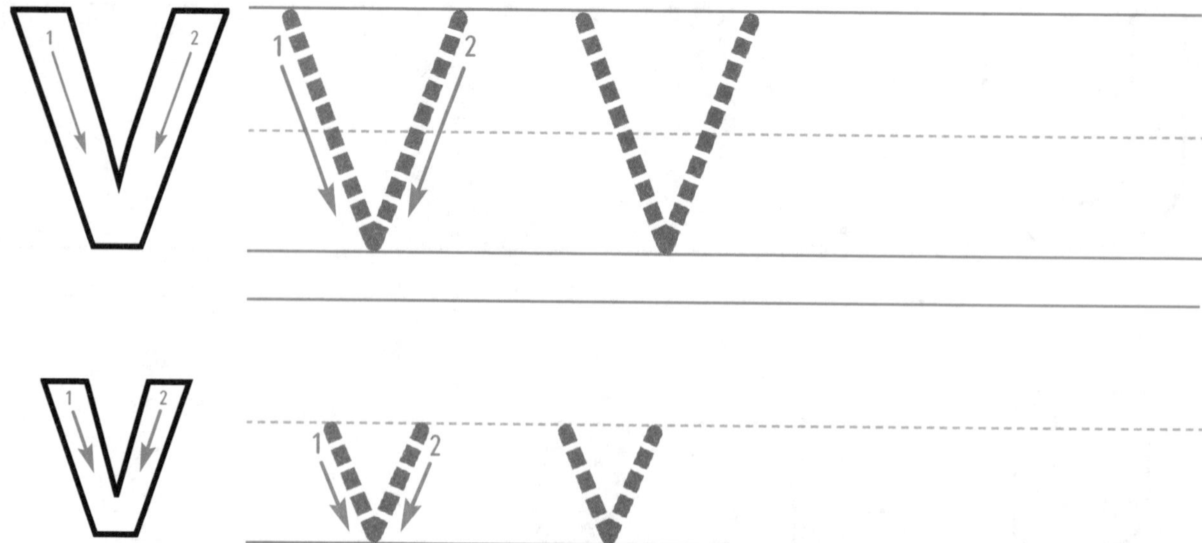

Parents: **(Top) Ask your child to identify the capital and lowercase letters *V* and *v*. Help him or her name the pictures that begin with the letter *V*. Encourage your child to trace the hollow letters with a finger, following the arrows. Then have him or her color the letters. (Bottom) Have your child use a pencil or crayon to trace and write the letters.**

Writing Ww

Color the letters.

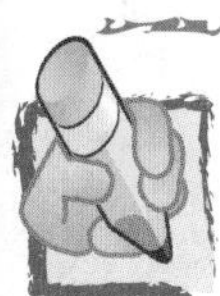

Trace and write the letters.

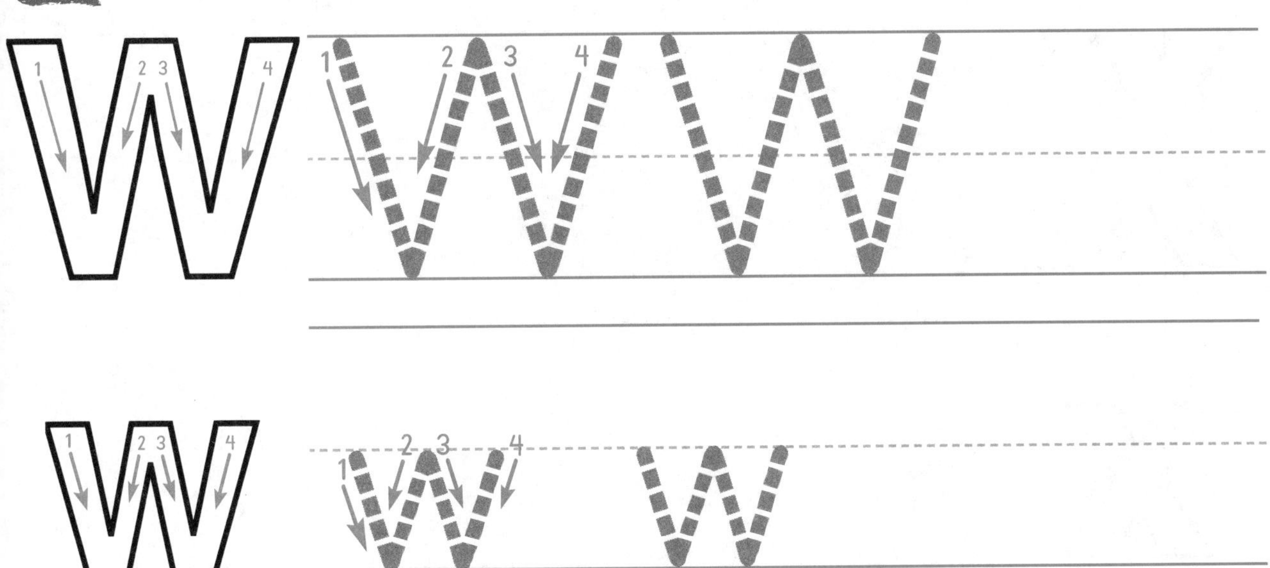

Parents: **(Top) Ask your child to identify the capital and lowercase letters *W* and *w*. Help him or her name the pictures that begin with the letter *W*. Encourage your child to trace the hollow letters with a finger, following the arrows. Then have him or her color the letters. (Bottom) Have your child use a pencil or crayon to trace and write the letters.**

Writing Xx

Color the letters.

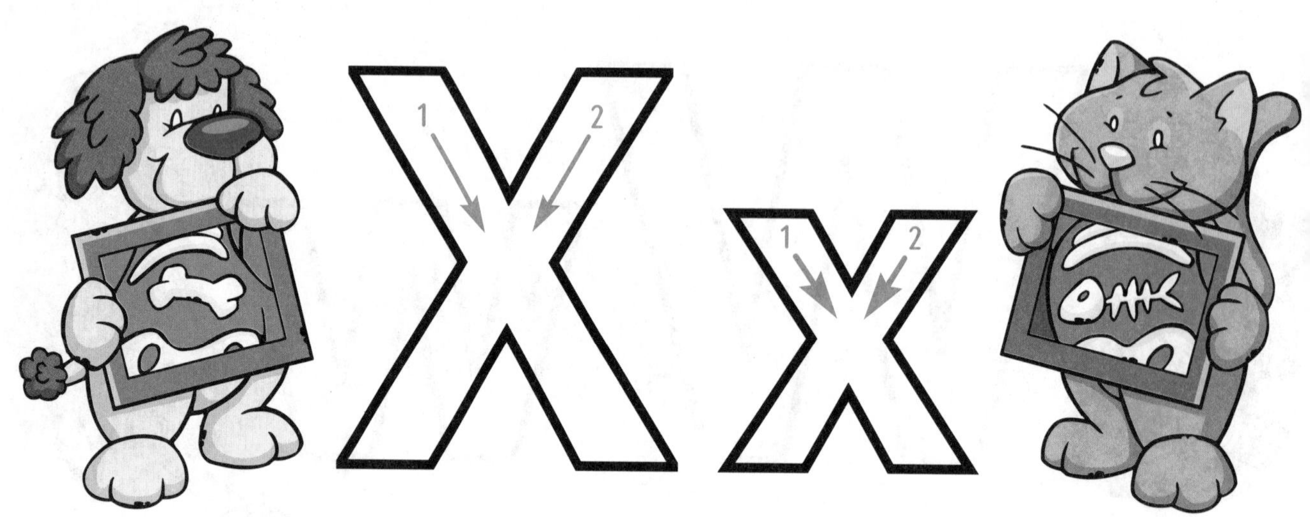

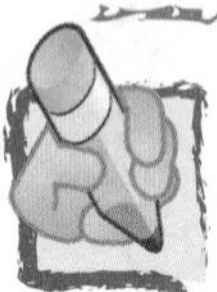

Trace and write the letters.

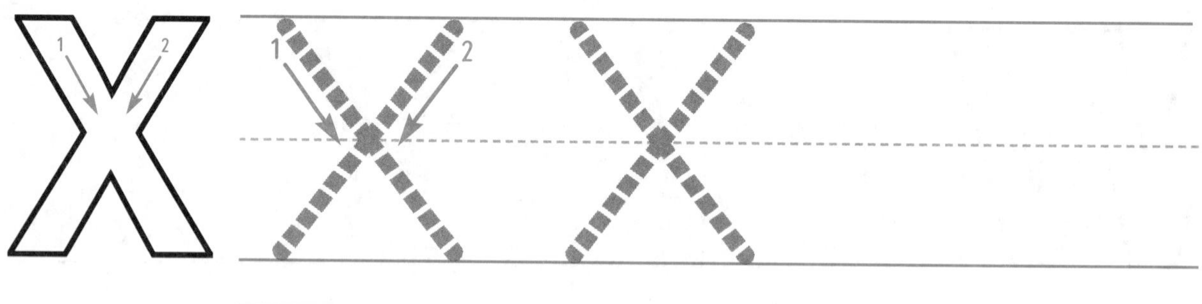

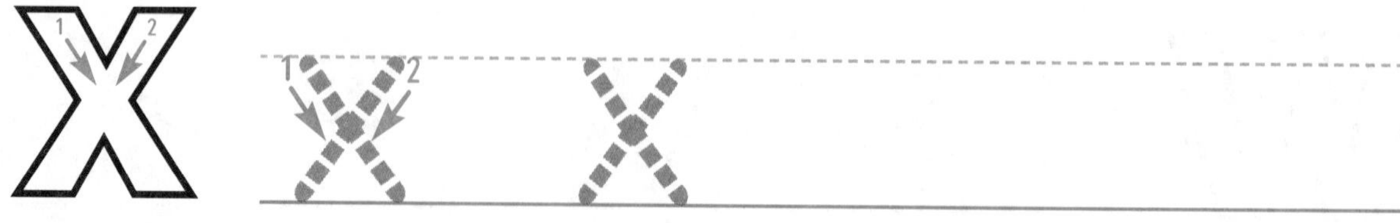

Parents: (Top) Ask your child to identify the capital and lowercase letters *X* and *x*. Help him or her name the pictures that begin with the letter *X*. Encourage your child to trace the hollow letters with a finger, following the arrows. Then have him or her color the letters. (Bottom) Have your child use a pencil or crayon to trace and write the letters.

Writing Y y

Color the letters.

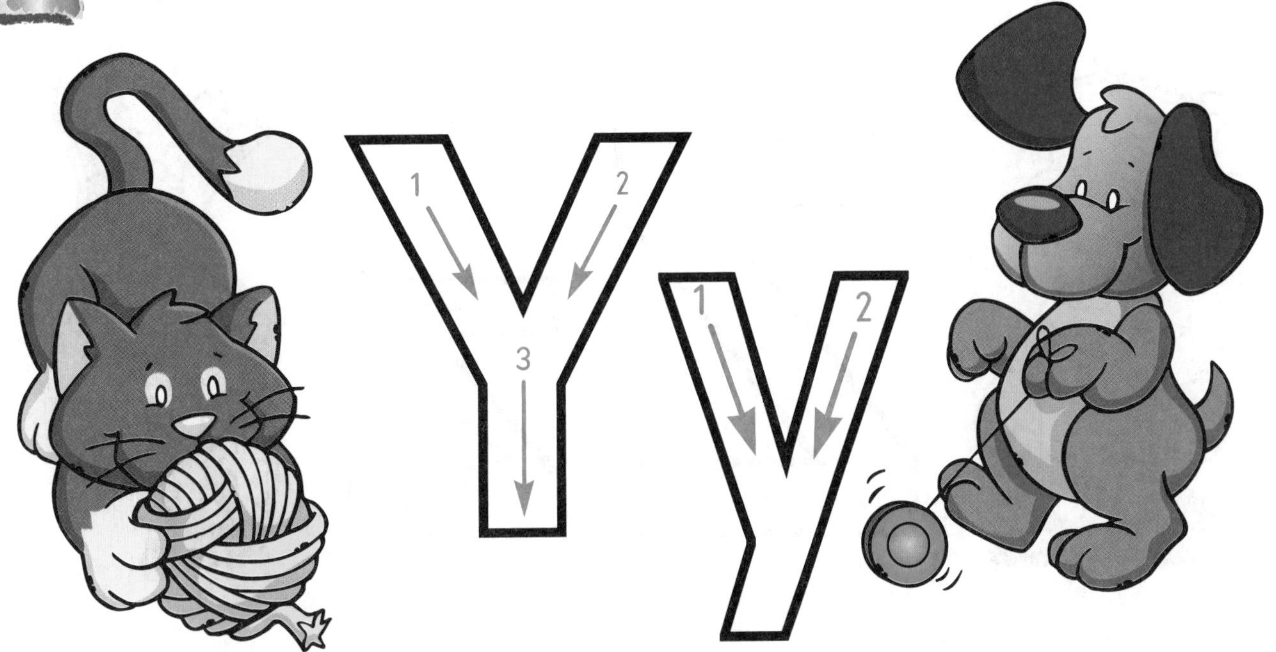

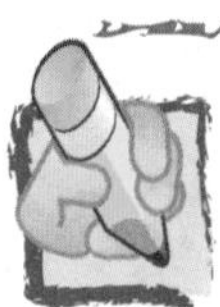

Trace and write the letters.

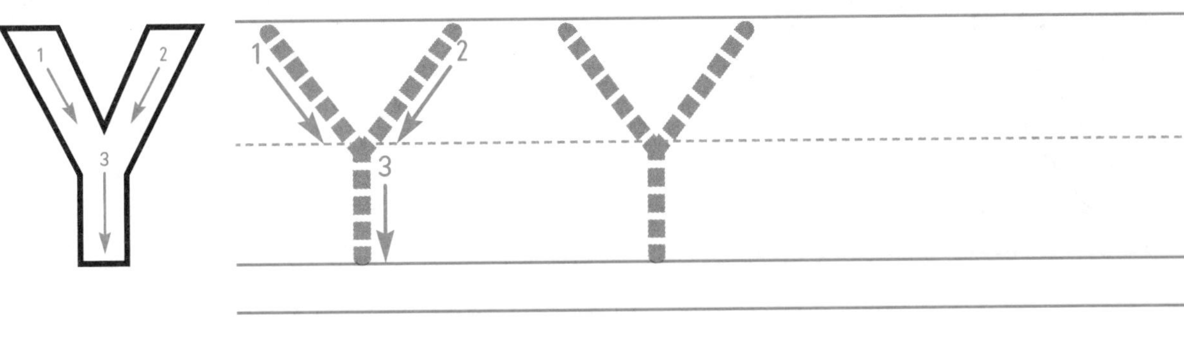

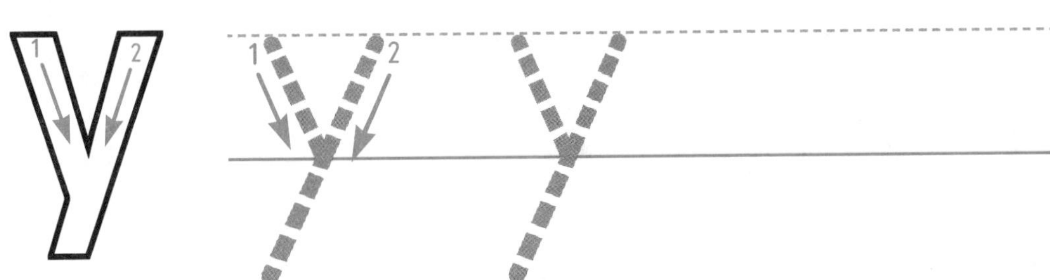

Parents: (Top) Ask your child to identify the capital and lowercase letters *Y* and *y*. Help him or her name the pictures that begin with the letter *Y*. Encourage your child to trace the hollow letters with a finger, following the arrows. Then have him or her color the letters. (Bottom) Have your child use a pencil or crayon to trace and write the letters.

ALPHABET

Writing Zz

Color the letters.

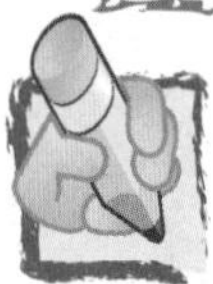

Trace and write the letters.

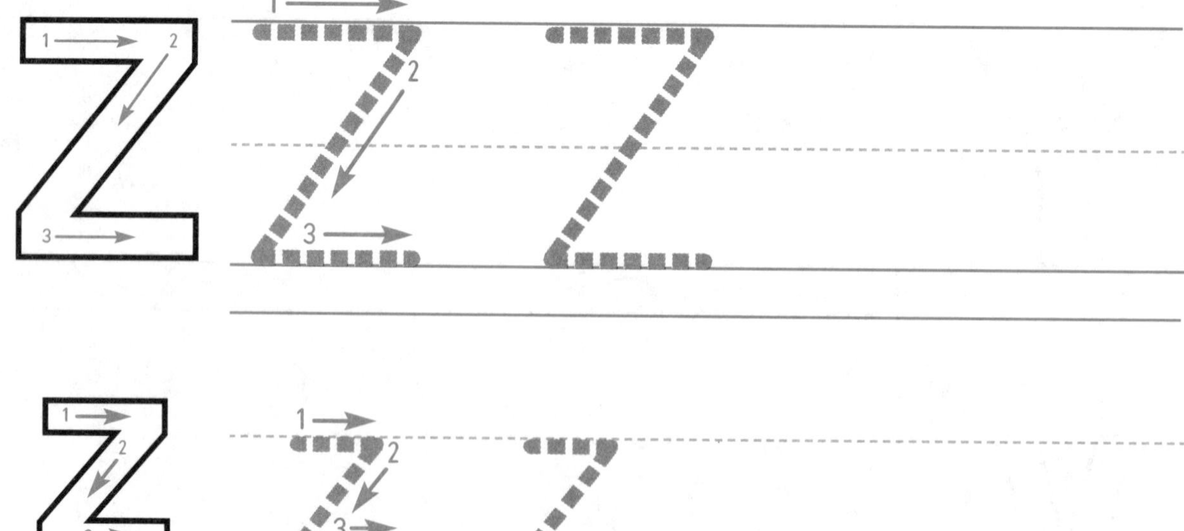

Parents: **(Top) Ask your child to identify the capital and lowercase letters *Z* and *z*. Help him or her name the pictures that begin with the letter *Z*. Encourage your child to trace the hollow letters with a finger, following the arrows. Then have him or her color the letters. (Bottom) Have your child use a pencil or crayon to trace and write the letters.**

Alphabet Cards

Cut out the cards.

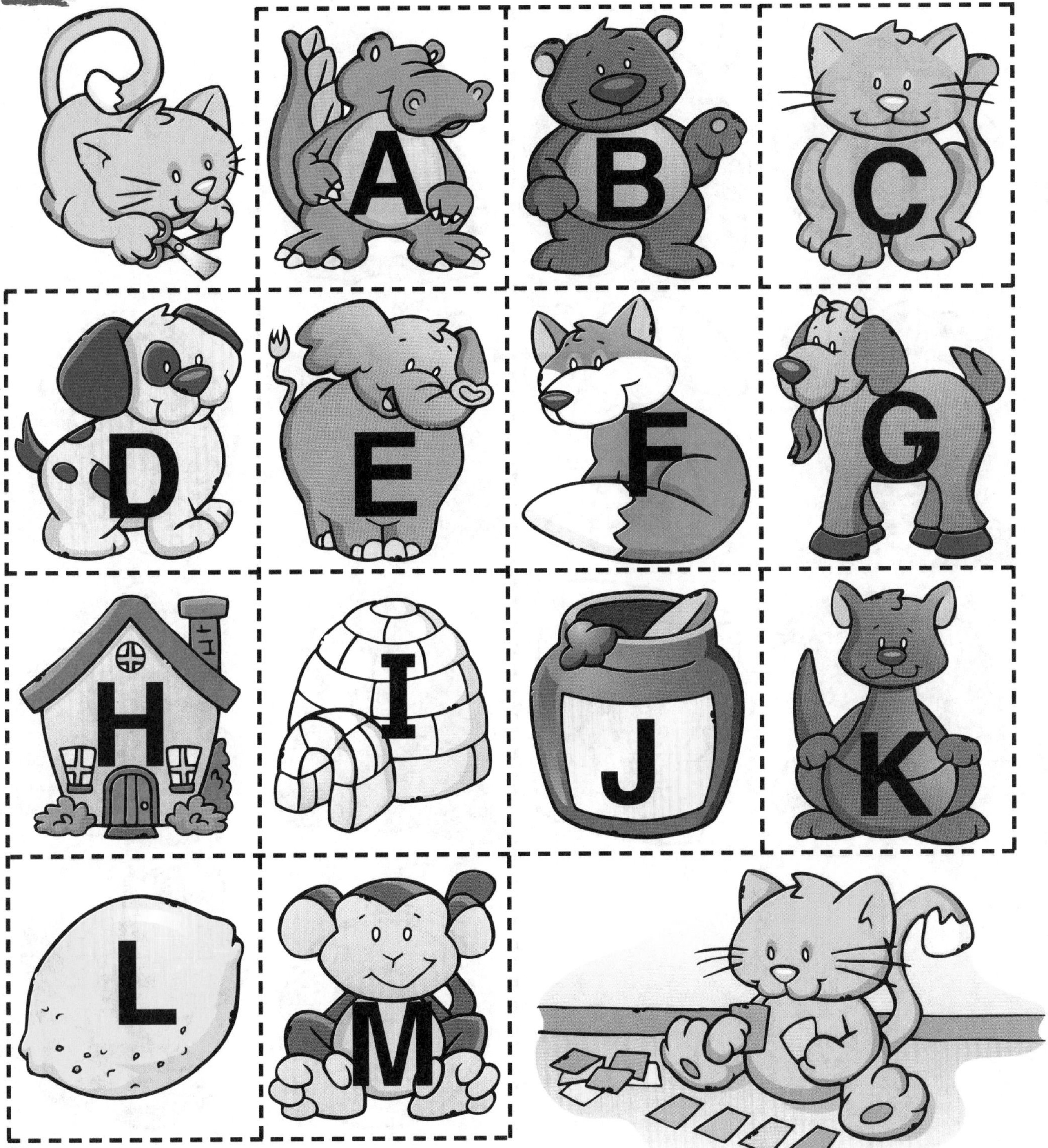

A B C

D E F G

H I J K

L M

Parents: Ask your child to trace each letter with a finger and say its name. Repeat for the letters pictured on the next page. Then have your child cut along the dashed lines to make alphabet cards. Shuffle the cards and place them on a table. Take turns picking cards from the deck, naming the letters, and tracing them with a finger.

Alphabet Cards

Cut out the cards.

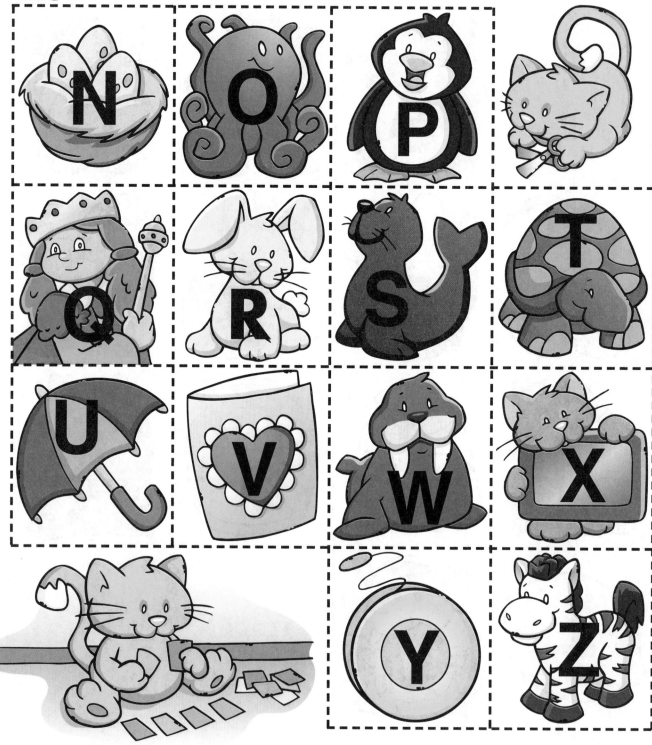

N O P

Q R S T

U V W X

Y Z

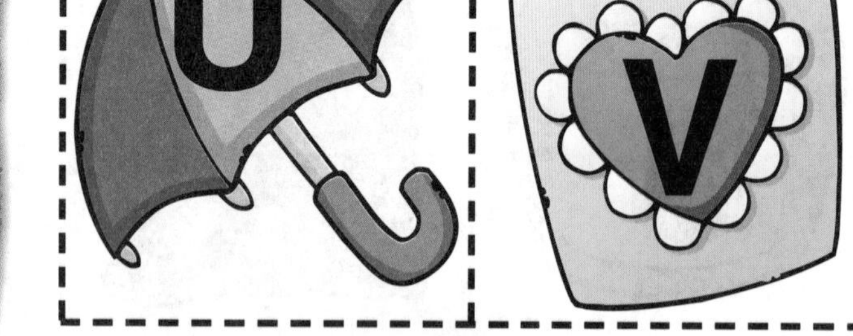

Alphabet Cards

Cut out the cards.

a b c

d e f g

h i j k

l m

Parents: Ask your child to trace each letter with a finger and say its name. Repeat for the letters pictured on the next page. Then have your child cut along the dashed lines to make alphabet cards. Shuffle the cards and place them on a table. Take turns picking cards from the deck, naming the letters, and tracing them with a finger. Also, combine these cards with the capital letter cards to play a matching game of capital and lowercase letters.

Alphabet Cards

Cut out the cards.

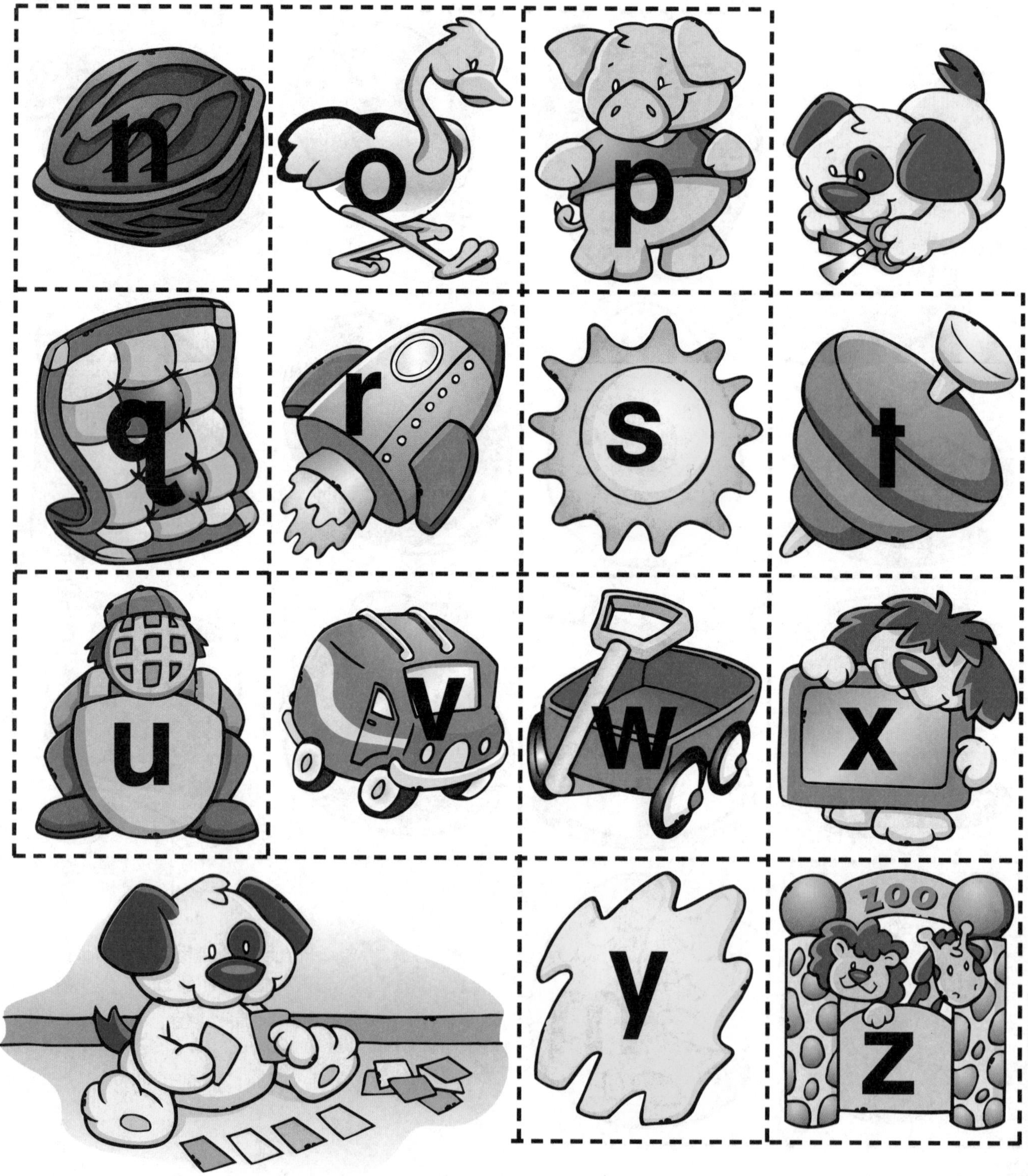

n o p

q r s t

u v w x

y z

Month 12 Checklist

Hands-on activities to help prepare your child for school!

READING

Same Words: pages 355–356
Making Words: pages 357–359
Matching Pictures and Words: pages 360–363
Help your child focus on developing recognition of beginning sounds and letter order in words through the following activities.

- ❑ Complete the worksheets.
- ❑ Recite a silly tongue twister, such as "babies bounce beach balls." Repeat the line, in this case emphasizing the *b* sound. Ask your child to join in. Point out that every word in this sentence begins with the same sound. Ask your child to write the letter that stands for the sound. Other examples of tongue twisters are "happy hippos hop home" and "just juggle, jump, and jiggle."
- ❑ Draw a simple picture of a pig on a sheet of paper. Write the letters *p, i,* and *g* beside it. Cut the paper between the *p* and *ig,* like a jigsaw puzzle. Have your child say the picture name and then put the pieces together to form the word *pig.* Repeat with *cap, dog, jet,* and *bug.*

Reading Words with Phonograms: pages 364–370
Words with phonograms follow patterns. Your child will learn to transfer these patterns to expand the set of words they can read and write. The following activities are examples of ways to practice phonograms.

- ❑ Complete the worksheets.
- ❑ Vary the activity on page 367 by drawing and cutting out an outline of a pot. Cut slits wide enough to pull a letter strip through. Write *-ot* to the right of the slits. Create a letter strip with the letters *c, d, h, l, p,* and *n* on it. Slide the strip through the slits on the pot. Help your child read the words that appear when you combine each initial consonant with the letters *-ot.* Repeat for other word endings, such as *-et.*
- ❑ Write *red, sit, hot, bun,* and *van* on separate index cards. Place the cards on a table and read each one aloud with your child. Then tell your child a riddle and ask him or her to answer it with one of the word cards. Try these riddles.
    - *It is the color of strawberries. It rhymes with bed. (red)*
    - *You do this in a chair. It rhymes with fit. (sit)*
    - *It is the opposite of cold. It rhymes with pot. (hot)*
    - *You put a hot dog on it. It rhymes with fun. (bun)*
    - *You ride in it. It rhymes with man. (van)*

  Also, make up your own set of riddles and word cards!
- ❑ Write *did, hid, kid, lid, hen, men, ten, pen, hop, mop, pop, top, lap, map, rap,* and *tap* on separate index cards. Help your child read each word and sort them by their ending sounds. Explain that the words in each pile rhyme.

READING

Reading Sight Words and Sentences: pages 371–382

Sight words, also known as "high-frequency words," are words your child will often encounter in reading. Many of these words are difficult to remember because they are not pronounced as thei spelling might suggest (for example: was/wuz). Still, sight words affect the flow of reading. In order for your child to automatically read a sight word, he or she needs many opportunities to see it and commit it to memory. You can help your child remember sight words through the following activities.

- ❑ Complete the worksheets.
- ❑ Practice sight words, one at a time. Use the words from the worksheet pages and others. Examples: *for, us, up, down, was, here, who, of, come, when, you,* and *he*. Write each word on a card and read it for your child. Have your child say it, spell it, and use it in a sentence.
- ❑ Put a thin layer of dry gelatin, drink mix, flour, salt, or sugar in a pie tin. Say a sight word and have your child use his or her finger to write it in the powder. Show your child how to shake the tin to erase the word.
- ❑ Have your child write a sight word in large letters on paper and then glue uncooked pasta or beans on the letters. Have your child trace the letters with a finger as he or she spells the word
- ❑ Read a story to your child. Have him or her point out the sight words as you say them.
- ❑ Give your child a newspaper or magazine ad that contains a particular sight word. Ask him or her cut out or circle the word.
- ❑ Have your child form sight words on bread using a squeeze bottle of mustard, ketchup, or jelly Try this with syrup on pancakes, waffles, or French toast.
- ❑ Invite your child to make sight words using alphabet cereal or alphabet macaroni.
- ❑ Go outdoors and use chalk to write sight words on the pavement.
- ❑ Write the individual letters of a sight word on separate index cards. Scramble the letters and have your child arrange them to spell the word.
- ❑ Have your child form sight words using snack foods such as cheese cubes, raisins, or nuts. Then invite your child to eat the sight words.

The Cave

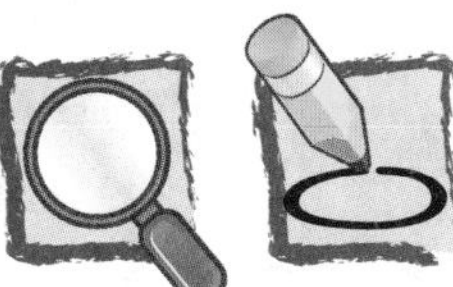

Circle the word that is the same.

we	is	we
go	go	am
in	to	in
it	it	do

Parents: Have your child look at the first word in each row. Then have him or her find and circle the word in that row that is the same. Repeat for the other rows. After your child has finished all the rows, help him or her read the circled words aloud.

Cubs In Their Den

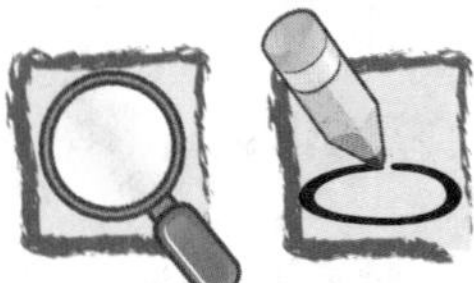

Circle the words that are the same.

den	ten	den
mom	mom	mug
rug	hug	hug
cub	tub	cub

Parents: Have your child look closely at the words in each row and circle the two that are the same. After your child has finished all the rows, help him or her read the circled words aloud.

Make a Word

Write the missing letter to make the word.

d **l**	**w** **p**
dog	_ig
b **c**	**h** **p**
_at	_en

Parents: **Ask your child to say the name of each picture and listen for the beginning sound. Then have him or her complete the word under each picture by writing the letter that stands for the missing beginning sound. Encourage your child to read the words aloud.**

Using picture, sound, and letter clues to make words

Make More Words

Write b or c to make the word.

c up

_ ap

_ ed

_ ox

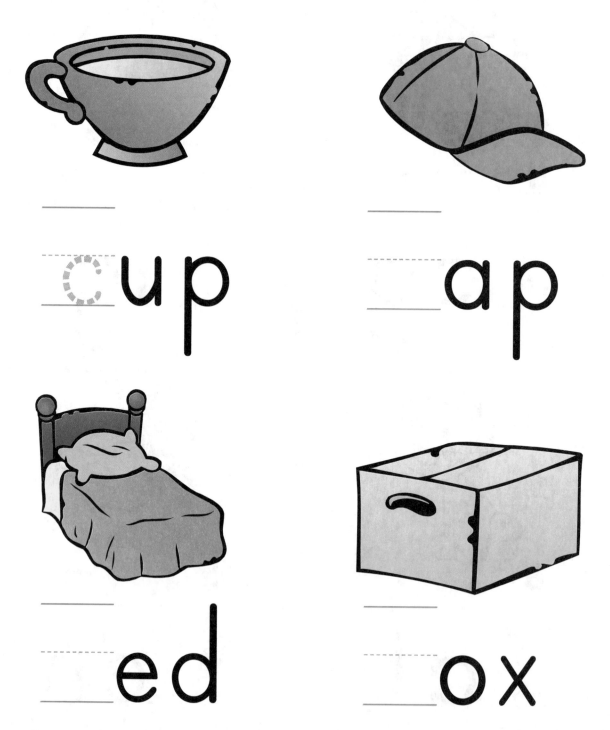

Parents: Ask your child to say the name of each picture and listen for the beginning sound. Then have him or her complete the word under each picture by writing the letter *b* or *c*, whichever stands for the missing beginning sound. Encourage your child to read the words aloud.

Find a Letter

Write the missing letter to make the word.

f	s	t	m

s un

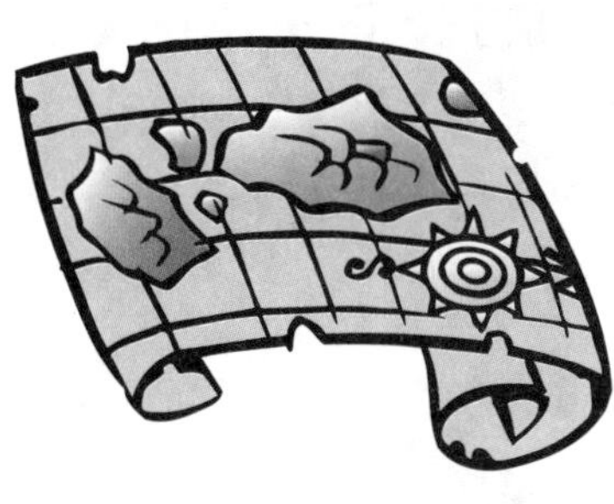

__ ap

__ en

__ ox

Parents: Ask your child to say the name of each picture and listen for the beginning sound. Then have him or her complete the word under each picture by writing the letter from the box that stands for the missing beginning sound. Encourage your child to read the words aloud.

READING

Match Them Up!

Match the pictures to the words.

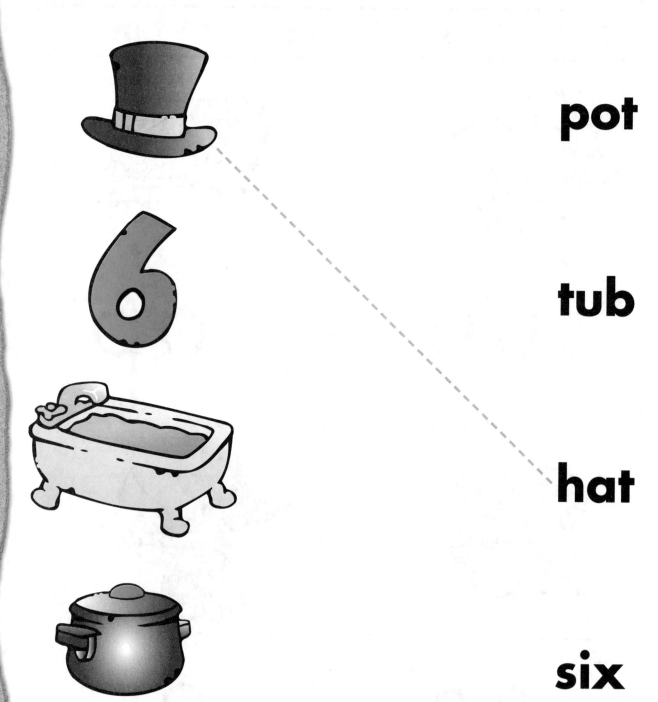

pot

tub

hat

six

Parents: Have your child say the name of each picture. Then ask him or her to draw a line from each picture to the word that says what it is. Have your child read each word aloud.

Picture Cards

Cut out the cards.

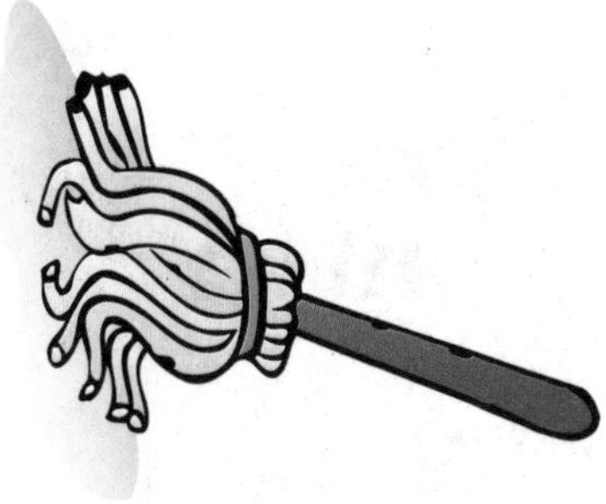

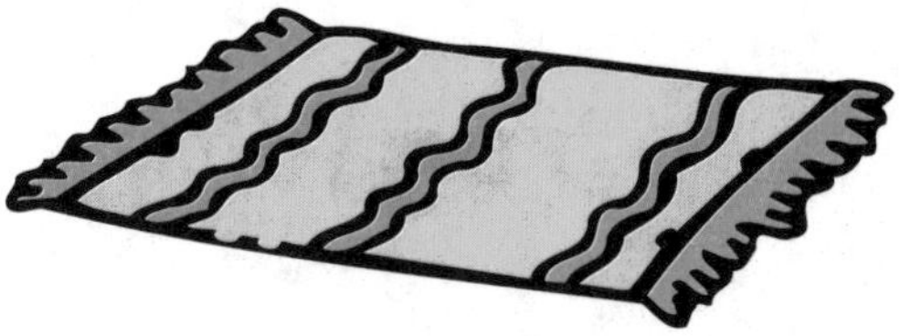

Parents: Cut out the picture cards and place them picture side up on a table. Say, "Pick a picture. Now, turn the card over. Read the word."

READING

Word Cards

Cut out the cards.

mop	**van**
tub	**pen**
ham	**bag**
web	**rug**

Parents: Place the cards word side up on a table. Read a word aloud but do not point to it. Ask your child to find the word. Say, "Read the word. Turn the card over to see the picture."

More Match-Ups!

Match the words to the pictures.

bug 

top 

net 

jam 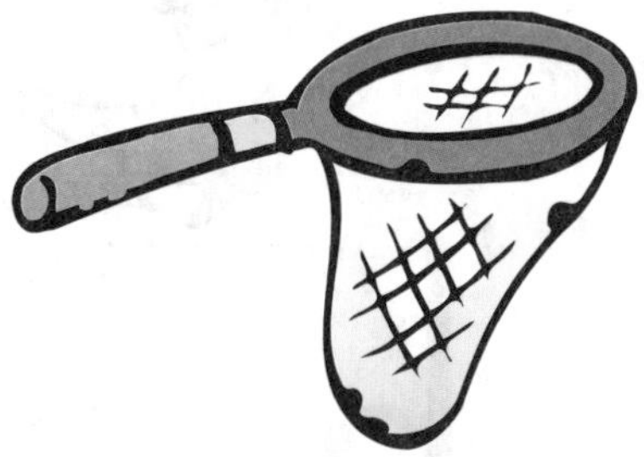

Parents: Have your child read each word aloud. Then ask him or her to draw a line from each word to the picture it names.

Reading Words With -en

Read the word.

hen

Circle the -en ending.

men **pen** **ten**

Trace the letters.

h e n

t e n

Parents: (Top) Have your child read the word *hen* and point to the letters *e* and *n* at the end. (Middle) Ask your child to name each picture, read the word below, and circle the *-en* ending. (Bottom) Have your child say the name of each picture, trace the letters *e* and *n,* and then read the word.

Reading Words With -an

Circle the pictures with names that rhyme.

can	 pan	 red	 van
 fan	Dan	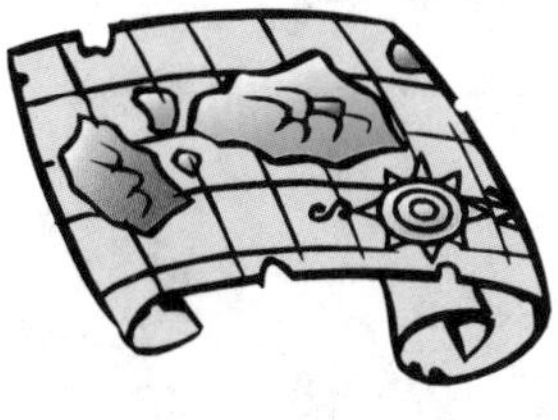 map	 man
 pan	 van	 jug	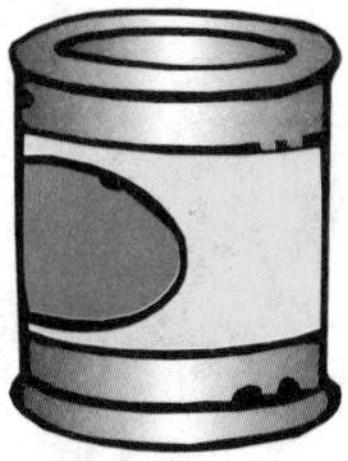 can
 man	 fan	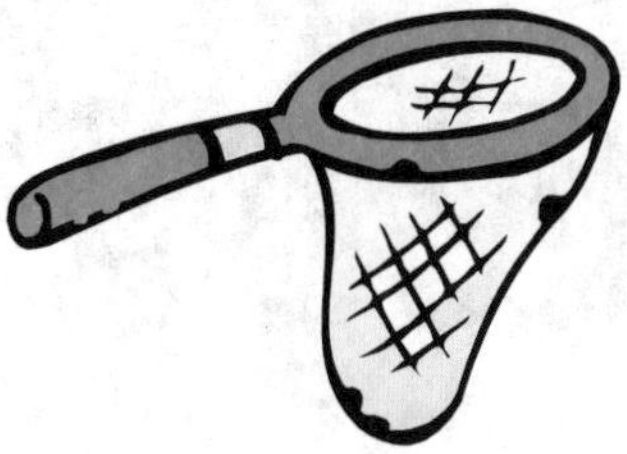 net	 pan

Parents: Have your child say the name of the first picture in the first row and read the word below it. Next, ask him or her to read the words below the other pictures in that row. Then have your child circle the pictures with names that rhyme with *can*. Help him or her finish the page.

Reading Words With -og

Read the word.

dog

Trace the letter.

dog

log

Parents: Have your child read the word *dog* and point to the letter *d* at the beginning. Help your child describe the picture and read the words. Then have him or her trace the beginning letters. Point out that the words rhyme.

Reading Words With -at

Cut out the cat.

at

c f h m p s

Parents: Help your child cut out the cat and letter strip. Cut along the dashed lines on the cat to make slits. Then slide the letter strip through the slits, positioning the letter *c* in the opening. Ask your child to read the word. Slide the strip and have him or her read each new word that appears.

Reading Words With -ig

Trace the letter.
Draw a line to the matching picture.

pig

wig

dig

big

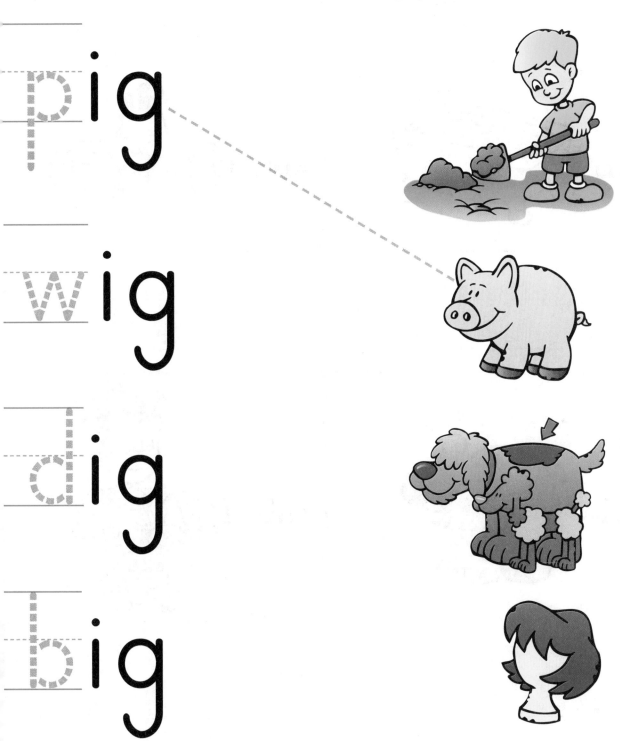

Parents: Have your child read each word on the left and say the beginning letter. Ask him or her to trace the letter, read the word again, and draw a line to the picture it names on the right. Point out that all the words rhyme.

Reading Words With -ub

Read the word.
Trace the word.

tub

tub

sub

sub

cub

cub

rub

rub

Parents: Have your child read each word. Help him or her see that the word names what is shown in the picture to the right. Then ask your child to trace the word on the line. Point out that all the words rhyme.

A Puppy In and Out

Read the word. Trace the word.

in **out**

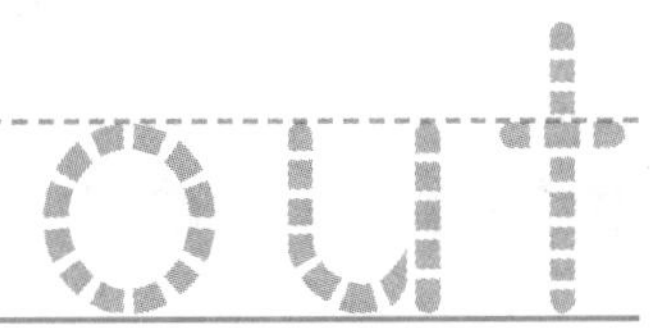

Write in or out to complete the sentence.

The is______.

The is______.

Parents: (Top) Read the word *in* aloud. Have your child repeat it and spell it. Then have him or her trace the word and read it. Repeat for the word *out*. (Bottom) Have your children write *in* or *out* to complete each sentence. Ask him or her to read the sentences.

Tigers Can Go!

  **Read the word. Trace the word.**

can **go**

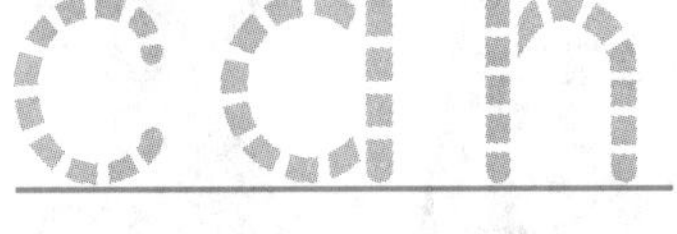

The [tiger]s can go!

 **Trace the paths with can and go.**

Parents: (Top) Read the word *can* aloud. Have your child repeat it and spell it. Then have him or her trace the word and read it. Repeat for the word *go*. (Bottom) Say, "Help the tigers get to the finish line." Have your child use a pencil or crayon to trace the path with the word *can*. Ask him or her to read each word as he or she passes it. Then have your child do the same for the path with the word *go*.

Is It A Pet?

Read the word. Trace the word.

yes **no**

Circle yes or no.

Is the a toy? yes no

Is the a toy? yes no

Is the a pet? yes no

Is the a pet? yes no

Parents: (Top) Read the word *yes* aloud. Have your child repeat it and spell it. Then have him or her trace the word and read it. Repeat for the word *no*. (Bottom) Help your child read each sentence. Say, "Circle *yes* or *no* to answer the questions."

Spots and Stripes

Read the word. Trace the word.

has **and**

has and

Write has or and to complete the sentence.

The dog __________ s.

The tiger __________ zebra have s.

Parents: (Top) Read the word *has* aloud. Have your child repeat it and spell it. Then have him or her trace the word and read it. Repeat for the word *and.* (Bottom) Have your children write *has* or *and* to complete each sentence. Ask him or her to read the sentences.

My, My, My!

Trace the word. Write the word.

Write **my** to complete each sentence.

That is ______ .

That is ______ .

That is ______ .

That is NOT ______ !

Parents: (Top) Read the word *my* aloud. Have your child repeat it and spell it. Then have him or her trace the word and read it. Ask your child to write *my* on the blank line. (Bottom) Have your child write *my* to complete each sentence. Then encourage him or her to read the sentences. Ask, "Whose nose is that?" (It's an elephant's nose!)

READING

I Can! Can You?

Look closely.

hug hop run sing

Circle yes or no.

Can a [tree] hug?	Can a [fish] sing?
yes no	yes no
Can a [rabbit] hop?	Can a [lion] run?
yes no	yes no

Parents: Help your child read each sentence. Ask him or her circle yes or no to answer the questions.

On the Playground

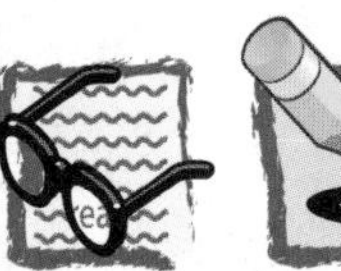

Read the word. Trace the word.

I **we**

I

Look closely at the picture.
Write I or We to complete each sentence.

_______________ **can go on the**  **.**

_______________ **can go on the**  **!**

Parents: (Top) Read the word *I* aloud. Have your child repeat it and spell it. Then have him or her trace the word and read it. Repeat for the word *we*. Explain that *I* is used for one and *we* is used for more than one. (Bottom) Have your child look closely at the pictures and write *I* or *We* to complete each sentence. Ask him or her to read the sentences.

Colors All Around

Read the color names.

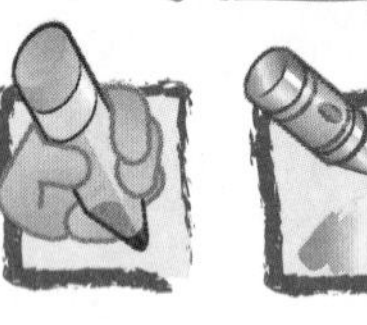

Write the color word. Color the picture.

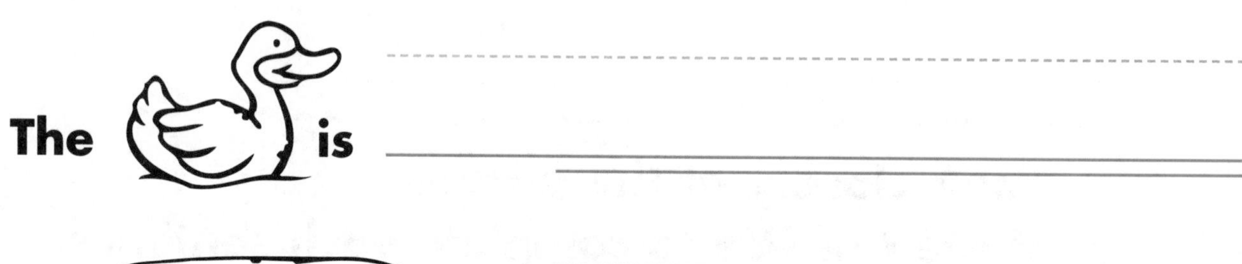

The [duck] is ____________________ .

The [pond] is ____________________ .

The [flower] is ____________________ .

The [tree] is ____________________ .

The [rainbow] is many colors!

Parents: (Top) Read the color words on the crayons aloud. Have your child point to each crayon, repeat the color word, and spell it. (Bottom) Say, "Write the missing color word to complete each sentence. Read the sentences." Then have your child color the pictures.

Parents: Remove pages 379-382 from this book. See directions for making mini storybooks on the inside front cover.

Goodbye bee!
Goodbye !
HONEY
Where Is the Bee?
HONE

Where is the bee?

It is in the 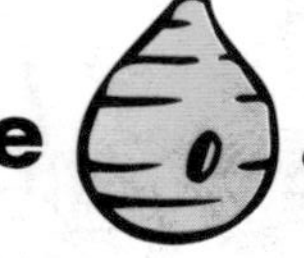.

Where is the bee?

The bee is on the .

Where is the bee?

It is in the  **.**

Where is the bee?

It is in the [tree icon] **.**

Where is the bee?

It is in the .

Where is the bee?

The bee is on the  .

Index

Alphabet. *See* Letters
Beginning Sounds, 131-160
    See also Letters
Checklists. *See* Hands-On Activity Checklists
Classifying
    Go-togethers, 29-32
    Grouping and sorting objects, 19-20
    Objects that belong, 21-24
    Objects that do not belong, 25-28
Colors, 37-48
Conclusions, *See* Drawing Conclusions
Consonants. *See* Letters
Counting,
    From one to five, 68-89, 95, 227
    From six to ten, 228-244, 248-249, 252-255
    See also Numbers and Numerals AND Numerical Order
Directions. *See* Hands-On Activity Checklists: Following Directions OR Visual Discrimination: Recognizing Directionality
Dot-to-Dot Puzzles, 181-183, 250-251
Drawing
    Lines, 163-172
    Missing parts, 210-213
    Pictures, 173-176, 189-192
    Shapes, 177-180
    See also Tracing, Writing
Drawing Conclusions, 216-217
Finding Objects in a Picture. *See* Visual Discrimination
Flashcards
    Action word cards, 303-304
    Alphabet cards, 349-352
    Matching cards, 33-34
    Number cards, 95-96
    Opposite cards, 119-120
    Picture and word cards, 361-362
    Rhyming cards, 107-108
    Sequence cards, 223-224
Following Directions
    Multi-step, 312-320
    Three-step, 315-317
    To color a picture, 47
    Two-step, 312-314
Grouping. *See* Classifying
Hands-on-Activity Checklists, 3-4, 35-36, 65-66, 97-98, 129-130, 161-162, 193-194, 225-226, 257-258, 291-292, 321-322, 353-354
Letters
    Beginning sounds, consonants, 131-153, 159-160
    Beginning sounds, vowels, 154-160
    Recognizing Aa-Zz, 259-290
    Review
        Beginning sounds, 159-160
        Recognizing letters, 263, 268, 273, 278, 284, 290
    Tracing and writing letters Aa-Zz, 323-352
Lines. *See* Tracing, Drawing
Matching. *See* Classifying AND Same and Different
Mazes, 184-188
Measurement. *See* Size
More and Less, 88-89
Motor Control. *See* Mazes, Dot-to-Dot Puzzles, Tracing, Writing, and Drawing
Naming Words
    For actions, 302-304
    For animals, 123-124
    For people, 121-122
    For places, 298-299
    For things, 300-301

Numbers and Numerals,
Counting from one to five, 68-89, 95-96, 227, 248-249
Counting from six to ten, 228-244, 248-249, 252-255
Matching sets, 67, 80, 87, 95
Recognizing numerals, 74-75, 81-86, 241-247
Sequence, 250-252, 256
Writing, 252-256 *See also Numerical Order*
Numerical Order, 250-256
See also Numbers and Numerals, Dot-to-Dot Puzzles, Sequence
Opposites, 110-120
Pairs, 15-16, 33-34
See also Same and Different
Part and Whole, 17-18
Patterns, color, 48
Pictures. *See* Tracing, Drawing
Position words, 305-311
Predicting, 218-219
Reading
Sentences, 375-382
Words, 355-374
Recognizing Differences. *See* Same and Different, Visual Discrimination
Rhyming Words, 99-109, 125-128, 293-297, 364-370
Same and Different
Identifying objects that are different, 11-14, 197
Identifying objects that are the same, 5-10, 195-196
Identifying words that are the same, 355-356
Matching one to one, 67
Matching pairs, 15-16, 33-34
Matching shapes, 58-59, 198-199
Sentences, 375-382 *See also* Reading
Sequence
First, Next, Last, 220-224
Matching, 198-199
Number, 250-252, 256
Recognizing, 49-64
Story, 223-224
Tracing, 177-180
Shapes, 49-64, 189-199
Sight Words, 371-374
See also Words
Sizes, comparing, 90-94
Sorting. *See* Classifying
Storybooks (Pull-out)
How to Draw a Frog! 189-192
Rhyming Riddles, 125-128
Where Is the Bee? 379-382
Telling a Story. *See* Sequence
Tracing
Letters, 323-352
Lines, 163-172
Pictures, 173-176, 189-192
Shapes, 177-180
See also Letters, Numbers
Visual Discrimination
Drawing missing parts, 210-213
Finding objects in a picture, 204-209
Finding shapes in a picture, 62
Identifying what's wrong with a picture, 214-215
Matching objects that are the same, 5-10, 195-196
Matching objects to shapes, 198-199
Matching pairs, 15-16, 33-34
Recognizing differences, 11-14, 197
Recognizing directionality, 200-203
Vowels. *See* Letters
Word Families *See also* Rhyming Words
Words
Making words, 357-359
Matching words, 355-356
Matching words and pictures, 360-363
Reading sight words, 371-374
Reading words with phonograms, 364-370
Writing
Letters. *See* Letters
Numerals. *See* Numbers and Numerals